THE GEORGE FISHER BAKER
NON-RESIDENT LECTURESHIP IN CHEMISTRY
AT CORNELL UNIVERSITY

THE PROTON IN CHEMISTRY

BY R. P. BELL

THE PROTON
in CHEMISTRY

BY R. P. BELL *Fellow of Balliol College* AND
University Reader in Physical Chemistry, Oxford University

Cornell University Press

Ithaca, New York, 1959

PRINTED IN THE UNITED STATES OF AMERICA

BY THE GEORGE BANTA COMPANY, INC.

Preface

THIS book is based on the lectures which I gave at Cornell University as George Fisher Baker Non-resident Lecturer during 1958. I wish to express my warmest thanks to Professor F. A. Long and the other members of the Department of Chemistry for giving me this opportunity and for their kindness and most helpful advice. Both my wife and I are also deeply indebted to the members of the Cornell branch of the Telluride Association for their hospitality in Telluride House and their stimulating company.

The material in this book is largely complementary to that in *Acid-Base Catalysis* (Oxford, 1941). Many of the theses which were argued in some detail in the earlier book have now become generally accepted, and the kinetic evidence obtained from catalyzed reactions has been supplemented by direct studies of acid-base reactions using a variety of modern techniques. The relation between molecular structure and acid-base properties has received much attention during the last twenty years and is dealt with in Chapters VII and X. I have attempted in Chapter VI to give some account of recent work on concentrated solutions of acids, and had originally intended to add a chapter on reaction kinetics in these solutions; however, this was finally abandoned in view of the confused state of the subject at present. The final chapter is devoted to the hydrogen isotope effect in acid-base reactions, which, after a period of comparative neglect, has attracted a good deal of interest during the last few years. I have tried here to clarify the quantitative factors involved in the simplest cases rather than to review a large mass of experimental data.

In conclusion, my best thanks are due to my wife for typing a large part of the book and for other assistance.

R. P. BELL

Balliol College
Oxford
May 1959

v

Contents

THE PROTON IN CHEMISTRY

CHAPTER I

Introduction

THE proton is most naturally thought of by the chemist as the cation derived from the hydrogen atom. Except in purely descriptive chemistry it is not usually profitable to consider a single element in isolation, still less a particular ion, and the topic chosen for these lectures therefore requires some justification.

The proton is unique among singly charged ions in having no electrons outside the nucleus, and although this property is shared by some multiply charged cations (e.g., He^{2+}, Li^{3+}) none of these are important in chemical processes taking place under ordinary conditions. This means that the proton has a radius of the order 10^{-13} cm., as compared with 10^{-8} cm. for all other ions. On account of this small radius it can exert an enormous polarizing power on any molecule or ion in the neighborhood, and for this reason the free proton is encountered only in a vacuum, or in a very dilute gas. However, we shall see that a wide variety of processes can be regarded as *proton-transfer reactions*, and since these involve only the movement of a nucleus, without any attendant electrons, they represent a particularly simple type of change. In particular, they can take place without any serious disorganization of bonding electrons and without bringing into play forces of repulsion between nonbonding electrons. In the terminology of modern organic chemistry, the proton has low steric requirements. Some reactions do, of course, involve the transfer of a hydrogen atom rather than a proton, but these usually take place under more drastic conditions, for example, in the gas phase at high temperatures or under the influence of radiation or bombardment by particles of high energy. There is rarely any doubt as to whether a reaction involves protons or hydrogen atoms, while for other elements (notably the halogens) it is often necessary to consider the possibility of both heterolytic and homolytic mechanisms.

The simple nature of proton transfers is probably responsible for the fact that such transfers are commonly facile and lead to mobile equilibria.   This circumstance underlies the general usefulness of the acid-base concept, especially in its quantitative aspects.   A large proportion of our knowledge about equilibria in solution relates to protolytic equilibria (dissociation constants and related quantities), and there is no other class of reaction for which such accurate data are available. This has played an important part in the development of theories of ionic solutions, on the one hand, and of the interpretation of substituent effects in organic chemistry, on the other.   In solution kinetics, as opposed to equilibria, the proton does not occupy such a special position; in fact, most acid-base reactions take place so rapidly that their velocities cannot be measured by ordinary means, and only recently have they become accessible through modern techniques for studying very fast reactions.   It has long been realized, however, that *catalysis by acids and bases* usually involves one or more proton transfers, and the simple nature of the proton appears again in regularities which have been observed in the kinetics of catalyzed reactions.

There are two classes of phenomena in which the proton acts as a link between two other atoms.   The first of these is in *hydrogen bonding*, which to a first approximation may be attributed to the electrostatic attraction between a proton and an unshared pair of electrons. It is again the absence of orbital electrons which makes the proton unique, and hydrogen bonding can often be regarded as an intermediate stage in a proton-transfer reaction.   The second type of binding is in *electron-deficient compounds* such as the boron hydrides, where (in the most recent interpretation) the proton forms part of a three-center bond involving two electrons.   This phenomenon differs fundamentally from hydrogen bonding in the usual sense of the term, and it does not necessarily involve a proton, though it usually does so.   The analogy with the other special properties of the proton is a thin one, and this topic will not be treated further.

The masses of nuclei are not usually of primary importance in chemical problems, since the forces concerned depend on electronic and nuclear charges rather than on masses.   There are, however, a number of situations in which it is of importance that the proton is the lightest nucleus known, having only one-twelfth of the mass of carbon, the next common element in the periodic table.   Since hydrogen forms strong bonds with many elements, the combination of low mass and high force constant produces stretching frequencies for bonds of the type X—H which are considerably higher than for any other bonds.   This would be of little importance if classical mechanics could be applied to molecular phenomena, but in terms of quantum theory it means that bonds containing hydrogen have large vibrational quanta $h\nu$, amounting to

5 to 10 kilocalories per mole. Any phenomena involving departures from classical behavior are therefore particularly prominent in compounds of hydrogen. A notable example of this is in the differences between the isotopes hydrogen, deuterium, and tritium. Isotopic differences depend primarily on differences in zero-point energies ($\frac{1}{2}h\nu$), and these depend in turn on vibrational frequencies and on the ratios of isotopic masses. For most elements the frequencies are low and the mass ratios close to unity, so that isotopes differ only slightly in their chemical behavior. For hydrogen, on the other hand, the frequencies are high and the masses in the ratio $1:2:3$; hence *hydrogen isotope effects* are very large, both for equilibria and in kinetic problems. Many investigations have been carried out on isotope effects in the equilibria and kinetics of proton-transfer reactions, and the results should ultimately constitute a severe test of the theory of isotope effects, besides providing information about the mechanism of the reactions concerned.

In the kinetic field there is another way in which the small mass of the proton may be important. It is well known that the behavior of electrons cannot be accounted for in terms of a particulate model but that it is necessary to take into account the wave nature of the electron; on the other hand, it is usually supposed that the motion of nuclei can be described with sufficient accuracy by the laws of classical mechanics. This is undoubtedly true for most nuclei, but calculation shows that the proton may, on account of its small mass, show considerable deviations from classical behavior. This phenomenon is often described as the *tunnel effect* and should be detectable experimentally, especially by a detailed analysis of kinetic isotope effects. At present the experimental evidence is meager, but the problem is an interesting one and will be treated in some detail.

Finally, the nuclear magnetic properties of the proton have recently become of great importance to chemists in the technique known as *proton magnetic resonance*. Because of the magnetic moment of the nucleus, when placed in a magnetic field it has two orientations of different energies, and transitions between these two levels can be brought about by the absorption of radiation in the radio-frequency range. These frequencies can be measured very accurately and will give information about the environment of the protons in the sample being examined, and also about the rate at which different protons can change places with one another. Similar considerations will, of course, apply to other nuclei having a magnetic moment, but a large proportion of the work done so far has dealt with protons, and the method offers great possibilities for investigating equilibria and kinetics in proton-transfer reactions.

There is thus some justification for taking "The Proton in Chemistry" as a title for bringing together various aspects of the behavior of this particle. As an alternative title "Properties of Acids and Bases" would have served the same purpose to a certain extent. This title, however, is too narrow to include some of the topics mentioned and at the same time the terms "acid" and "base" are often used in a wider sense, without reference to the proton. In any case, Walden published *Salts, Acids, and Bases* in the Baker Non-resident Lectureship series thirty years ago, and it is just as well to have a different title for the present book.

CHAPTER II

The Qualitative Nature of Acids and Bases

THE exact verbal definition of qualitative concepts is more often the province of philosophy than of physical science. However, the various definitions suggested for acids and bases have been closely linked with the development of physical chemistry and have often served to stimulate experimental work and to further our understanding of chemical processes, and we shall therefore devote some time to this subject. The definitions used in the remainder of this book will be those proposed by Brönsted[1] in 1923, namely, *An acid is a species having a tendency to lose a proton, and a base is a species having a tendency to add on a proton.* This can be represented schematically by $A \rightleftharpoons B + H^+$, where A and B are termed a *conjugate (or corresponding) acid-base pair.*[2] Before examining the consequences of this definition and its relation to more recent concepts, we shall consider briefly the previous history of the terms "acid" and "base."

A detailed account of the early history of this subject has been given in an earlier series of Baker Lectures,[3] and only a summary will be attempted here. Like most scientific terms of long standing, the terms "acid" and "base" originated in empirical observations of chemical or

---

[1] J. N. Brönsted, *Rec. trav. chim.*, **42,** 718 (1923).

[2] It is frequently stated that the acid-base definition given here was put forward almost simultaneously by Brönsted and by T. M. Lowry (*Chem. and Ind.,* **42,** 43 [1923]). However, although Lowry's paper undoubtedly contains many of the ideas underlying this definition, especially for bases, it does not contain an explicit definition, and it is nowhere made clear that Lowry at that time regarded NH_4^+ as an acid or $CH_3CO_2^-$ as a base. In fact, in a later paper (*J. Chem. Soc.*, 2562 [1927]) Lowry himself writes, "More novelty is to be found in the perfectly logical conclusion of Brönsted that the anion of an acid is also a base or proton acceptor, in view of the fact that it can combine with a proton to form a molecule of the undissociated acid"; hence it does not seem justifiable to regard Lowry as one of the originators of the definition. I am indebted to Professor E. A. Guggenheim for calling my attention to this point.

[3] P. Walden, *Salts, Acids, and Bases: Electrolytes: Stereochemistry* (New York, 1929).

physical properties, rather than in any theoretical interpretation of the nature of the substances concerned or of their reactions.   Etymologically, the English "acid" and the German *Saüre* both derive from the sour taste of acids in dilute solution (cf. Latin *acetum* "vinegar," and Latin *acidus*, German *sauer*, Old Norse *suur*, all meaning "sour"). Soon, however, other properties were added to this; for example, Boyle (end of the seventeenth century) included solvent power and the ability to turn blue vegetable dyes red, and William Lewis (1746) included effervescence with chalk.   Acids were also recognized by their power of combining with bases (or alkalis) to form salts, usually with the liberation of water, while bases were chiefly characterized, apart from their part in salt formation, by their negative properties of destroying or reversing the effects caused by acids.   The complementary nature of acids and bases was at one time emphasized very strongly, as may be illustrated by a quotation from Gay-Lussac: "Acidity and alkalinity are properties which are related interchangeably to one another, one of which can be defined only through the other.   Thus oil in soaps behaves like an acid, because it satisfies the alkalis.   In several ethereal substances alcohol behaves as an alkali, because it satisfies acids."[4]

Apart from these phenomenological definitions, the first theory of acidic behavior which is comprehensible in modern terms is that of Lavoisier (end of the eighteenth century), who regarded oxygen as the "acidifying principle" which converted elements such as carbon, nitrogen, and sulfur into acids like carbonic, nitric, and sulfuric.   The assumption that all acids must contain oxygen led to the view that hydrochloric acid, and therefore chlorine, contained oxygen; in fact, hydrochloric acid and chlorine were known as muriatic acid and oxymuriatic acid respectively.   It was Davy (1810–1815) who first questioned this interpretation, and the discovery of hydrobromic, hydriodic, and hydrocyanic acids cast further doubt on the oxygen theory.   In fact, by 1830 the following oxygen-free acids were known: HF, HCl, HBr, HI, HCN, $HSCN$, H_2S, H_2Se, H_2Te, H_2SiF_6, and HBF_4. In spite of this, the oxygen theory was strongly supported by some chemists, notably Berzelius and Gay-Lussac, up to about 1840.   A reminder of Lavoisier's views still persists in the word "oxygen," which is derived through the French *oxygéne* from the Greek οξοs, "vinegar," οξυs, "sour," and γενναω, "I produce."

Davy at first expressed the opinion that "acidity does not depend upon any particular elementary substance, but upon peculiar arrangement of various substances," a view which we shall meet again in dis-

---

[4] J. L. Gay-Lussac, *Gilb. Ann. d. Phys.*, **48**, 341 (1814)

cussing Lewis' definition of acids. It soon became clear, however, that all the substances commonly accepted as acids did contain hydrogen, and Davy soon recognized hydrogen as the essential element in an acid. Liebig adopted the same idea, especially in relation to organic acids, and in 1838 he defined acids as "compounds containing hydrogen, in which the hydrogen can be replaced by a metal," a definition which held the field until the advent of the ionic theory, and which would still be regarded as essentially correct. Bases were still regarded as substances that reacted with acids to form salts, and there was no theory as to their constitution corresponding to the hydrogen theory of acids.

The theory of electrolytic dissociation (Ostwald and Arrhenius,1880–1890) showed that hydrogen compounds with acidic properties were also those which gave rise to hydrogen ions in aqueous solutions, and the application of the law of mass action to the dissociation equilibrium leads to the dissociation constant as a rational quantitative measure of the strength of an acid. Similarly, basic properties were associated with the production of hydroxyl ions in solution, and the mutually antagonistic effect of acids and bases was explained in terms of the reaction $H^+ + OH^- \rightarrow H_2O$. This led naturally to the definition or acids and bases as substances giving rise to hydrogen and hydroxyl ions respectively in aqueous solution, and this definition was generally accepted for the next thirty or forty years. Many quantitative relations were worked out for dissociation, hydrolysis, buffer solutions, and indicator equilibria, and a satisfactory account was given of a large mass of data.

The success of these quantitative developments helped to obscure some logical weaknesses in the qualitative definitions. For example, it was not clear whether a pure nonconducting substance like anhydrous hydrogen chloride should be called an acid or whether it became one only on contact with water. The definition did not apply directly to nonaqueous solvents, where the ions formed differed from those in water, and this difficulty was particularly acute when it was realized that "typical" acid-base properties such as neutralization, indicator effects, and catalysis often appeared in solvents such as benzene and chloroform where free ions could barely be detected by conductivity methods. A particular ambiguity appears in the definition of bases, some of which (e.g., metallic hydroxides) contain a hydroxyl group, whereas others (e.g., amines) produce hydroxyl ions in solution by abstracting a proton from a water molecule. Some authors[5] distinguished

[5] E.g., A. Werner, *Z. anorg. Chem.*, **3**, 267 (1893); **15**, 1 (1897); *Ber.*, **40**, 4133 (1907).

these two classes as "aquo-bases" and "anhydro-bases" respectively, but there was no general agreement.

Most of these difficulties and ambiguities are removed by the Brönsted definition in terms of the scheme $A \rightleftharpoons B + H^+$. This is now in such general use that only a few points will be mentioned here.[6] The symbol H^+ represents the proton, and not the "hydrogen ion" of variable nature existing in different solvents, so that the definition is independent of the solvent. Acids need not be neutral molecules such as HCl and CH_3CO_2H but may also be anions (HSO_4^-, $CO_2H \cdot CO_2^-$) and cations (NH_4^+, $Fe(H_2O)^{3+}$). The same is true of bases, where the three classes can be illustrated by RNH_2, H_2O, $CH_3CO_2^-$, HPO_4^{2-}, and $Fe(H_2O)_5OH^{2+}$. Since the free proton cannot exist in solution in measurable concentrations, all actual acid-base reactions are of the type $A_1 + B_2 \rightleftharpoons B_1 + A_2$, where A_1—B_1 and A_2—B_2 are two conjugate acid-base pairs. This scheme includes reactions formerly described by a variety of names, such as dissociation, neutralization, hydrolysis, and buffer action. One acid-base pair may involve the solvent (in water H_3O^+—H_2O or H_2O—OH^-), showing that ions such as H_3O^+ and OH^- are in principle only particular examples of an extended class of acids and bases, though of course they do occupy a particularly important place in practice.

The only acid-base definition which is now a serious rival to that of Brönsted is the one formulated by Lewis.[7] Originally put forward in 1923, it did not receive much attention at first, but more recently it has attracted many supporters; for example, the preface to a book written in 1946[8] compares its importance in chemistry with that of the theory of relativity in physics. In view of such claims it is wise to state at once that it is misleading to speak of an "electronic theory" of acids and bases; the question is essentially one of the convenience and consistency of different verbal usages, and not of any fundamental differences in the interpretation of experimental facts. We shall examine briefly some of the arguments for and against the usage proposed by Lewis.[9]

Lewis aims at broadening the acid-base definition both from the ex-

[6] For a fuller account see R. P. Bell, *Chem. Soc. Quart. Rev.*, 1, 115 (1947).

[7] G. N. Lewis, *Valency and the Structure of Atoms and Molecules* (New York, 1923).

[8] W. F. Luder and S. Zuffanti, *The Electronic Theory of Acids and Bases* (New York, 1946).

[9] For a further discussion see I. M. Kolthoff, *J. Phys. Chem.*, 44, 51 (1944); Bell, *loc. cit.* (6).

perimental and from the theoretical standpoint.[10] From the experimental point of view he includes in the definition all substances which exhibit "typical" acid-base properties (neutralization, replacement, effect on indicators, and catalysis) irrespective of their chemical nature or mode of action. On the theoretical side he relates these properties to the acceptance (by acids) and the donation (by bases) of electron pairs to form covalent bonds, regardless of whether protons are involved. The theoretical definition of bases is substantially the same as in the Brönsted scheme, since species which can add on a proton contain an unshared pair of electrons and will also combine with other electron acceptors. Thus the base NH_3 combines with a proton to give NH_4 and with boron trifluoride to give $H_3\overset{+}{N}$—$\overset{-}{B}F_3$. On the other hand, the list of acids is radically altered. Lewis writes, "Any similar and instructive extension of the idea of acids has been prevented by what I am tempted to call the modern cult of the proton." The typical acids of the Lewis definition are molecules like $AlCl_3$, BF_3, and SO_3, which are able to expand their shell of valency electrons by receiving one or more electron pairs. These are not acids at all in the Brönsted sense, since they contain no hydrogen. Classical acid-base reactions as usually written do not reveal any electron deficiencies, and, in fact, the acids of the older definitions (HCl, H_2SO_4, CH_3COOH, etc.) can only be included in the Lewis scheme by rather indirect means. The reaction between an acid HX and a base B is pictured as taking place through an initial stage XH----B in which the hydrogen accepts extra electrons from the base. Proton-transfer reactions are undoubtedly often initiated by the formation of a hydrogen bond, but it is not now believed that the hydrogen in this bond ever receives more than the two electrons which it originally possessed. Lewis himself has said: "Evidently what has become known as the hydrogen bond differs not only in degree but in kind from a true chemical bond,"[11] and for this reason the proton acids are sometimes referred to as "secondary acids" by Lewis and his school.[12]

[10] See particularly G. N. Lewis, *J. Franklin Inst.*, **226**, 293 (1938); W. F. Luder, *Chem. Rev.*, **27**, 247 (1940).

[11] G. N. Lewis, T. T. Magel, and D. Lipkin, *J. Am. Chem. Soc.*, **64**, 1774 (1942).

[12] They also use the term "secondary acid" in a different sense, to denote some acidic oxides and other substances which, as usually written, cannot expand their electron shell but nevertheless give rise to acidic properties (e.g., CO_2, $R \cdot COCl$). Thus CO_2 can be logically termed a Lewis acid only by writing it in the form $O{=}\overset{+}{C}{-}\overset{-}{O}$.

On the experimental side it is certainly true that Lewis' definition brings together a wide range of qualitative phenomena: for example, solutions of BF_3 or SO_3 in inert solvents cause color changes in indicators very similar to those produced by HCl, and these changes are reversed by bases, so that titrations can be carried out. Similarly, the same substances catalyze a large number of organic reactions, some of which are also catalyzed by proton acids. This analogy is, however, a somewhat superficial one; thus every proton acid will react with the base NH_3 to form the conjugate acid $\overset{+}{N}H_4$, but with Lewis acids the initial product $\overset{-}{X}—\overset{+}{N}H_3$ will be different in every reaction and may or may not dissociate further. Consequently, the similar catalytic effects and indicator colors represent analogous electronic displacements rather than a strict parallelism in the nature of the reactions.

We have seen that the Lewis definition of acids does not really represent an extension or generalization of the older concepts, but rather the use of the word "acid" in a fundamentally different sense, and for this reason alone there would be some grounds for treating proton acids separately. However, the greatest justification for such a separate treatment lies in the quantitative relationships involved. In the proton-transfer reactions the knowledge of one constant for each conjugate acid-base pair (for a given temperature and solvent) is sufficient to determine the position of equilibrium in any dilute mixture of acids and bases provided that the dielectric constant is not too low. Similar predictions can be made to a limited extent about reaction velocities, which are commonly closely related to acid-base strengths. In fact, the most important aspects of the classical acid-base concepts are the quantitative relationships to which they lead. No such general quantitative treatment can be envisaged for Lewis acids. Although little quantitative work has yet been done, many facts are already known which show (to quote Lewis, *loc. cit.* [10]) that "the relative strengths of acids and bases depend not only upon the chosen solvent, but also upon the particular acid or base used for reference." For example, in the classical sense ammonia is a much weaker base than hydroxyl ion, but if referred to the Lewis acid Ag^+ the order is reversed, since AgOH is a strong electrolyte while $Ag(NH_3)_2^+$ is a stable complex.

These lectures will be devoted mainly to the quantitative aspects of proton-transfer reactions. The question of nomenclature is not in itself of fundamental importance, and the situation has been much confused by the various uses of terms like "primary acid," "secondary acid," "pseudo acid," and "proto-acid" (the last being proposed by Kolthoff for acids which do *not* contain a proton!). We shall use the terms "acid" and "base" only in relation to the Brönsted definition $A \rightleftharpoons B + H^+$ and shall refer to molecules such as BF_3, as *Lewis acids* or *electron acceptors*, the latter being fully descriptive of their functions. In some cases there may be doubt as to the nature of the acidic function, especially when some of the species concerned may be hydrated in solution. For example, the first dissociation of boric acid is commonly written as $H_3BO_3 \rightleftharpoons H_2BO_3^- + H^+$, representing it as a Brönsted acid. Recent work on the Raman spectrum of borate solutions[13] shows, however, that the borate ion in aqueous solution is almost certainly $B(OH)_4^-$ (analogous to BF_4^-), so that the dissociation of boric acid would be more correctly written as $B(OH)_3 + H_2O \rightleftharpoons B(OH)_4^- + H^+$, or $B(OH)_3 + OH^- \rightleftharpoons B(OH)_4^-$, thus representing boric acid as an electron acceptor or Lewis acid. On the other hand, it is quite possible that the boric acid molecule itself exists in aqueous solution as $(OH)_3\overset{-}{B}\!-\!\overset{+}{O}H_2$, in which case its dissociation would again involve the loss of a proton. For most purposes these distinctions are quite unimportant, but they may be significant when considering time-dependent processes (cf. pp. 178–179).

The terms *pseudo acid* and *pseudo base* have been widely used in the older literature, before the advent of Lewis' concepts, and it is convenient to consider here the present status of this description. The most commonly quoted example of a pseudo acid is nitromethane, which is a weak acid of dissociation constant about 10^{-10}. Whereas most acids are neutralized effectively instantaneously by strong bases such as aqueous sodium hydroxide, with nitromethane this process takes place at a measurable rate. This slow neutralization was first observed by Hantzsch,[14] who regarded it as the characteristic property of a pseudo acid. He also observed later that the absorption spectrum of the nitromethane anion differs considerably from that of the parent substance, which could be interpreted (using modern structural formulas) in terms of the structural change

$$CH_3\cdot\overset{+}{N}\!\!\overset{\displaystyle O}{\underset{\displaystyle O^-}{\diagdown}} \quad \rightarrow \quad CH_2\!:\!\overset{+}{N}\!\!\overset{\displaystyle O^-}{\underset{\displaystyle O^-}{\diagup}} \ .$$

The anion can be regarded as derived from a "true acid" or an *aci*-isomer of nitromethane, having the structure

[13] J. O. Edwards, G. C. Morrison, V. F. Ross, and J. W. Schulz, *J. Am. Chem. Soc.*, **77**, 266 (1955).

[14] A. Hantzsch, *Ber.*, **32**, 575 (1899).

$$CH_2 : \overset{+}{N} \overset{\displaystyle O^-}{\underset{\displaystyle OH}{<}} \quad ,$$

and although this actual substance cannot be isolated or detected the analogous $C_6H_5 \cdot CH : NO \cdot OH$ and several similar compounds can be obtained as pure solids, though they are thermodynamically unstable and revert readily to the normal isomers. Since it was regarded as unthinkable that a neutralization reaction could take place at a measurable speed, Hantzsch supposed that the slow process was the conversion of the ordinary form of nitromethane (a pseudo acid) into the *aci*-form (a true acid), which was then neutralized rapidly by the alkali, i.e.,

$$CH_3 \cdot \overset{+}{N} \overset{\displaystyle O^-}{\underset{\displaystyle O}{\diagdown}} \quad \xrightarrow[\text{Slow}]{} \quad CH_2 : \overset{+}{N} \overset{\displaystyle O^-}{\underset{\displaystyle OH}{<}}$$

$$CH_2 : \overset{+}{N} \overset{\displaystyle O^-}{\underset{\displaystyle OH}{<}} \quad + \ OH^- \quad \xrightarrow[\text{Fast}]{} \quad CH_2 : \overset{+}{N} \overset{\displaystyle O^-}{\underset{\displaystyle O^-}{<}} \quad + \ H_2O.$$

This reaction scheme as it stands would predict a velocity independent of the alkali concentration, but the observed dependence is restored if we suppose that the isomerization reaction is catalyzed by hydroxyl ions. This is quite reasonable, since analogous changes, such as keto-enol tautomerism, are known to be very sensitive to catalysis by bases. A similar two-stage process was suggested by Hantzsch for many other neutralizations involving a change in absorption spectra, even when they are effectively instantaneous. Finally, in fact, Hantzsch himself was led to describe almost every acid as a pseudo acid on the basis of slight optical changes on ionization.[15] Such a wide extension of the term destroys its usefulness, and few other authors have followed him here.

Later developments have largely removed the justification for speaking of a separate class of pseudo acids, even if restricted to the nitroparaffins and similar substances. In the first place (as was first pointed

[15] A. Hantzsch, *Z. Elektrochem.*, **29**, 244 (1923); **30**, 202 (1924); *Ber.*, **58**, 953 (1925).

out clearly by Pedersen[16]), we do not now believe that the neutralization of nitromethane involves the intermediate formation of the *aci*-form, but rather that the removal of a proton from CH_3NO_2 to give

is itself a relatively slow process, because of the degree of electronic reorganization involved; the charge on the anion is not associated with the atom from which the proton has been removed. As will be seen later, many of the phenomena of acid-base catalysis can be explained in terms of slow proton transfers of this kind. In fact, Hantzsch's explanation has effectively been turned inside out, since we do not now think that a change such as *aci*-form → *nitro*-form (or keto → enol) commonly takes place by a single-stage migration of a hydrogen atom, and current mechanisms for these changes involve the anion as an intermediate.

In the second place, it is now realized that the direct observation of a measurable reaction rate with hydroxyl ions is an arbitrary criterion to adopt. Thus the neutralization of nitromethane by strong alkalis has a velocity constant of about 25 l. mole^{-1} sec.$^{-1}$ at 25°C, which is uncomfortably fast for measurements by conventional methods.[17] However, techniques are now available for studying reactions in solution with velocity constants up to 10^{11} l. mole^{-1} sec.$^{-1}$, a value of 1.5×10^{11} having been recently given for the reaction $H_3O^+ + OH^- \rightarrow 2H_2O$.[18] There is no doubt that acid-base reactions exist which cover the whole intermediate range of velocities, and the concept of a "measurable" velocity thus depends entirely on the experimental facilities available.

Equally unsatisfactory is the suggestion of defining a pseudo acid on the basis of the structural change (or charge shift) which it undergoes on ionization, as revealed by the change in optical properties. In the nitroparaffins this change is a fairly clear-cut one, consisting of a shift of charge from the carbon to the oxygen atoms, but changes of this

[16] K. J. Pedersen, *Kgl. Danske Vid. Selsk. Math.-fys. Medd.*, **12**, No. 1 (1932); *J. Phys. Chem.*, **38**, 581 (1934).

[17] Hantzsch, and most later workers, made measurements in the neighborhood of 0°C.

[18] M. Eigen and J. Schoen, *Z. Elektrochem.*, **59**, 483 (1955); M. Eigen and L. De Maeyer, *ibid.*, **59**, 986 (1955).

kind are now believed to take place in varying degrees over a wide range of acid-base systems. For example, nitramide, NH_2NO_2, gives an anion which can be written either as $NH^- \cdot NO_2$ or

$$HN:\overset{+}{N}\overset{\displaystyle O^-}{\underset{\displaystyle O^-}{\big<}} ,$$

and the negative charge in the phenate ion is believed to reside partly on the *ortho* and *para* carbon atoms in the ring. Even familiar acids such as carboxylic acids and inorganic oxyacids ionize with a change of structure, since in their anions the negative charge is shared between two or more equivalent oxygen atoms. All of these could be logically termed pseudo acids, but the term would now include the vast majority of known acids. It seems better on the whole to avoid the use of a term which is difficult to define satisfactorily.

The description "pseudo base" could logically have been applied to bases which undergo a structural change on the addition of a proton and are therefore the conjugate bases of pseudo acids. Examples would be the anions of nitroparaffins, or derivatives of γ-pyrone, which acts as a base in the following way:

$$O\overset{\displaystyle CH:CH}{\underset{\displaystyle CH:CH}{\big<}\big>}C{=}O + H^+ \rightleftharpoons {}^+O\overset{\displaystyle CH \cdot CH}{\underset{\displaystyle CH:CH}{\big<}\big>}C \cdot OH;$$

similar changes are responsible for the color change of many plant pigments (anthocyanines and flavones) with pH. However, the term has been more commonly used for a class of organic substances which react with acids (sometimes slowly) to form a cation and water, rather than to add on a proton. The best-known examples are the "carbinol bases" of various triphenylmethane dyes. Thus the carbinol base of crystal violet is $(NMe_2 \cdot C_6H_4)_3C \cdot OH$, and it reacts slowly with acids with the loss of a water molecule to give the ion of the dye, which has the structure

$$(NMe_2 \cdot C_6H_4)_2C{=}\!\!\big<\!\!\!=\!\!\!\big>\!\!={}\overset{+}{N}Me_2$$

where the quinonoid structure and positive charge can be associated with any one of the three benzene rings. This ion reacts slowly with hydroxyl ions to re-form the carbinol base. Similar behavior is met with in simpler compounds such as the pyrazines and acridines,[19] and in strongly acid solvents such as sulfuric acid analogous changes take place with a number of compounds, e.g.,

$$(C_6H_5)_3C \cdot OH + 2H_2SO_4 \rightarrow (C_6H_5)_3C^+ + H_3O^+ + 2HSO_4^-$$
$$R \cdot COOH + 2H_2SO_4 \rightarrow R \cdot CO^+ + H_3O^+ + 2HSO_4^-$$

(with certain carboxylic acids)

$$HNO_3 + 2H_2SO_4 \rightarrow NO_2^+ + H_3O^+ + 2HSO_4^-.$$

These substances would not be termed bases in the Brönsted nomenclature, since they do not accept protons, but it would be convenient to have a term for describing them. It seems undesirable to retain "pseudo base," because of a misleading analogy with "pseudo acid," and a more descriptive term would be "aquo-base," originally used by Werner to distinguish the metallic hydroxides from the "anhydrobases" like ammonia and the amines.[20]

[19] A. Hantzsch and M Kalb, *Ber.*, **32**, 3116 (1899); J. G. Aston, *J. Am. Chem. Soc.*, **52**, 5254 (1930); **53**, 1448 (1931).

[20] Werner, *loc. cit.* (5); *Neuere Anchauungen auf dem Gebiete der anorganischen Chemie*, 2nd ed. (Braunschweig, 1909), p. 218.

CHAPTER III

The Definition and Measurement of Acid-Base Strengths in Aqueous Solution

SINCE the free proton is never encountered in solution, the equation $A \rightleftharpoons B + H^+$, defining an acid-base pair, does not represent a realizable equilibrium, and all actual acid-base equilibria are of the form $A_1 + B_2 \rightleftharpoons B_1 + A_2$. Any qualitatively sensible concept of acid-base strength would imply that the equilibrium conversion of $A_1 + B_2$ to $B_1 + A_2$ will be more complete the stronger the acid A_1 and the base B_2 and the weaker the acid A_2 and the base B_1. Quantitatively, the equilibrium constant $[B_1][A_2]/[A_1][B_2]$ is equal to the ratio of the (hypothetical) constants $[B_1][H^+]/[A_1]$ and $[B_2][H^+]/[A_2]$, and it will therefore measure the ratio of the acid strengths of A_1 and A_2, or the ratio of the base strengths of B_2 and B_1. Since these two ratios are equal, there is no point in considering the acid and base strengths separately, and it has become usual to describe the properties of any acid-base pair A—B in terms of the acid strength of A. Thus for the pair CH_3COOH—CH_3COO^- we speak of the acid strength of acetic acid rather than the base strength of acetate ion, and for the pair NH_4^+—NH_3 of the acid strength of the ammonium ion rather than the base strength of ammonia.

This approach leads only to the relative strengths of acids (or bases), and it does not seem possible, even in principle, to attach a meaning to the "absolute" strength of an acid or base. Under these circumstances it is natural to measure strengths relative to some standard acid-base pair A_0—B_0, the acid strength for another pair A—B then being given by the equilibrium constant $[B][A_0]/[A][B_0]$. The usual procedure is to use the *solvent* as the source of the standard pair A_0—B_0. In aqueous solution there are two possible pairs, H_3O^+—H_2O, or H_2O—OH^-, and the first of these is commonly used. The rational measure of the strength of any acid A is then $[B][H_3O^+]/[A][H_2O]$, but since the concentration of water is effectively constant in dilute aqueous solutions it is usual to omit it from the equation, thus giving the usual ex-

18

pression for the *acid dissociation constant* $K_c = [\text{B}][\text{H}_3\text{O}^+]/[\text{A}]$. This is strictly a constant only in very dilute solution, partly because of the omission of the term $[\text{H}_2\text{O}]$, but more significantly because at least two of the species A, B, and H_3O^+ are ions, and therefore do not obey the simple law of mass action except in very dilute solutions. This can, of course, be formally corrected by replacing concentrations by activities, but for the sake of simplicity we shall in many cases use the simpler concentration constants K_c. The symbol K will be reserved for the thermodynamic dissociation constant (equal to K_c in very dilute solution). Similarly, since the observed constants vary through many powers of ten, it is often convenient to use the quantities $pK = -\log K$ and $pK_c = -\log K_c$. Obviously, the higher the pK, the weaker the acid and the stronger the base in the pair A—B.

We have written the hydrogen ion in water as H_3O^+, and although the treatment of dilute solutions is not affected by the assumptions made about the hydration of the proton (because of the high and constant concentration of water) this is a convenient point for considering the evidence for the existence of the species H_3O^+, often referred to as the *oxonium* or *hydronium* ion.

The clearest evidence for the existence of H_3O^+ comes from the solid hydrates of strong acids such as nitric, perchloric, and sulfuric acid and the hydrogen halides. Thus it was shown by Volmer[1] that the monohydrate of perchloric acid is isomorphous with ammonium perchlorate and gives a very similar set of X-ray reflections. This suggests strongly that it is an ionic crystal $\text{H}_3\text{O}^+ \cdot \text{ClO}_4^-$, and analogous structures are likely for the other hydrates. A definite proof of this, however, had to wait for modern methods of locating hydrogen atoms in crystals, of which the most powerful is proton magnetic resonance. The characteristic frequencies for the transition between different orientations of the proton nuclear magnetic moment are very sensitive to the environment of the proton, and in particular to the proximity of other protons. A group of several protons gives a pattern of frequencies which is characteristic of their number and of their geometrical arrangement, and a quantitative treatment of this pattern yields information about the distances between the protons. Thus Richards and Smith[2] studied the proton magnetic resonance spectra of the solid hydrates $\text{HNO}_3 \cdot \text{H}_2\text{O}$, $\text{HClO}_4 \cdot \text{H}_2\text{O}$, and $\text{H}_2\text{SO}_4 \cdot \text{H}_2\text{O}$ and in each case concluded that the crystals contained three protons in an equilateral triangle; alternative

[1] A. Volmer, *Ann.*, **440**, 200 (1924).

[2] R. E. Richards and J. A. S. Smith, *Trans. Faraday Soc.*, **47**, 1261 (1951). See also Y. Kakiuchi, H. Shono, H. Matsu, and K. Kigoshi, *J. Chem. Phys.*, 19, 1069 (1951); *J. Phys. Soc. Japan*, **7**, 102 (1952), for $\text{HClO}_4 \cdot \text{H}_2\text{O}$.

structures such as a hydrogen-bonded $H_2O\cdots H-X$ would have given an entirely different type of spectrum. This points to a pyramidal or planar ion H_3O^+, and by combining the observed proton-proton distances with reasonable values of the $O-H$ bond length Richards and Smith concluded that it was a flat pyramid with $H-O-H$ about 115 degrees. Further evidence comes from the infrared spectra of the same solids. Bethell and Sheppard[3] concluded that the spectrum of $HNO_3 \cdot H_2O$ contained bonds characteristic of the ion H_3O^+, but there are complications due to overlapping by NO_3^- frequencies. Ferriso and Hornig[4] examined the monohydrates of the four hydrogen halides and detected in each of them four infrared fundamental frequencies characteristic of a pyramidal H_3O^+. (A planar ion H_3O^+ would have only three frequencies active in the infrared spectrum.) The Raman spectrum of H_3O^+ is more difficult to observe, and observations on powdered $H_3O^+ \cdot ClO_4^-$, $H_3O^+ \cdot HSO_4^-$, $H_3O^+ \cdot NO_3^-$, and $(H_3O^+)_2 \cdot SO_4^{2-}$[5] served only to establish the presence of the anions indicated in these formulas, from which the presence of the H_3O^+ cation can be inferred indirectly. Raman frequencies characteristic of H_3O^+ itself have been found with single crystals of $H_3O^+ \cdot ClO_4^-$,[6] and show a satisfactory correspondence with the infrared frequencies.

The existence of ionic crystals with the formula $H_3O^+X^-$ makes it possible to estimate thermochemically the energy change in the gas reaction $H^+ + H_2O \rightarrow H_3O^+$, i.e., the proton affinity of water, P_{H_2O}. This is done by means of the following cycle:

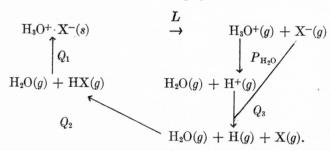

Q_1 is the calorimetric heat of formation of the hydrate from HX gas and water vapor, Q_2 the heat of dissociation of gaseous HX, and Q_3 the sum of the ionization potential of H and the electron affinity of X.

[3] D. E. Bethell and N. Sheppard, *J. Chem. Phys.*, **21**, 1421 (1953).

[4] C. C. Ferriso and D. F. Hornig, *J. Chem. Phys.*, **23**, 1464 (1955).

[5] D. J. Millen and E. G. Vaal, *J. Chem. Soc.*, 2913 (1956).

[6] J. T. Mullhaupt and D. F. Hornig, *J. Chem. Phys.*, **24**, 169 (1956); R. C. Taylor and G. L. Vidale, *J. Am. Chem. Soc.*, **78**, 5999 (1956).

The two unknown quantities are thus L, the lattice energy of the crystal, and P_{H_2O}. In order to obtain the latter it is necessary to make an estimate of the lattice energy, and since the detailed crystal structures of the hydrates are not known this is usually done by analogy with similar crystals. Thus Grimm[7] assumed that $H_3O^+ \cdot Cl^-$ and KCl had the same lattice energies and arrived at the value $P_{H_2O} = 160$ kcal/mole. A more reliable procedure is that employed by Sherman.[8] He first derives the energy of the process $NH_3 + H^+ \rightarrow NH_4^+$, $P_{NH_3} = 207$ kcal/mole, by applying a cycle like that given above to the crystals NH_4Cl, NH_4Br, and NH_4I; these have accurately known crystal structures, and their lattice energies can therefore be calculated with fair certainty. He then considers analogous cycles for the crystals NH_4ClO_4 and H_3OClO_4, making the very reasonable assumption that their lattice energies are the same. Each cycle involves the energy of the process $H^+(g) + ClO_4^-(g) \rightarrow HClO_4(l)$, which is unknown, but this quantity is eliminated by subtraction, and we have finally $P_{NH_3} - P_{H_2O} = Q_1' - Q_1$, where Q_1' and Q_1 are the calorimetric heats of reaction for the reactions $NH_3(g) + HClO_4(l) \rightarrow NH_4ClO_4(s)$ and $H_2O(g) + HClO_4(l) \rightarrow H_3ClO_4(s)$. This leads finally to $P_{H_2O} = 182$ kcal/mole, and it is interesting to note that two attempts to calculate P_{H_2O} theoretically gave approximate values of 200 and 180 kcal/mole.[9]

There is thus good evidence of the existence in the solid state of the species H_3O^+, with a stability comparable with that of the ammonium ion, and this ion would be expected to retain its individuality in solution. Some of the earliest evidence on this point came from a study of nonaqueous solutions. For example, Goldschmidt[10] studied the retarding effect of small quantities of water on acid-catalyzed esterification reactions in various alcohols and interpreted his results in terms of the equilibrium $H^+(ROH)_n + H_2O \rightleftharpoons nROH + H_3O^+$, it being assumed that the catalytic effect of H_3O^+ is small compared with that of $H^+(ROH)_n$. This reaction scheme gave quantitative agreement with the observed results, while any other assumption about the hydration of the proton would destroy this agreement.[11] The same con-

[7] H. G. Grimm, *Z. Elektrochem.*, **31**, 474 (1925).

[8] J. Sherman, *Chem. Rev.*, **11**, 164 (1932).

[9] K. Fajans, *Ber. d. deutscher phys. Gesell.*, **21**, 709 (1919); F. Hund, *Z. Physik*, **32**, 1 (1925).

[10] H. Goldschmidt and O. Udby, *Z. physikal. Chem.*, **60**, 728 (1907); H. Goldschmidt, *Z. Elektrochem.*, **15**, 4 (1909).

[11] It is reasonable to assume by analogy that the "hydrogen ion" in an alcohol ROH has the formula ROH_2^+, hence that the equilibrium can be written

clusion was reached by other authors, who studied the inhibiting effect
of water on the hydrogen-ion-catalyzed alcoholysis of ethyl diazoacetate,[12] and a similar treatment has been applied to the effect of small
quantities of water upon the conductivity of solutions of strong acids
in methyl and ethyl alcohol,[13] and to the effect of water additions on
the dissociation constant of picric acid in ethyl alcohol.[14]   The following observation also gives a clear illustration of the strong tendency of
the proton to attach a single molecule of water.   Liquid sulfur dioxide
alone dissolves very little water, but a nonconducting solution of hydrogen bromide in liquid sulfur dioxide dissolves an equivalent amount
of water and becomes a good conductor.   When this solution is elec-
trolyzed, one equivalent of water per Faraday is liberated at the
cathode.[15]

It has proved much more difficult to get clear evidence of the existence of recognizable H_3O^+ ions in aqueous solutions of acids, and there
are three reasons why this is so.   Firstly, the characteristic properties
of H_3O^+ (for example, its spectral frequencies) will not differ very much
from those of H_2O, which is present in very large excess.   Secondly, the
ion H_3O^+ in aqueous solution will undoubtedly be further hydrated by
the more or less firm attachment of additional water molecules, and
this will make it difficult to recognize it.   Thirdly, there is good evidence that the protons in H_3O^+ can exchange very rapidly with those
in liquid water, so that the lifetime of any individual H_3O^+ ion may be
too short to endow it with characteristic properties.   This last circumstance makes it impossible to obtain any structural information from
studies of proton magnetic resonance in solution, since because of the
rapid interchange the observed frequency is averaged over the different kinds of proton present.   Many attempts to detect the hydronium
ion in aqueous solution by its infrared or Raman spectrum have been
unsuccessful.   Pure water gives a diffuse vibrational spectrum without
any well-defined frequencies, and although this is modified by the addition of acid most workers have failed to detect any new frequencies.[16]
Recently, however, Falk and Giguère[17] have reported measurements of

$ROH_2^+ + H_2O \rightleftharpoons ROH + H_3O^+$; however, this cannot be deduced from experiments in which the concentration of the alcohol is effectively constant.

[12] G. Bredig, *Z. Elektrochem.*, **18**, 535 (1912); W. S. Millar, *Z. physikal. Chem.*,
85, 129 (1913).

[13] G. Nonhebel and H. B. Hartley, *Phil. Mag.*, **50**, 734 (1925); L. Thomas and
E. Marum, *Z. physikal. Chem.*, **143**, 213 (1929).

[14] P. Gross, A. Jamöck, and F. Patat, *Monatsh.*, **63**, 124 (1933).

[15] L. S. Bagster and G. Cooling, *J. Chem. Soc.*, 693 (1920).

[16] See, e.g., R. Suhrmann and F. Breyer, *Z. physikal. Chem.*, **23B**, 193 (1933).

[17] M. Falk and P. A. Giguère, *Canad. J. Chem.*, **35**, 1195 (1957).

infrared spectra which clearly characterize the H_3O^+ ion in solution. They examined very thin layers of concentrated solutions of HCl, HBr, HNO_3, $HClO_4$, and H_3PO_4 and of some acid salts of the last two acids. In every case they were able to detect three broad absorption bands at 1,205, 1,750, and 2,900 cm.$^{-1}$ which are in good agreement with three of the frequencies attributed to H_3O^+ in the solid state. Measurements with DCl in D_2O give correspondingly lower frequencies of 960, 1,400, and 2,170 cm.$^{-1}$ The detection of an H_3O^+ vibrational frequency of 1,205 cm.$^{-1}$ means that the lifetime of the vibrating species must be greater than about $1/(3 \times 10^{10} \times 1,205)$ $= 3 \times 10^{-13}$ sec. It is possible that the lifetime is in fact only just long enough to produce an observable vibrational spectrum, since a recent analysis of the rate processes involved in the mobility of the hydrogen ion leads to an average lifetime of 2.4×10^{-13} sec.[18] This estimate is, however, subject to some uncertainty, and there will in any case be an appreciable number of hydronium ions with lifetimes exceeding the average value.

There is thus evidence for the existence in the solid state of the ion H_3O^+ with a stability comparable to that of the ammonium ion, and also for retention of identity by this ion in solution. Thermochemical data for the hydrogen ion in solution are in harmony with this view. Various estimates have been made for the heat evolved in the process $H^+(g) + \infty H_2O(liq) \rightarrow H_3O^+(aq)$, which we shall denote by $Q_s(H^+)$, the heat of solution of the proton. Early estimates of the quantity were about 250 kcal/mole,[19] but the most reliable value is probably that given by Baughan,[20] who considered the cycle

$$
\begin{array}{ccc}
 & \overset{D}{\nearrow} H(g) + X(g) \xrightarrow{\;\;Q'\;\;} H^+(g) + X^-(g) & \\
HX(g) \; \longleftarrow \quad\quad Q_s(H^+) \;\Big\downarrow \quad\Big\downarrow Q_s(X^-) & \\
Q_s(HX) \quad\quad\quad\quad H_3O^+(aq) + X^-(aq) &
\end{array}
$$

where X is a halogen. D is the dissociation energy of HX gas, and Q_s is the sum of the ionization energy of H and the electron affinity of X. HCl, HBr, and HI are completely dissociated in solution, so that $- Q_s(HX)$ is the measured heat of solution of HX gas, but for HF corrections have to be applied for incomplete dissociation in solution

[18] B. E. Conway, J. O'M. Bockris, and H. Linton, *J. Chem. Phys.*, **24**, 834 (1956).

[19] T. J. Webb, *J. Am. Chem. Soc.*, **48**, 2589 (1926); F. J. Garrick, *Phil. Mag.*, [7], **8**, 101 (1929).

[20] E. C. Baughan, *J. Chem. Soc.*, 1403 (1940).

and polymerization in the gas. It is thus possible to obtain unambiguous values for $Q_s(H^+) + Q_s(X^-)$, and the chief uncertainty in the calculation lies in the value adopted for $Q_s(X^-)$, which depends upon an arbitrary splitting up of the experimental values of $Q(M^+) + Q(X^-)$, where M is an alkali metal. The uncertainty thus introduced is not, however, large, and Baughan obtained concordant values of $Q_s(H^+)$ = 283 ± 3 kcal/mole from all four hydrogen halides.[21]

This value of $Q_s(H^+)$ is greater than the heat of solution of any other univalent ion by more than 100 kcal/mole. However, we can think of the solution of the proton as taking place in two stages: (1) $H^+(g)$ + $H_2O(g) \rightarrow H_3O^+(g)$ and (2) $H_3O^+(g) \rightarrow H_3O^+(aq)$, and we have already seen that the energy liberated in the first stage is $P(H_2O) = 182$ kcal/mole. This leaves about 100 kcal/mole for the second stage, which is close to the value for $Q_s(Na^+)$, which is 95 to 116 kcal/mole according to different authors. This is a reasonable conclusion, since Na^+ and H_3O^+ are isoelectronic.

There is thus ample justification for writing the hydrogen ion in aqueous solution as H_3O^+, and it is likely by analogy that the hydrogen ion in nonaqueous solvents is attached particularly firmly to one solvent molecule, so that we normally write ROH_2^+ in an alcohol, R_2COH^+ in a ketone, RNH_3^+ in an amine, and so on. The use of these formulas does not of course deny the looser attachment of further solvent molecules, since these are not usually included when writing the formulas of ions in solution; for example, we commonly write Li^+ and Fe^{3+}, although there is good reason to believe that these ions are actually $Li(H_2O)_4^+$ and $Fe(H_2O)_6^{3+}$. The further hydration of the hydronium ion can be very important in some contexts, as we shall see later in dealing with concentrated solutions.

After this digression on the hydronium ion, we shall survey briefly the methods available for measuring acid-base strengths, especially in aqueous solution. The most obvious methods involve a direct determination of the concentration of A or B in a solution of known total concentration. The best way to estimate these concentrations without disturbing the equilibrium is to use optical properties such as the absorption spectrum (visible or ultraviolet) or the Raman spectrum. For acids or bases of moderate strength the spectrum of pure A or pure B can be obtained experimentally by adding an excess of hydrogen or hydroxyl ions to the solution. If an acid is fairly strong ($K > 10^{-1}$),

[21] In treating the results for HF, Baughan used values for its dissociation energy and for the electron affinity of fluorine which are now known to be considerably in error. These errors cancel out, however, since they both depend on an erroneous value for the dissociation energy of the fluorine molecule.

the reaction $A + H_2O \rightleftharpoons B + H_3O^+$ will go very far to the right, and it may be necessary to use concentrated solutions to get a sufficiently large value of the ratio $[A]/[B]$. The use of concentrated solutions introduces some uncertainty, since the spectrum of any species varies somewhat with environment, especially in its intensity. It appears that optical spectra are considerably influenced in this way, but Raman spectra considerably less so; recently it has been shown that nuclear magnetic resonance measurements are particularly suitable for this purpose, since the "chemical shift" in the observed frequency is determined almost exclusively by the immediate surroundings of the nucleus being observed, i.e., by the bonds and atoms attached to it. Any of these methods will of course in the first instance give K_c, the concentration equilibrium constant, and the evaluation of the thermodynamic K involves extrapolation and the use of other experimental observations. Nevertheless, the use of Raman spectra and nuclear magnetic resonance has made it possible to assign dissociation constants with fair certainty to a number of acids formerly regarded as "strong" in aqueous solution, e.g., nitric acid ($K = 23.5$) and trifluoroacetic acid ($K = 1.8$).[22]

If an acid is very weak, it is often more convenient to use a solution of the conjugate base. For example, phenol has $K \simeq 10^{-10}$, and it would be necessary to go down to concentrations of about 10^{-6}M to obtain 1 percent conversion to phenate ion; on the other hand, a 10^{-2}M solution of sodium phenate is hydrolyzed to the extent of about 10 percent according to the equation $C_6H_5O^- + H_2O \rightleftharpoons C_6H_5OH + OH^-$, and the ratio $[C_6H_5O^-]/[C_6H_5OH]$ could be readily determined by optical means. Similarly, the anilinium ion ($K = 2 \times 10^{-5}$) is converted appreciably into aniline according to the equation $C_6H_5NH_3^+ + H_2O \rightleftharpoons C_6H_5NH_2 + H_3O^+$ at 10^{-3}M, while aniline itself reacts with water to give hydroxyl ions to an extent of less than 1 percent even at a concentration of 10^{-5}M. From this point of view the most awkward acid-base pairs are those with $K \simeq 10^{-3}$, since here either the acid or the base must be diluted to 10^{-5}M in order to obtain 10 percent conversion. In equilibria of the type $B + H_2O \rightleftharpoons A + OH^-$ the acid strength of the pair A—B is of course being compared with H_2O—OH^- rather than with the usual standard H_3O^+—H_2O, but the relation between the two is easily expressed in terms of the ionic product of water.

The use of optical properties is of course restricted to a limited selection of acid-base systems, and methods of more general applicabil-

---

[22] For a critical summary, with references, see O. Redlich and G. C. Hood, *Disc. Faraday Soc.*, **24**, 87 (1957).

ity are based on the properties of the hydronium ion, in particular the e.m.f. of cells containing a reversible hydrogen electrode or some equivalent, such as a glass electrode. Since we are now measuring a thermodynamic quantity, the free energy, the expressions for the e.m.f. of such cells contain the activity rather than the concentration of the hydronium ion, and this type of measurement therefore leads to the thermodynamic K rather than K_c. However, the observed e.m.f. also involves the activities of other ions in the solution in a manner depending on the construction of the cell, and some extrapolation is always necessary to obtain the true value of K. Measurements are best made, not on solutions of the acid or the base alone, but on buffer mixtures, i.e., solutions containing comparable amounts of A and B, often prepared by the partial neutralization of A or B by a strong base or a strong acid respectively. Such solutions are insensitive to small quantities of impurities in the materials used, or derived from the vessels or the atmosphere. It is usual to regard the potential of a hydrogen electrode as being determined by the process $\frac{1}{2}H_2 + H_2O \rightleftharpoons H_3O^+ + \epsilon$, but this is probably unrealistic in a solution of low hydrogen ion concentration. For example, in an alkaline solution the potential-determining process may well be $\frac{1}{2}H_2 + OH^- \rightleftharpoons H_2O + \epsilon$, and in a buffer solution containing a high concentration of an acid-base pair A—B another possible process is $\frac{1}{2}H_2 + B \rightleftharpoons A + \epsilon$. However, if all the acid-base pairs are in equilibrium with one another, it is immaterial which is regarded as determining the potential, since it is a thermodynamic necessity that each pair give the same potential.

The oldest method of determining dissociation constants is of course by measurements of electrolytic conductivity. If the solution is prepared from either an uncharged acid or an uncharged base, the equilibria involved are $BH + H_2O \rightleftharpoons B^- + H_3O^+$ and $B + H_2O \rightleftharpoons BH^+ + OH^-$, and since ions appear on only one side of these equations the method can be used even for very weak acids and bases provided that conducting impurities can be kept down to a very low level. If the solution is made up from the salt of a charged acid or base, e.g., $BH^+ \cdot Cl^-$ or $K^+ \cdot B^-$, the corresponding equations are $BH^+ + H_2O + Cl^- \rightleftharpoons B + H_3O^+ + Cl^-$ and $B^- + H_2O + K^+ \rightleftharpoons BH + OH^- + K^+$, and the situation is clearly less favorable for using the conductivity method. However, the ions H_3O^+ and OH^- have considerably higher mobilities than any other ions, and the measurement of conductivity can be carried out with very high accuracy, so that the method is still applicable provided that the position of equilibrium is not too far to one side.

Conductivity measurements do not lead directly either to K or to K_c, but by making an allowance for the variation of ionic mobilities with environment K_c can be obtained, and hence K by extrapolation to infinite dilution. Since the solutions used have low ionic concentrations, these corrections and extrapolations involve little uncertainty, and the most accurately known dissociation constants are probably those derived from modern conductivity measurements.[23]

The pK of a pair A_1—B_1 is often determined by the addition of a second pair A_2—B_2 (other than the solvent) of known pK, and this can be done in two ways. In the first a buffer solution of A_1—B_1 is prepared, and a very small amount of A_2—B_2 is added, the equilibrium ratio $[A_2]/[B_2]$ being measured by an optical method. The ratio $[A_1]/[B_1]$ is little affected by the addition of A_2—B_2, and the equilibrium constant $[B_1][A_2]/[A_1][B_2]$ is thus known, leading directly to pK_1—pK_2. This is of course the familiar indicator method, A_2—B_2 usually consisting of an organic acid or base absorbing in the visible region. Alternatively, the known system A_2—B_2 can be used to make a buffer solution of fairly high concentration, to which is added a small amount of A_1—B_1, the ratio $[A_1]/[B_1]$ being again determined by optical means, usually by ultraviolet absorption measurements. This procedure is naturally limited in its application but has been successful for certain classes of compound, for example, the pyridine bases,[24] where the conjugate acid and base differ considerably in their ultraviolet absorption.

There are some systems for which ambiguities arise in defining a dissociation constant, independently of the methods used for determining it. One of the long-standing problems of this kind concerns ammonia and the amines. The usual expression for the acid constant is $K_c = [NH_3^*][H_3O^+]/[NH_4^+]$, where $[NH_3^*]$ denotes the total concentration of unionized ammonia in the solution. It has commonly been supposed that ammonia exists in aqueous solution partly as the molecule NH_3 and partly as "ammonium hydroxide" NH_4OH, so that K_c as usually defined is more properly written

$$[H_3O^+][NH_3 + NH_4OH]/[NH_4^+].$$

If it were possible to determine the extent to which NH_3 is converted to NH_4OH in solution, then "true" dissociation constants could be specified for the separate species.[25] The equilibrium $NH_3 + H_2O$

---

[23] See, e.g., F. S. Feates and D. J. G. Ives, *J. Chem. Soc.*, 2798 (1956).

[24] R. J. L. Andon, J. D. Cox and E. F. G. Herington, *Trans. Faraday Soc.*, 50, 918 (1954).

[25] By the Brönsted definition NH_3 would be the true base, and NH_4OH an "aquo-base" (cf. p. 10). Earlier workers concentrated more on the production of hydroxyl ions and defined the "true" basic dissociation constant in terms of the equilibrium $NH_4OH \rightleftharpoons NH_4^+ + OH^-$.

$\rightleftharpoons$ NH$_4$OH is presumably highly mobile, and since water is present in large excess equilibrium measurements in general give no information about the extent of hydration of NH$_3$. Moore and Winmill[26] attempted to solve this problem by measuring the distribution coefficients of ammonia and amines between water and organic solvents over a range of temperature, and their conclusions have often been quoted.[27] These are, however, based on unverifiable assumptions about the distribution coefficients of the individual species, and it is interesting to note that a recent use of the same experimental method has led to conclusions which differ widely from those of Moore and Winmill, though it is doubtful whether they are more trustworthy.[28]

Modern opinion discounts the existence of a definite species such as NH$_4$OH in aqueous solution. It is not possible to write a covalent structure for NH$_4$OH, and the only alternatives are an ion pair NH$_4^+ \cdot$OH$^-$ or a hydrogen-bonded structure such as H—O—H$\cdots$NH$_3$. We do not now believe that ion pairs involving univalent ions exist in appreciable concentrations in aqueous solution, and the energies involved in hydrogen-bond formation are much smaller than ordinary bond energies. Various lines of evidence indicate that the interaction between ammonia and water is a comparatively weak one; thus the solid hydrates NH$_3 \cdot$H$_2$O and 2NH$_3 \cdot$H$_2$O are formed only at low temperatures and are unstable.[29] In a recent thermodynamic study of these solid hydrates[30] they were formulated as NH$_4^+$OH$^-$ and (NH$_4$)$_2$O^{2-}, but their infrared spectra[31] show none of the characteristic frequencies of NH$_4^+$ or OH$^-$ and resemble a superposition of the spectra of NH$_3$ and H$_2$O, with some modifications due to hydrogen bonding. Similarly, the Raman spectrum of ammonia in aqueous solution is very similar to that of anhydrous liquid ammonia,[32] and in general "ammonium hydroxide" differs markedly from the hydrates of the strong acids. Evidence of this kind has led many authors to doubt the existence of hydrates of ammonia or amines as species whose con-

[26] T. S. Moore and T. F. Winmill, *J. Chem. Soc.*, **91**, 1373 (1907); **101**, 1635 (1912).

[27] E.g., N. V. Sidgwick, *Chemical Elements and Their Compounds* (Oxford, 1950), p. 659.

[28] I. B. Khakham, *Zhur. Obshchei Khim.*, **18**, 1215 (1948); *Chem. Abs.*, **43**, 6891 (1949).

[29] L. D. Elliott, *J. Phys. Chem.*, **28**, 887 (1924); I. L. Clifford and E. Hunter, *ibid.*, **37**, 101 (1933).

[30] D. L. Hildenbrand and W. F. Giauque, *J. Am. Chem. Soc.*, **75**, 2811 (1953).

[31] R. D. Waldron and D. F. Hornig, *J. Am. Chem. Soc.*, **75**, 6079 (1953).

[32] B. P. Rao, *Proc. Ind. Acad. Sci.*, **20A**, 292 (1944).

centrations can be specified.[33] It is not of course denied that ammonia and the amines interact with water by hydrogen-bond formation, and interaction of this kind is revealed in the thermodynamic properties of their aqueous solutions[34] and in the variation with concentration of proton magnetic resonance frequencies,[35] the latter measurements showing also that these interactions fluctuate very rapidly. Hydrogen bonding in aqueous solution is, however, common to many solutes and is not usually taken into account in specifying the formula or concentration of the solute. In fact, in the equilibrium $NH_3 + H_2O \rightleftharpoons NH_4^+ + OH^-$ (or the analogous one for amines) the ions NH_4^+ and OH^- certainly interact more strongly with the solvent than does the molecule NH_3, and it would be inconsistent to indicate solvation of the molecule by the formula NH_4OH unless we are also going to express the solvation of the ions. The acid constant of the ion NH_4^+ can thus be expressed simply as $[NH_3][H_3O^+]/[NH_4^+]$, where $[NH_3]$ represents the total concentration of unionized ammonia in the solution irrespective of hydration.

A somewhat similar problem arises in defining the acid strength of carbonic acid. When carbon dioxide is dissolved in water, the following equilibria are set up:

$$CO_2 + H_2O \rightleftharpoons H_2CO_3 \rightleftharpoons HCO_3^- + H_3O^+,$$

and we can define two acid constants,

$$K_c(CO_2) = [HCO_3^-][H_3O^+]/[CO_2 + H_2CO_3],$$

and

$$K_c(H_2CO_3) = [HCO_3^-][H_3O^+]/[H_2CO_3].$$

The normal methods of determining acid strengths do not distinguish between CO_2 and H_2CO_3, and since the equilibrium $CO_2 + H_2O \rightleftharpoons H_2CO_3$ is set up rapidly the quantity usually given as the first dissociation constant of carbonic acid (4.45×10^{-7} at 25°C) is thus $K_c(CO_2)$. So far the problem appears to be very similar to that of ammonia and the amines, but it is in fact a more amenable one. From the theoretical point of view H_2CO_3 (unlike NH_4OH) can be given a normal covalent structure, $O{=}C(OH)_2$, and although it has not been isolated its organic derivatives are well known; thus it is reasonable to speak of the concentra-

[33] See, e.g., P. F. van Velden and J. A. Ketelaar, *Chem. Weekblad*, **43**, 401 (1947).
[34] J. L. Copp and D. H. Everett, *Disc. Faraday Soc.*, **15**, 174 (1953).
[35] H. S. Gutowsky and S. Fujiwara, *J. Chem. Phys.*, **22**, 1782 (1954).

tion of H_2CO_3 in an aqueous solution.   It might be possible in principle to measure the ratio $[H_2CO_3]/[CO_2]$ by some optical method, but this has not been achieved, mainly because this ratio turns out to be a very small one.

All the estimates which have been made depend on the fact that the reversible reaction $H_2O + CO_2 \rightleftharpoons H_2CO_3$ and other reactions involving the CO_2 molecule take place much more slowly than the simple acid-base reactions $H_2CO_3 + H_2O \rightleftharpoons HCO_3^- + H_3O^+$ and $H_2CO_3 + OH^- \rightleftharpoons HCO_3^- + H_2O$, although they are still too fast to study quantitatively by conventional methods.   It was observed at an early date[36] that when carbon dioxide or carbonates are titrated with phenolphthalein as indicator the color change is not instantaneous.   The earliest estimate of the ratio $[H_2CO_3]/[CO_2]$ was given by Thiel,[37] who assumed that the concentration of carbonic acid in aqueous carbon dioxide was given by the amount neutralized by alkali in less than 0.4 seconds.   Though not accurate, his estimate (0.6 percent) was of the right order of magnitude, and later workers used essentially similar methods.   Faurholt[38] added dimethylamine to aqueous carbon dioxide.   This reacts rapidly with carbon dioxide (but not with carbonic acid or its ions) according to the equation $2NHMe_2 + CO_2 \rightarrow NMe_2COO^- + Me_2NH_2^+$, and the remaining carbonic acid is precipitated by adding barium chloride immediately afterward.   The success of this method depends upon the fact that the reaction $H_2CO_3 \rightarrow H_2O + CO_2$ does not proceed to a considerable extent before the barium carbonate is precipitated; actually it has a half-time of only a few seconds at 0°C, so that the method is not capable of great accuracy.   More reliable values for the equilibrium constant for $CO_2 + H_2O \rightleftharpoons H_2CO_3$ have been obtained by direct determinations of the reaction velocities in the two directions.   These can be determined by means of flow methods in conjunction with the measurement of temperature changes, or of changes in pH by indicators[39] or with the glass electrode,[40] or by studying the rate of exchange of the isotope ^{18}O between carbon dioxide and water.[41]   Finally, the most accurate values for the ratio $[H_2CO_3]/[CO_2]$ have been obtained by studying

[36] J. W. McBain, *J. Chem. Soc.*, **101**, 814 (1912); D. Vorländer and S. Strube, *Ber.*, **46**, 172 (1913).

[37] A. Thiel, *Ber.*, **46**, 241 (1912).

[38] C. Faurholt, *J. chim. phys.*, **21**, 400 (1924); **22**, 1 (1925).

[39] F. J. W. Roughton, *J. Am. Chem. Soc.*, **63**, 2930 (1941).

[40] J. Meier and G. Schwarzenbach, *Helv. Chim. Acta*, **40**, 907 (1957).

[41] G. A. Mills and H. C. Urey, *J. Am. Chem. Soc.*, **62**, 1019 (1940).

the conductivity of aqueous carbon dioxide at very high field strengths.[42] This method depends upon the so-called "dissociation field effect," in which the degree of dissociation of a weak electrolyte according to the scheme $AB \rightleftharpoons A^+ + B^-$ is increased by the application of a strong field.[43] The magnitude of this increase can be predicted theoretically in terms of the dissociation constant at low field strengths and the ionic mobilities, and the prediction agrees with experiment for a number of weak electrolytes. In a solution of carbon dioxide the equilibrium $H_2CO_3 + H_2O \rightleftharpoons H_3O^+ + HCO_3^-$ will be affected by the field strength, but not the equilibrium $H_2CO_3 \rightleftharpoons H_2O + CO_2$. Moreover, since the times involved in the measurement are very short (a few microseconds) there is no readjustment of the second equilibrium, and the observed change of conductivity with field strength can be used to obtain the true dissociation constant of H_2CO_3. This leads to the values $K(H_2CO_3) = 1.3 \times 10^{-4}$, $K(CO_2) = 4.5 \times 10^{-7}$, $[H_2CO_3]/[CO_2] = 0.0037$ at 25°C, in satisfactory agreement with earlier values.

Carbonic acid is thus a relatively strong acid, comparable with formic acid, and its apparent weakness is due to the small proportion of dissolved carbon dioxide which is in the form H_2CO_3. As long as we are dealing with equilibrium properties, the distinction between CO_2 and H_2CO_3 is unimportant, and it is quite satisfactory to operate with the "apparent" dissociation constant $K(CO_2)$. However, the distinction does become important as soon as we are dealing with time-dependent phenomena, especially rapid ones, and we shall see later (Chapter X) that the catalytic effect of solutions containing carbon dioxide or bicarbonate ions can be understood only if we know both the true and apparent dissociation constants. An exactly similar situation presumably occurs in solutions of sulfurous acid on account of the equilibrium $SO_2 + H_2O \rightleftharpoons H_2SO_3$. There is evidence[44] from measurements of rates of gas absorption that this equilibrium is not set up instantaneously, but the position of equilibrium is unknown. It would be interesting to make conductivity measurements at high field strengths on this and similar systems.

[42] D. Berg and A. Patterson, *J. Am. Chem. Soc.*, **75**, 5197 (1953); K. F. Wissbrunn, D. M. French, and A. Patterson, *J. Phys. Chem.*, **58**, 693 (1954).

[43] The conductivity of a strong electrolyte is also increased at high field strengths because the ions are moving so fast that the ionic atmospheres are unable to form completely. This is known as the Wien effect: it will also operate in solutions of weak electrolytes, but it is considerably smaller than the dissociation field effect and can be eliminated at sufficiently high field strengths

[44] R. P. Whitney and J. A. Vivian, *Chem. Eng. Progress*, **45**, 323 (1949).

In the system carbon dioxide–carbonic acid, only the latter would be regarded as an acid in the sense of the Brönsted definition, since carbon dioxide has no proton to lose. There are, however, cases in which two isomeric acids are in equilibrium in solution, each being in equilibrium with the same anion. The commonest example involves keto-enol equilibria. If we write the two isomers as SH (keto) and HS (enol), the equilibrium scheme becomes

$$\text{SH} \underset{}{\overset{K_t}{\rightleftharpoons}} \text{HS}$$

$$K_k \searrow \qquad \swarrow K_e,$$

$$\text{S}^- + \text{H}^+$$

omitting the hydration of the hydrogen ion for the sake of brevity. We then have the three equilibrium constants

$$K_t = [\text{HS}]/[\text{SH}], \quad K_k = [\text{S}^-][\text{H}^+]/[\text{SH}], \quad K_e = [\text{S}^-][\text{H}^+]/[\text{HS}]$$

whence

$$K_t = K_k/K_e.$$

If we measure the acid constant for this system by a static method, equilibrium having been attained, the total concentration of undissociated acid is $[\text{SH}] + [\text{HS}]$ and the measured equilibrium constant is

$$K' = [\text{S}^-][\text{H}^+]/[\text{SH} + \text{HS}] = K_k/(K_t + 1) = K_e K_t/(K_t + 1).$$

For example, a dilute aqueous solution of ethyl acetoacetate contains 0.4 percent of enol (determined by bromine titration) and the measured dissociation constant is 2×10^{-11}. This is therefore effectively the dissociation constant of the keto form, and the constant for the enol form is 5×10^{-8}. Since the keto form usually predominates in aqueous solution, the enol form is commonly the stronger acid, but this is not always the case. For example, dimedone (5,5-dimethylcyclohexane-1,3-dione) exists in aqueous solution as 95 percent enol and 5 percent keto, and its apparent dissociation constant is 5.9×10^{-6}; hence in this case the dissociation constants of the keto and enol forms are respectively 1.2×10^{-4} and 5.6×10^{-6}.[45]

The interconversion of the two isomeric forms of an acid is often a relatively slow process, so that it may be possible to measure the dissociation constants of the two forms separately. Thus when acid is added to an alkaline solution of nitroethane (containing the anion

[45] G. Schwarzenbach and E. Felder, *Helv. Chim. Acta*, **27**, 1701 (1944).

$CH_3CH:NOO^-$), the species produced initially is the *aci*-form $CH_3CH:NOOH$, which changes only slowly into the *nitro*-isomer $CH_3CH_2NO_2$; hence if pH measurements are made directly after the addition of acid, they can be used to calculate the dissociation constant of the *aci*-form, which is found to be $K_{aci} = 3.9 \times 10^{-5}$. If similar measurements are made after the system has come to equilibrium, the *aci*-form has been transformed almost completely into the *nitro*-form, and we obtain $K_{nitro} = 3.5 \times 10^{-9}$. The same value is obtained if a solution of nitroethane is partly neutralized with sodium hydroxide. By combining the two dissociation constants, we find at equilibrium $[aci]/[nitro] = K_{nitro}/K_{aci} = 9 \times 10^{-5}$, and in this and similar cases the measurement of the two dissociation constants is the only way of estimating the very small proportion of the *aci*-form which is present at equilibrium.[46]

The acid-base properties of the ion HF_2^- pose a special problem. This species is well defined both in the solid state and in solution. Recent estimates based on the lattice energies of the salts KHF_2 and $RbHF_2$ show that the process $HF + F^- \rightarrow HF_2^-$ in the gas phase is exothermic to the extent of 58 ± 5 kcal/mole,[47] and the equilibrium constant for the same process in aqueous solution has the value 3.9 at 25°C.[48] There is no doubt that the species HF_2^- possesses both acidic and basic properties, since it can both lose and gain a proton; for example, in water we have the equilibria $HF_2^- + H_2O \rightleftharpoons H_3O^+ + 2F^-$ and $HF_2^- + H_3O^+ \rightleftharpoons H_2O + 2HF$. We cannot, however adopt the usual procedure of using these equilibria to define the acidic or basic strength of HF_2^-, since the equilibrium constants contain the terms $[F^-]^2$ and $[HF]^2$ and thus have physical dimensions differing from those of the usual acid dissociation constants. A logical measure of the acid-base properties of HF_2^- would involve the hypothetical equilibria $HF_2 + H_2O \rightleftharpoons H_3O^+ + F_2^{2-}$ and $HF_2^- + H_3O^+ \rightleftharpoons H_2O + H_2F_2$. Actually the species F_2^{2-} is unknown, and there is no evidence for the existence of H_2F_2 in aqueous solutions, though it is of course present in the vapor and in nondissociating solvents. We thus have the rather paradoxical situation that H_2F_2 may be regarded as a strong acid in aqueous solution (because the equilibrium $H_2F_2 + H_2O \rightleftharpoons HF_2^- + H_3O^+$ is far to the right), while the conjugate species HF_2^- has appreciable basic properties in virtue of the reaction $HF_2^- + H_3O^+ \rightarrow H_2O + 2HF$. Similar difficulties in defining acid-base strengths arise whenever there is not a one-to-one correspondence between

[46] D. Turnbull and S. H Maron, *J. Am. Chem. Soc.*, **65**, 212 (1943).

[47] T. C. Waddington, *Trans. Faraday Soc.*, **54**, 25 (1958).

[48] H. H. Broene and T. de Vries, *J. Am. Chem. Soc.*, **69**, 1644 (1947).

acidic and basic species. For example, when a glycol is added to a solution of boric acid, the following equilibrium is set up:

$$2\;\begin{array}{c}-\!\!\overset{|}{\underset{|}{C}}\!-\!OH\\[2mm]-\!\!\overset{|}{\underset{|}{C}}\!-\!OH\end{array}\;+\;H_3BO_3\;\rightleftharpoons\;\begin{array}{c}-\!\!\overset{|}{C}\!-\!O\;\;\;\;\;O\!-\!\overset{|}{C}\!-\\[1mm]\diagdown\;\diagup\\B\\[-1mm]\diagup\;\diagdown\\-\!\!\overset{|}{C}\!-\!O\;\;\;\;\;O\!-\!\overset{|}{C}\end{array}\;+\;H_3O^+\;+\;2H_2O,$$

and it is clearly impossible to define the acid-base properties of the system in the usual way. There is no difficulty in representing the equilibrium properties of such systems, but we shall see that special problems arise in connection with time-dependent phenomena such as the kinetics of proton transfer.

The fundamental acid-base equation $A \rightleftharpoons B + H^+$ is formally very similar to the redox equation $R \rightleftharpoons Ox + \epsilon$, and in both cases the processes realized in practice are obtained by combining two acid-base or redox systems. It is therefore of interest to consider the main differences between the two classes of phenomena. In the first place, equilibrium between two acid-base systems is almost always set up rapidly, whereas two redox systems frequently react very slowly; further, water and similar solvents take part reversibly in acid-base reactions, but are usually indifferent solvents in redox reactions (unless they are irreversibly oxidized or reduced). For this reason acid-base strengths are always expressed in terms of equilibrium with a standard system, usually the solvent, while redox systems are characterized by a potential relative to a standard electrode. Standard redox potentials are of course closely related to equilibrium constants; for example, if a system R—Ox is measured relative to a standard hydrogen electrode, the redox potential is given by $FE = RT\ln K$, where K is the equilibrium constant for the process $R + H_3O^+ \rightleftharpoons Ox + \frac{1}{2}H_2 + H_2O$. In general, however, these equilibria cannot be studied directly, and their equilibrium constants vary through 50 to 60 powers of ten.[49] In principle acid-base equilibria could equally well be characterized by potentials, since the potential of a hydrogen electrode in solution containing an acid-base system A—B is determined by the process $A + \epsilon \rightleftharpoons B + \frac{1}{2}H_2$, and if this potential is measured relative to a standard hydrogen electrode the e.m.f. is directly related to the

[49] Because of the slowness of many redox reactions it is possible to study in aqueous solution many redox systems which are thermodynamically capable of oxidizing water completely to oxygen or hydrogen peroxide, or of reducing it to hydrogen.

equilibrium constant of the reaction $A + H_2O \rightleftharpoons B + H_3O^+$. These constants can be determined by a number of other methods, and the range of directly accessible values is limited by the acid-base properties of the solvent: thus in aqueous solution the range is limited to about 14 powers of ten. For this reason acid-base strengths are usually specified in terms of equilibrium constants rather than potentials. In aprotic solvents (i.e., solvents lacking appreciable acidic or basic properties) it is impossible to use the solvent as a reference system, and it might then be useful to employ a potential scale, though this has not commonly been done.[50]

[50] See, however, E. Wiberg, *Z. physikal. Chem.*, **171A,** 1 (1934).

CHAPTER IV

The Effect of the Solvent on Acid-Base Equilibria

SOLVENT effects on acid-base equilibria are naturally most marked when the solvent itself enters into the equilibrium, as is the case for the conventional definition of acid strength by means of the equilibrium $A + SH \rightleftharpoons B + SH_2^+$ (where SH is the solvent). The existence of such an equilibrium implies that the solvent has some basic properties. Similarly, the occurrence of the reaction $B + SH \rightleftharpoons A + S^-$ (where S^- is the anion derived by abstracting a proton from the solvent) implies that the solvent is acidic. The most important factor determining qualitative behavior in a wide range of solvents is the acidic or basic nature of the solvent, as determined by its chemical nature. In a preliminary classification we can neglect other factors, notably the effect of dielectric constant on the association of ions or the forces between them. Only a small number of examples will be considered to illustrate the range of chemical behavior, and in the first instance we shall deal only with systems in which the reaction of acids or bases with the solvent can be studied directly without the addition of other acid-base pairs such as indicators.

The *lower alcohols* are qualitatively very smiliar to water, in that they are *amphoteric*, forming the ions ROH_2^+ and RO^-. Substances which dissociate as acids or bases in water will also do so in the alcohols, though to a smaller extent, and the same methods of investigation are applicable, e.g., conductivity, e.m.f., and indicators. A number of acids, e.g., perchloric acid and the hydrogen halides, are "strong" in the alcohols, i.e., their dissociation constants are so high that they appear to be completely dissociated. There appear to be no uncharged bases which are "strong" in the alcohols, in the sense that they react completely according to the equation $B + ROH \rightleftharpoons BH^+$

+ RO⁻.[1]   Because of their amphoteric nature the alcohols show self-dissociation according to the scheme $2ROH \rightleftharpoons ROH_2^+ + RO^-$, but the ionic products are much lower than for water, being $10^{-16.7}$ and $10^{-19.1}$ for methyl and ethyl alcohol respectively.   We shall see later that these differences can be attributed mainly to the decrease in dielectric constant, which also makes much more difficult a quantitative interpretation of experimental data since it increases the interionic forces.   It is possible, however, to obtain information about acids and bases in the alcohols which can be compared directly with data for aqueous solutions, and a large amount of accurate work has been done.

There is no other class of solvent to which the last sentence applies, but much semiquantitative information is available, especially for solvents which are more strongly acidic than water.   Anhydrous *acetic acid* has been widely studied,[2] mostly by indicator measurements or by e.m.f. measurements using a platinum electrode in contact with solid tetrachloroquinone and tetrachlorohydroquinone (chloranil), which serves as a substitute for the hydrogen electrode as does the quinhydrone electrode.   Because of its low dielectric constant ($\epsilon = 6.3$) all salts have dissociation constants less than about 10^{-5} and are therefore incompletely dissociated even at very low concentrations.   This complicates the quantitative interpretation of the results, but the general picture is clear.   Acetic acid is clearly much more acidic than water, and correspondingly it is found that all bases which in water are stronger than aniline give almost identical titration curves with a given acid in acetic acid; this implies that they have reacted almost completely with the solvent according to the equation $B + MeCO_2H \rightarrow BH^+ \cdot MeCO_2^-$.   Much weaker bases, for example the nitroanilines, react with anhydrous acetic acid to a considerable

---

[1] Very few uncharged bases are strong in aqueous solution, exceptions being guanidine and the amidines, which have not been investigated quantitatively in the alcohols.

[2] See, e.g., N. F. Hall and J. B. Conant, *J. Am. Chem. Soc.*, **49**, 3047, 3062 (1927); J. B. Conant and G. M. Bramann, *ibid.*, **50**, 2305 (1928); N. F. Hall and T. H. Werner, *ibid.*, **50**, 2367 (1928); J. B. Conant and T. H. Werner, *ibid.*, **52**, 4436 (1930); N. F. Hall, *ibid.*, **52**, 5116 (1930); A. Hantzsch and W. Langbein, *Z. anorg. Chem.*, **204**, 193 (1932); N. F. Hall and H. H. Voge, *J. Am. Chem. Soc.*, **55**, 239 (1933); W. C. Eichelberger and V. K. LaMer, *ibid.*, **55**, 3635 (1933); I. M. Kolthoff and A. Willman, *ibid.*, **56**, 1007 (1934); B. V. Weidtner, A. W. Hutchinson, and G. C. Chandlee, *ibid.*, **56**, 1285 (1934); M. A. Paul and L. P. Hammett, *ibid.*, **58**, 2182 (1936); N. F. Hall and W. F. Spengeman, *ibid.*, **62**, 2487 (1940); V. Gold and B. W. V. Hawes, *J. Chem. Soc.*, 2102 (1951); I. M. Kolthoff and S. Bruckenstein, *J. Am. Chem. Soc.*, **78**, 1, 10 (1956); T. L. Smith and J. H. Elliott, *ibid.*, **75**, 3566 (1953); T. Higuchi, J. A. Feldman, and C. R. Rehm, *Analyt. Chem.*, **28**, 1128 (1956).

extent, and many substances which barely exhibit basic character in water show measurable basic properties in this solvent, for example, urea, the oximes, and triphenylcarbinol.

The ionic product of pure acetic acid (K_s) is not known with any certainty, but since the solvent can be prepared with a specific conductivity as low as 10^{-8} mhos[3] K_s must be less than 10^{-13}, assuming that the limiting mobility for $MeCO_2^- + MeCO_2H_2^+$ is about 40. Since a base as weak as aniline is completely protonated in acetic acid, it follows that this solvent must possess very weak proton-accepting powers, perhaps 10^6 to 10^8 times weaker than water. It would therefore be expected to react to a very small extent with most acids, and this is fully borne out in practice. The acids $HClO_4$, HBr, H_2SO_4, p-toluene-sulfonic, and HCl, all of which are completely dissociated in water, form a series of decreasing strength, judged by conductivity or indicator measurements, and also by the potentials recorded by a chloranil electrode either in solutions of the acids alone, or in titration with a base. Because of the low dielectric constant the concentrations of free ions are very low, but it has been concluded by Kolthoff and Bruckenstein (*loc. cit.* [2]) that even for the strongest acid, perchloric, only about one-half of the acid is converted into the ion pair $MeCO_2H_2^+ \cdot ClO_4^-$, thus showing that acetic acid is a very weakly basic medium, and not merely one which has a low dissociating power because of its low dielectric constant. Solutions of perchloric or hydrobromic acid in glacial acetic acid have much stronger acidic powers than any aqueous solutions, and they have found practical application in titrating very weak bases such as oximes or amides, which cannot be estimated by titration in aqueous solution.[4]

Anhydrous *formic acid* is more strongly acidic than acetic acid but in general it exhibits a similar behavior toward uncharged bases.[5] It differs from acetic acid in having a high dielectric constant ($\epsilon = 62$) and also a high ionic product, $[HCO_2^-][HCO_2H_2^+] = 10^{-6}$, the latter fact showing that it has considerable basic as well as acidic properties. A number of acids (perchloric, sulfuric, and benzenesulfonic) react completely with the solvent, producing completely dissociated prod-

---

[3] D. A. McInnes and T. Shedlovsky, *J. Am. Chem. Soc.*, **54**, 1429 (1932); Eichelberger and LaMer, *loc. cit.* (2), Kolthoff and Willman, *loc. cit.* (2). Since J. Kendall and P. M. Gross (*J. Am. Chem. Soc.*, **43**, 1426 [1921]) prepared propionic acid with $\kappa = 10^{-9}$, it seems likely that the true specific conductivity of acetic acid is less than 10^{-8}.

[4] See, e.g., S. R. Palit, M. H. Das, and G. R. Somayajulu, *Non-aqueous Titrations* (Calcutta, 1954).

[5] L. P. Hammett and A. J. Deyrup, *J. Am. Chem. Soc.*, **54**, 4239 (1932); L. P. Hammett and N. Dietz, *ibid.*, **52**, 4795 (1930).

ucts, though hydrochloric acid is a weak acid. The existence of strong, completely dissociated acids makes it possible to measure acidity constants defined by $[B][HCO_2H_2^+]/[A]$, and this has been done especially for systems of the type $RNH_3^+ - RNH_2$.

A great deal of work has been done in the strongly acidic solvent *sulfuric acid*, which has a high dielectric constant (110)[6] and also a high ionic product, $[HSO_4^-][H_3SO_4^-] = 1.7 \times 10^{-4}$, the position being further complicated by the existence of another type of dissociation, $2H_2SO_4 \rightleftharpoons H_3O^+ + HS_2O_7^-$, with an equilibrium constant

$$[H_3O^+][HS_2O_7^-] = 7 \times 10^{-5}.$$

Because of the large self-ionization, investigation by conductivity or e.m.f. measurements is not practicable, and most of the information on the behavior of solutes comes from cryoscopic measurements.[7] Sulfuric acid is such a strongly acid medium that almost all compounds containing oxygen or nitrogen will accept a proton from it to some degree, thus behaving as bases. For example, not only amines, but also amides, ethers, ketones, and esters give a twofold freezing point depression, corresponding to complete reaction according to schemes such as

$$\diagdown \!\! O + H_2SO_4 \rightarrow \overset{+}{O}H + HSO_4^-.$$

Many substances which behave as acids in hydroxylic solvents exhibit basic properties in sulfuric acid. Thus most carboxylic acids are strong bases, forming the ion $R \cdot COOH_2^+$, though reaction is incomplete for strong acids such as di- and trichloroacetic acids, which are thus weak bases in this solvent. Nitrocompounds, sulfones, and sulfonic acids also behave as weak bases, and it is in fact difficult to find substances which are soluble in sulfuric acid without detectable ionization; sulfuryl chloride and chlorosulfonic acid are the only recorded examples. Since cryoscopic measurements lead only to the total number of solute particles, it is not possible to obtain quantitative measurements of base strength over a wide range, especially since there are complications caused by the self-dissociation of the solvent, and interionic effects, though small, must be taken into account.

[6] J. C. D. Brand, J. C. James, and A. Rutherford, *J. Chem. Soc.*, 2247 (1953).

[7] Recent accurate investigations are due to R. J. Gillespie and his collaborators, *J. Chem. Soc.*, 2473, 2997 (1950); 204, 964 (1953); 1851 (1954); 80, 607, 1925, 3850 (1956). The first of these papers contains full references to earlier measurements by Hammett (1933–1937) and to the pioneer work of Hantzsch (1907–1930).

Very few substances behave as acids in sulfuric acid, and even such a strong acid as perchloric acid has a dissociation constant of only 10^{-4}. Both of the ions $H_3SO_4^+$ and HSO_4^- show abnormally high mobilities, presumably because of a proton-jump mechanism analogous to that assumed for hydrogen and hydroxyl ions in water. Many substances undergo reactions in sulfuric acid which are more complicated than simple proton transfers, for example,

$$EtOH + 2H_2SO_4 \rightarrow EtOSO_3H + H_3O^+ + HSO_4^-$$

$$(MeCO)_2O + 2H_2SO_4 \rightarrow MeCO^+ + MeCO_2H_2^+ + 2HSO_4^-$$

$$(C_6H_5)_3C \cdot OH + 2H_2SO_4 \rightarrow (C_6H_5)_3C^+ + 2HSO_4^-$$

$$HNO_3 + 2H_2SO_4 \rightarrow NO_2^+ + H_3O^+ + 2HSO_4^-.$$

Ions like CH_3CO^+ and NO_2^+ are of course important in relation to the chemical reactivity of sulfuric acid solutions.

Hydrogen fluoride is a solvent of similar acidic strength to sulfuric acid; it also has a high dielectric constant ($\epsilon = 84$). In contrast to sulfuric acid, its self-dissociation is small, so that conductivity measurements are the usual method of investigation. A wide range of nitrogen and oxygen compounds behave as bases, but acids are usually undissociated. Like sulfuric acid, hydrogen fluoride is sufficiently acidic to protonate some aromatic hydrocarbons to an appreciable extent.[8]

Behavior in hydrogen fluoride has recently been reviewed in several books and will not be treated further here.[9]

There are of course many solvents which are more strongly basic than water, but these have been much less investigated than the acidic ones. Thus although liquid *ammonia* has been extensively studied, not many of the data relate to acids and bases in the sense in which we are using the terms. Conductivity measurements have been widely used but are difficult to interpret quantitatively because of the fairly low dielectric constant ($\epsilon = 22$) and the relatively high concentrations which have been used. It is clear, however, that a wide range of acids (e.g., acetic, benzoic, formic, nitric, hydrochloric, and perchloric) react almost completely with the solvent according to the scheme

[8] See, e.g., D. A. McCaulay and A. P. Lien, *J. Am. Chem. Soc.*, **73**, 2013 (1951); M. Kilpatrick and F. E. Luborsky, *ibid.*, **75**, 577 (1953); E. L. Mackor, G. Dallinga, J. H. Kruizinga, and A. Hofstra, *Rec. trav. chim.*, **75**, 836 (1956); H. H. Hyman and M. Kilpatrick, *J. Am. Chem. Soc.*, **79**, 3668 (1957).

[9] E.g., J. H. Simons, article in *Fluorine Chemistry* (New York, 1950); K. Wiechert, in *Newer Methods of Preparative Organic Chemistry* (New York, 1948).

$HX + NH_3 \rightarrow NH_4^+ \cdot X^-$, though the salt produced is incompletely dissociated and the degree of dissociation varies considerably from one case to another. Liquid ammonia also has weak acidic properties, and the dissociation $2NH_3 \rightleftharpoons NH_4^+ + NH_2^-$ takes place to a small extent ($[NH_4^+][NH_2^-] = 10^{-33}$ at $-33°C$), but little is known about its behavior toward other bases.

There are many other solvents which fall between the extreme cases which we have so far considered, for example, solvents of moderate basicity like the amides or acetonitrile, solvents with basic but no acidic properties such as the ethers, and solvents of moderate acidity such as the phenols. There are also the so-called *aprotic* solvents, such as the hydrocarbons, which have no appreciable acidic or basic properties and therefore do not take any direct part in acid-base equilibria. Some of these solvents will be dealt with later in connection with relative acid-base strengths in different solvents.

The solvents so far mentioned provide several examples of the *leveling effect*, a term first introduced by Hantzsch. If in any solvent we have three different acids that are dissociated to the extent of 99 percent, 99.9 percent, and 99.99 percent, their dissociation constants will be 10^{+1}, 10^{+2}, and 10^{+3} respectively, but their solutions will be experimentally indistinguishable from the acid-base point of view, since the solvated proton will be effectively the only acid species present. Thus in water, dilute solutions of the acids $HClO_4$, HI, HBr, and HCl and the sulfonic acids are virtually indistinguishable in their acid properties, though in less basic solvents such as acetic and sulfuric acid or a hydrocarbon they behave very differently. On the other hand, in a basic solvent such as ammonia the list of "strong" acids is greatly extended, including now many carboxylic acids. Similar leveling effects are observed with bases in acidic solvents. In aqueous solutions guanidine and amidines are the only common bases which react completely according to the scheme $B + H_2O \rightarrow BH^+ + OH^-$, but in acetic acid all bases stronger than aniline are completely protonated, while in sulfuric or hydrofluoric acid the list of "strong" bases includes a wide range of nitrogen and oxygen compounds. In general we can say that any solvent possessing both acidic and basic properties can be characterized by two approximate values pK' and pK''. If an acid-base system has pK (in water) $< pK'$, then on dissolving in this solvent it will be converted almost completely to base + solvent cation, whereas if pK (in water) $> pK''$, the base will be converted completely to acid + solvent anion. The range between pK' and pK'' represents the range of acid-base pairs whose equilibrium can be usefully studied in the solvent in question, without being "leveled" in either direction. Figure 1 illustrates the approximate state of affairs for a number of different solvents. Since ether has no acidic properties, no limit of pK is shown on the upper side. Similarly, for the aprotic solvent hexane there is no limit in either direction.

Although information like that contained in Figure 1 makes good sense from the general chemical point of view, it is difficult to obtain any quantitative interpretation of conventional acid or base constants, defined by the equilibria $A + SH \rightleftharpoons B + SH_2^+$ and $B + SH \rightleftharpoons A + S^-$

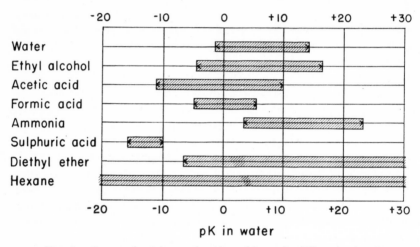

FIG. 1.—Range of existence of acids and bases in different solvents.

in terms of the properties of the solvent S. This is partly because these constants are only accessible in solvents in which we can obtain strong, completely dissociated acids and bases in order to prepare solutions with known concentrations of SH_2^+ or S^-. This limits our consideration to solvents which have appreciable acidic and basic properties, and also to those whose dielectric constant is not too low. Of the solvents which have been carefully studied, this restricts us to the lower alcohols and formamide.

If we are dealing with an equilibrium of the type $RH + SH \rightleftharpoons R^- + SH_2^+$ or $R + SH \rightleftharpoons RH^+ + S^-$, the right-hand side in each case contains more ions than the left, and the position of equilibrium should depend considerably on the dielectric constant of the medium, quite apart from other factors. In order to minimize this electrostatic effect we must consider equilibria such as $RH^+ + SH \rightleftharpoons R + SH_2^+$ or $R^- + SH \rightleftharpoons RH + S^-$. The first of these is expressed by the conventional acid dissociation constant of a cation acid (e.g., the ammonium ion), while the second is often described as the solvolysis of the anion of a weak acid, and its equilibrium constant is obtained from the conventional dissociation constant of RH and the ionic product of the solvent.

Table 1 contains some values for these constants in water, methyl alcohol, and ethyl alcohol.[10] Considering first the reactions RNH_3^+ + SH $\rightleftharpoons$ RNH_2 + SH_2^+, we see that the differences Δ_I, and Δ_{II} are roughly constant at about 1.1 over a wide range of acid strengths. This could be expressed by saying that methyl and ethyl alcohol are less basic than water by a factor of ten in their behavior toward cation acids, and since the effect of dielectric constant should be small for this reaction this effect can be thought of in chemical terms.[11] To obtain comparable values we must allow for the fact that in defining the equilibrium constants for the reaction RNH_3^+ + SH $\rightleftharpoons$ RNH_2 + SH_2^+ the concentration of the solvent is omitted from the constant, and if we divide by these concentrations (56, 25, and 17 moles/liter for H_2O, MeOH, and EtOH respectively) we find that the basic strengths of the three molecules are in the ratio 1, 0.13, 0.33. This result is in the opposite direction to what would be expected in terms of the electron-releasing power of the alkyl groups, as shown by their effect on the basic strength of alkylamines relative to ammonia. These conclusions must not be taken too seriously, since we are comparing pure liquids, in which the position is complicated by association.

[10] Most of the values are taken from the compilations of E. Larsson, *Z. physikal. Chem.*, **169A**, 207 (1934); and L. D. Goodhue and R. M. Hixon, *J. Am. Chem. Soc.*, **56**, 1329 (1934). More accurate data exist for mono-substituted benzoic acids (J. H. Elliott and M. Kilpatrick, *J. Phys. Chem.*, **45**, 454, 566, [1941]) and anilines (M. Kilpatrick and C. A. Arenberg, *J. Am. Chem. Soc.*, **75**, 3812 [1953]), and these have been used to fill in gaps in the table. High accuracy is not important for present purposes. The values used for the ionic products of the alcohols are pK_s = 16.7 and 19.1 for methyl and ethyl alcohol respectively.

[11] L. P. Hammett (*Physical Organic Chemistry* [New York, 1940], p. 261) states that the ammonium acids are *stronger* by 0.8 logarithmic units in ethyl alcohol than in water, and this statement is often quoted in support of the view that the alcohols are more basic solvents than water, for example, by A. E. Remick (*Electronic Interpretation of Organic Chemistry* [New York, 1949]. p. 258) and by Brown, McDaniel, and Häfliger (*Determination of Organic Structures by Physical Methods*, ed. E. A. Braude and F. C. Nachod [New York, 1955], p. 619). Hammett's statement is based on a small number of measurements by A. J. Deyrup (*J. Am. Chem. Soc.*, **56**, 60 [1934]) using a catalytic method of measuring hydrogen ion concentrations. Deyrup's dissociation constants differ widely from those obtained by other methods, and it seems probable that the amines reacted to some extent with the acetaldehyde used in his reaction.

The Proton in Chemistry

TABLE 1.—ACID-BASE CONSTANTS IN WATER AND THE ALCOHOLS

$$K_1 = [SH_2^+][RNH_2]/[RNH_3^+], \qquad K_2 = [S^-][RCO_2H]/[RCO_2^-],$$
$$\Delta_I = pK_1(MeOH) - pK_1(H_2O), \qquad \Delta_{II} = pK_1(EtOH) - pK_1(H_2O),$$
$$\Delta_{III} = pK_2(MeOH) - pK_2(H_2O), \qquad \Delta_{IV} = pK_2(EtOH) - pK_2(H_2O).$$

Primary amines	pK_1			Δ_I	Δ_{II}
	H_2O	MeOH	EtOH		
n-Butylamine	10.6	11.8	12.1	1.2	1.5
Ammonia	9.3	10.8	10.4	1.5	1.1
o-Chlorobenzylamine	8.8	10.1	—	1.3	—
p-Toluidine	5.2	6.7	6.2	1.5	1.2
m-Toluidine	4.8	5.9	5.9	1.1	1.1
Aniline	4.7	6.2	5.7	1.5	1.5
o-Toluidine	4.5	5.9	5.6	1.4	1.4
α-Naphthylamine	4.3	5.5	5.3	1.2	1.0
p-Chloroaniline	4.0	4.9	4.7	0.9	0.7
p-Bromoaniline	3.9	4.8	4.5	0.9	0.6
m-Chloroaniline	3.6	4.6	4.2	1.0	0.6
m-Bromoaniline	3.6	4.4	4.2	0.8	0.6
o-Chloroaniline	1.9	3.5	3.3	1.6	1.4
			Mean	1.2	1.0

Carboxylic acids	pK_2			Δ_{III}	Δ_{IV}
	H_2O	MeOH	EtOH		
Acetic	9.3	7.4	8.8	−1.9	−0.5
Phenylacetic	9.7	—	8.8	—	−0.9
p-Toluic	9.7	7.4	8.8	−2.3	−3.9
Benzoic	9.2	7.6	8.7	−1.6	−0.5
p-Bromobenzoic	10.1	8.0	9.5	−2.1	−0.6
m-Chlorobenzoic	10.2	8.1	9.6	−2.1	−0.7
m-Nitrobenzoic	10.5	8.3	9.9	−2.2	−0.6
Salicylic	11.0	8.8	10.7	−2.2	−0.3
3,5-Dinitrobenzoic	11.2	9.3	11.0	−1.9	−0.2
o-Nitrobenzoic	11.8	9.1	10.5	−2.7	−1.3
2,4-Dinitrobenzoic	12.6	10.2	11.8	−2.4	−0.8
Dichloroacetic	12.7	10.3	11.8	−2.4	−0.9
			Mean	−2.1	−0.7

Qualitatively, however, the same conclusions are reached in experiments where the species H_2O, MeOH, and EtOH are present in dilute solution in acetic acid. Kolthoff and Bruckenstein (*loc. cit.* [2], 1), measured the basic strength of these molecules with respect to perchloric acid, using an indicator method, and obtained the ratios $1:0.13:0.22$. This shows surprisingly good agreement with the above figures, especially since the products $ROH_2^+ \cdot ClO_4^-$ are certainly incompletely dissociated in acetic acid. Similar information follows from a study of the equilibrium $ROH_2^+ + H_2O \rightleftharpoons ROH + H_3O^+$ which is set up when a little water is added to an alcoholic solution of a strong acid, but this is much more difficult to interpret quantitatively, since of the two bases which we are comparing one is present in dilute solution and the other as an almost pure liquid. It seems certain, however, that the basic properties of the alcohols are not in accord with the simple picture of electron release by alkyl groups.[12]

A similar treatment can be applied to the data for the equilibrium $RCO_2^- + SH \rightleftharpoons RCO_2H + S^-$. The values of Δ_{III} and Δ_{IV} in Table 1 are each reasonably constant, and would suggest that methyl and ethyl alcohols are respectively about 100 and 5 times as acidic as water, again showing an effect in the opposite direction to that expected. It seems doubtful, however, whether these figures can be accepted. Hine and Hine[13] have used indicators to study the equilibrium $i\text{-}PrO^- + ROH \rightleftharpoons RO^- + i\text{-}PrO^-$ for dilute solutions of water, methyl, and ethyl alcohols in isopropyl alcohol and thus arrive at the values 1, 3.3, and 0.8 for the relative acidities of the molecules H_2O, MeOH, and EtOH. Although dissociation may not be complete in this solvent ($\epsilon = 20$), these ratios seem more probable than $1:100:5$ derived from Table 1, and it is likely that the effect of dielectric constant is not really eliminated in the reaction $RCO_2^- + SH \rightleftharpoons RCO_2H + S^-$. Measurements of the equilibrium $RO^- + H_2O \rightleftharpoons ROH + OH^-$[14] certainly suggest that the acidities of H_2O, MeOH, and EtOH do not differ by more than a power of ten at the most, though they are difficult to interpret quantitatively.

In equilibria of the type $RCO_2H + SH \rightleftharpoons RCO_2^- + SH_2^+$ and $RNH_2 + SH \rightleftharpoons RNH_3^+ + S^-$, in which charges appear only on one side of the equation, there is of course a considerable effect of dielectric constant, such reactions occurring to a much smaller extent in the alcohols than in water. In terms of the constants in Table 1 these equilibrium constants are given by

[12] Other factors which may be operative have been discussed by P. Bartlett and J. D. McCollum (*J. Am. Chem. Soc.*, **78**, 1441 [1956]), who conclude from a combination of kinetic and indicator measurements that isopropyl alcohol is a very much weaker base than water.

[13] J. Hine and M. Hine, *J. Am. Chem. Soc.*, **74**, 5267 (1952).

[14] A. Unmack, *Z. physikal. Chem.*, **133**, 45 (1927); E. F. Caldin and G. Long, *J. Chem. Soc.*, 3737 (1954); A. Koivisto, *Acta Chem. Scand.*, **8**, 1218, 1223, 1229 (1955).

$$K_4 = [RCO_2^-][SH_2^+]/[RCO_2H] = K_s/K_2$$

$$K_5 = [RNH_3^+][S^-]/[RNH_2] \quad = K_s/K_1$$

where K_s is the ionic product of the solvent, and the concentration of the solvent is omitted as usual in the equilibrium expressions. The effect of solvent is then represented by the differences

$$\Delta_V \ = pK_5(\text{MeOH}) - pK_5(\text{H}_2\text{O}) = pK_s(\text{MeOH}) - pK_s(\text{H}_2\text{O}) - \Delta_{III}$$

$$\Delta_{VI} = pK_5(\text{EtOH}) \ - pK_5(\text{H}_2\text{O}) = pK_s(\text{EtOH}) \ - pK_s(\text{H}_2\text{O}) - \Delta_{IV}$$

$$\Delta_{VII} = pK_4(\text{MeOH}) - pK_4(\text{H}_2\text{O}) = pK_s(\text{MeOH}) - pK_s(\text{H}_2\text{O}) - \Delta_I$$

$$\Delta_{VIII} = pK_4(\text{EtOH}) - pK_4(\text{H}_2\text{O}) = pK_s(\text{EtOH}) \ - pK_s(\text{H}_2\text{O}) - \Delta_{II}.$$

If we take $pK_s(\text{H}_2\text{O}) = 14.0$, $pK_s(\text{MeOH}) = 16.7$, $pK_s(\text{EtOH}) = 19.1$, the data in Table 1 give the following average values:

$$\Delta_V = 4.8, \qquad \Delta_{VI} = 5.8, \qquad \Delta_{VII} = 1.5, \qquad \Delta_{VIII} = 4.1.$$

These values involve both the changes in dielectric constant and in the acid-base properties of the solvent and cannot be interpreted in any simple way, though their sign is in each case what would be expected from the electrostatic effect. If we wish to examine the electrostatic effect independent of the acid-base properties of the solvent, we must consider the equilibrium $RCO_2H + R'NH_2 \rightleftharpoons RCO_2^- + R'NH_3^+$, not involving the solvent. The equilibrium constant K for this reaction is given in terms of the constants in Table 1 as $K = K_s/K_1K_2$, and if we again take the average values we find

$$\Delta_{IX} = pK(\text{MeOH}) - pK(\text{H}_2\text{O}) = 3.6$$

$$\Delta_X \ = pK(\text{EtOH}) \ - pK(H_2O) = 4.8.$$

It is of interest to see how far these figures can be accounted for on a simple electrostatic basis. The electrical free energy of a pair of separated ions of charges $+e$ and $-e$ and radius r in a medium of dielectric constant ϵ is given by $e^2/\epsilon r$, and if we apply this to two media of dielectric constants ϵ' and ϵ'' we have

$$-\Delta G^\circ = kT \ln \frac{K'}{K''} = -\frac{e^2}{r}\left(\frac{1}{\epsilon'} - \frac{1}{\epsilon''}\right). \tag{1}$$

Applying this to the data for water and ethyl alchol, we find for the mean ionic radius $r = 1.5$ Å. Similarly, the data for water and methyl alcohol give $r = 1.3$ Å. Although these are of the right order of magnitude, they are smaller than would be anticipated, though it is clearly difficult to define the effective radius of unsymmetrical ions like those concerned here. On the same basis we can attribute most of the differences in the ionic products of H_2O, MeOH, and EtOH to the differences in their dielectric constants, since we have seen that the differences in their acidic and basic strengths are not large.

The generalized picture just given for the behavior of acids and bases in water and the alcohols involves some simplification. In the first place, there are clearly variations among the individual acids and bases in Table 1 which exceed the experimental error. These individual variations would have been much greater if we had not restricted ourselves to the two series of closely similar compounds, carboxylic acids and primary amines. For example, the phenols differ from the carboxylic acids in their values of ΔpK. Similarly, there are considerable differences in the behavior of primary, secondary, and tertiary amines, the last class often differing from the first two in the sign of ΔpK. These individual deviations are considered in the next section. In the second place, the three solvents considered are of the same chemical type, and the macroscopic dielectric constant becomes an even less adequate measure of the solvent effect if we compare solvents of differing chemical character. This may be illustrated by the behavior of acids and bases in *formamide*,[15] which is a solvent having a dielectric constant ($\epsilon = 110$) somewhat greater than water and possessing both weakly acidic and weakly basic properties. Several acids are strong in formamide, and it was possible to determine pK_s (16.8) from e.m.f. measurements, so that the acid-base strengths could be referred to the solvent species SH_2^+—SH—S^-. Constants were obtained for twelve carboxylic acids and eight amines; when these are compared with the corresponding constants in water, the differences show individual variations somewhat greater than those in Table 1, but no trend with acid strength. The mean differences are as follows, Δ in each case representing pK (formamide)—$pK(H_2O)$:

$$RNH_3^+ + SH \rightleftharpoons SH_2^+ + RNH_2, \qquad \Delta_{XI} = -0.6$$

$$RCO_2^- + SH \rightleftharpoons S^- + RCO_2H, \qquad \Delta_{XII} = 0.9$$

$$RCO_2H + SH \rightleftharpoons SH_2^+ + RCO_2^-, \qquad \Delta_{XIII} = 1.9$$

$$RNH_2 + SH \rightleftharpoons S^- + RNH_3^+, \qquad \Delta_{XIV} = 3.4$$

$$RCO_2H + R'NH_2 \rightleftharpoons RCO_2^- + R'NH_3^+, \qquad \Delta_{XV} = 2.5.$$

The values of Δ_{XI} and Δ_{XII} indicate that formamide is a somewhat

[15] F. H. Verhoek, *J. Am. Chem. Soc.*, **58**, 2577 (1936).

stronger base and a weaker acid than water, which is reasonable on chemical grounds. On the other hand, Δ_{XIII} and Δ_{XIV} are each 2.5 units greater than Δ_{XI} and Δ_{XII} respectively, showing that when the reaction involves the production of charge formamide is considerably less effective in reacting with both acids and bases. This is not at all what would be expected electrostatically, since the dielectric constant of formamide is somewhat greater than that of water, which should favor the production of charge. The same anomaly is shown in the value of Δ_{XV}, which does not involve participation of the solvent. On the other hand, freezing point measurements for salts in formamide[16] show that their activity coefficients are close to those found in water, so that the above anomalies cannot be due to incomplete dissociation. There is of course ample evidence that the dielectric constant does not give a satisfactory account of the effect of solvent upon the free energy of ions, and this may be particularly the case in dealing with charged acids and bases, which depart very far from the picture of spherical ions. Thus in considering the ion SH_2^+, we are making a sharp distinction between the interaction of the proton with one solvent molecule (regarded as a chemical effect) and its interaction with the remainder of the solvent (represented by the dielectric constant term). Since most of the solvents considered are highly associated by means of hydrogen bonds, this distinction is somewhat artificial, and in some solvents it may be a truer picture to regard the ion SH_2^+ as formed by adding a proton to a large aggregate of associated molecules. Similarly, the S^- ion would be formed by removing a proton from a large aggregate. We shall see later that such a concept is helpful in interpreting the properties of concentrated aqueous solutions, but in general it lacks any quantitative basis, and we shall continue to use the electrostatic picture as a standard, especially for equilibria not involving the ions of the solvent.

Most of the equilibria discussed so far do involve solvent ions, and for many purposes it is convenient to consider the equilibrium between two added acid-base systems. In this way the acidity or basicity of the solvent is eliminated, and the problem now involves only the less intimate interactions with the solvent. We have already mentioned reactions of the type $RCO_2H + R'NH_2 \rightleftharpoons RCO_2^- + R'NH_3^+$, but it is more useful to evaluate constants for the equilibria $R_1CO_2H + R_2CO_2^- \rightleftharpoons R_1CO_2^- + R_2CO_2H$ or $R_1NH_3^+ + R_2NH_2 \rightleftharpoons R_1NH_2 + R_2NH_3^+$; these measure the *relative strength* K_r of two acids in the same class and should

[16] E. N. Vasenko, *Zhur. Fiz. Khim.*, **21**, 361 (1947); **22**, 999 (1948); **23**, 959 (1949).

give a rough cancellation of electrostatic effects. These relative strengths can be measured more accurately than the individual values of acid-base constants involving the solvent, and it is often possible to measure relative strengths when nothing quantitative is known about the acid-base properties of the solvent, which may even be completely inert in this respect. Thus K_r can sometimes be measured directly by spectrophotometric methods or, more frequently, by using an indicator in conjunction with the two separate systems. Provided that there is no association of the ionic species produced, K_r is given directly as the ratio of the two equilibrium constants with the indicator. Alternatively K_r can be derived from the e.m.f. of cells containing a hydrogen electrode (or some substitute such as the glass or quinhydrone electrode) in conjunction with a standard electrode. The difference between the e.m.f. of two similar cells (which may, for example, contain buffer solutions of two different carboxylic acids) will give reliable values for K_r, even when it is difficult to interpret the e.m.f. of a single cell because of uncertainties about standard electrode potentials and liquid junction potentials. Most of the reliable values of K_r in nonaqueous solvents have been obtained by these two methods.

The approximate constancy of the last two columns in Table 1 shows that to a first approximation relative acid strengths are the same in water, methyl alcohol, and ethyl alcohol, provided that we remain within a group of similar substances, e.g., carboxylic acids or amine cations. However, there are certainly variations considerably greater than experimental error, and we must now consider these. Kilpatrick and his co-workers have made accurate measurements of relative strengths of benzoic acids[17] and of anilinium ions[18] the results of which are given in Tables 2 and 3. Although the values of K_r run roughly parallel in each solvent, K_r is certainly not independent of the solvent in spite of the fact that we are considering series of closely related compounds. Some of the variations are large, but they do not depend on the value of K_r, nor in any obvious way on the nature of the substituent. There is some regularity, however, in that K_r usually varies monotonically with the dielectric constant, though the magnitude and direction of this variation are different for different compounds.

As was first pointed out by Wynne-Jones,[19] this behavior can be accounted for, at least formally, on an electrostatic basis. For an equilib-

[17] J. H. Elliott and M. Kilpatrick, *J. Phys. Chem.*, **45**, 454, 466, 473 (1941).

[18] Kilpatrick and Arenberg, *loc. cit.* (10).

[19] W. F. K. Wynne-Jones, *Proc. Roy. Soc.*, A, **140**, 440 (1933).

TABLE 2.—RELATIVE STRENGTHS OF SUBSTITUTED BENZOIC ACIDS
IN HYDROXYLIC SOLVENTS AT 25°C

Values of log K_r relative to benzoic acid

Substituents	H₂O ($\epsilon = 78.5$)	(CH₂OH)₂ ($\epsilon = 37.7$)	CH₃OH ($\epsilon = 31.5$)	C₂H₅OH ($\epsilon = 24.2$)	n—C₄H₉OH ($\epsilon = 17.4$)
p-OH	−0.36	−0.45	−0.53	−0.55	−0.57
p-OMe	−0.27	−0.32	−0.36	−0.32	−0.36
p-Me	−0.17	−0.17	−0.18	−0.18	−0.19
m-Me	−0.06	−0.09	−0.09	−0.06	−0.10
p-F	−0.06	−0.17	−0.18	−0.23	−0.22
m-OH	0.10	−0.03	−0.11	−0.16	−0.16
o-OMe	0.11	0.18	0.17	0.24	0.28
p-Cl	0.22	0.30	0.34	0.42	0.39
p-Br	0.23	0.37	0.42	0.47	0.42
o-CH₃	0.30	0.05	0.09	0.02	0.00
m-F	0.34	0.45	0.51	0.53	0.42
m-I	0.35	0.49	0.55	0.62	0.57
m-Cl	0.38	0.52	0.59	0.63	0.59
m-Br	0.39	0.54	0.60	0.65	0.58
m-NO₂	0.72	0.93	1.05	1.17	1.10
p-NO₂	0.78	0.97	1.02	1.17	1.14
o-F	0.94	0.69	1.00	1.03	0.93
o-Cl	1.28	1.14	1.21	1.12	1.08
o-I	1.34	1.11	1.19	1.08	1.04
o-Br	1.34	1.20	1.27	1.16	1.09
o-NO₂	2.03	1.74	1.83	1.77	1.78

rium $A + B_0 \rightleftharpoons A_0 + B$, if A and A_0 have a positive charge ze, an electrostatic calculation gives for the values of K_r in media of dielectric constants ϵ and ϵ' (cf. Equation 1)

$$\ln \frac{K_r}{K_r'} = \frac{e^2}{2kT}\left(\frac{1}{\epsilon} - \frac{1}{\epsilon'}\right)\left\{ z^2\left(\frac{1}{r_{A0}} - \frac{1}{r_A}\right)\right.$$

$$\left. - (z-1)^2\left(\frac{1}{r_{B0}} - \frac{1}{r_B}\right)\right\} \quad (2)$$

For uncharged acids $z = 0$, and for cation acids $z = 1$, so that (2) becomes

$$\ln K_r = \ln K_r^\infty \pm \frac{e^2}{2kT\epsilon}\left(\frac{1}{r_0} + \frac{1}{r}\right) \quad (3)$$

where K_r^∞ is the value of K_r in a hypothetical medium of infinite dielectric constant. The positive and negative signs refer to cationic and uncharged acids respectively, and the radii are those of the ions concerned. Equation (3) predicts that for a given acid in different sol-

TABLE 3.—RELATIVE STRENGTHS OF SUBSTITUTED ANILINIUM IONS
IN HYDROXYLIC SOLVENTS AT 25°C

Values of log K_r relative to anilinium ion

Substituent	H₂O	MeOH	EtOH
p-Me	−0.49	−0.54	−0.57
m-Me	−0.09	−0.19	−0.29
p-F	0.06	0.32	0.35
o-Me	0.20	0.10	0.10
p-Cl	0.77	1.00	1.07
m-F	1.20	1.46	1.47
m-Cl	1.26	1.53	1.55
o-Cl	1.96	2.40	2.43
m-NO₂	2.13	2.91	3.24
p-NO₂	3.60	4.52	5.21
o-NO₂	4.88	5.64	6.44

vents log K_r should be a linear function of $1/\epsilon$, the slope depending on the values of r_0 and r.

Figure 2 shows a plot of log K_r against $1/\epsilon$ for selected acids from Table 3.[20] If we omit *n*-butyl alcohol, in which ions are probably appreciably associated, the linear relation is fairly well obeyed, and the observed slopes can be accounted for by Equation (3) by assuming that r and r_0 differ by a few tenths of an Ångström. Positive and negative slopes are about equally common, which at first sight seems unreasonable, since a substituent should always increase the over-all size of the benzoate ion. However, the effective radius will be determined more by the charge distribution in the neighborhood of the carboxyl group than by the over-all size of the ion, and variations in both directions could be explained on this basis, though it is difficult to account for the individual variations. It seems better to regard the slopes as empirical parameters for each substance which are useful in correlating the effect of dielectric constant, rather than as related to any easily definable radius.

The data for anilinium ions (Table 3) do not include enough solvents to test Equation (3). Some of the changes in K_r are much greater than for carboxylic acids and would demand rather large changes in effective radius if they are to be explained electrostatically.

Much larger discrepancies appear if we compare solvents of differing chemical types and acids which differ more among themselves than the series of benzoic acids or anilinium ions. Both points are illustrated by the results of Verhoek (*loc. cit.* [15]) for solutions in formamide,

[20] Further plots, covering all the acids studied, are given by J. H. Elliott and M. Kilpatrick, *J. Phys. Chem.*, **45**, 466 (1941).

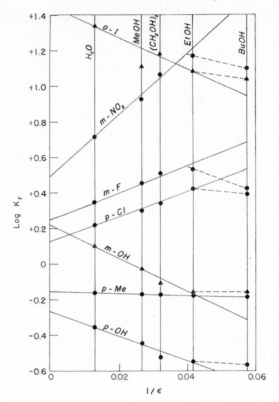

Fig. 2.—Relative strengths of substituted benzoic acids in hydroxylic solvents.

some of which are given in Table 4. We have already seen that for equilibria involving the solvent the effect of changing from water to formamide cannot be explained in any simple way, and the same is true for relative strengths in the two solvents.

Since water and formamide have high and similar dielectric constants, the electrostatic effect represented by (3) will be small; in fact, even if r and r_0 are respectively 4 Å and 2 Å, Equation (3) predicts a difference of only 0.1 in log K_r in the two solvents. The differences in Table 4 are much larger than this and could not be accounted for by any plausible values for the radii. In comparing solvents as different as water and formamide, it is clear that more specific solute-solvent interactions must play a part, for example, hydrogen bonding of both ions and uncharged species. It is noticeable that some of the largest discrepancies in Table 4 refer to acid-base pairs whose possibilities for hydrogen bonding differ considerably from those of the standard acid.

TABLE 4.—RELATIVE ACID STRENGTHS IN WATER AND FORMAMIDE AT 20°C

Carboxylic acids	Values of log K_r relative to benzoic acid	
	Water	Formamide
	($\epsilon = 80.4$)	($\epsilon = 111.5$)
Trimethylacetic	−0.82	−1.15
Propionic	−0.68	−0.84
Succinic	−0.01	0.33
m-Chlorobenzoic	0.38	0.51
m-Nitrobenzoic	0.75	0.87
Salicylic	1.21	1.83
Monochloroacetic	1.33	1.63
o-Nitrobenzoic	2.00	1.95
α-β-Dibromopropionic	2.07	2.15
Dichloroacetic	2.89	3.48
Amine cations	Values of log K_r relative to anilinium	
Piperidinium	−6.44	−6.98
Triethylammonium	−6.28	−5.89
Benzylammonium	−4.68	−5.67
Pyridinium	−1.23	−0.38
p-Chloroanilinium	0.66	0.84
o-Chloroanilinium	2.01	2.53
2,4-Dichloroanilinium	2.55	3.02

Thus succinic and salicylic acids possess —CO₂H and —OH groups additional to those in benzoic acid. Similarly, in the amine series there are large deviations when we go from the standard aniline, a primary aromatic amine, to amines which are secondary or tertiary or aliphatic.

There are considerable differences in the behavior of primary, secondary, and tertiary amines even when we compare two solvents as similar as water and ethyl alcohol, as has been pointed out by Trotman-Dickenson.[21] Thus if we continue to use anilinium as our standard acid, the data of Goldschmidt and Mathiesen[22] show that for ten primary amines log K_r(EtOH) is within ± 0.2 units of log K_r(H₂O), while for three secondary amines log K_r(EtOH) − log K_r(H₂O) = 0.4 ± 0.2 and for six tertiary amines log K_r(EtOH) − log K_r(H₂O) = 1.3 ± 0.3. Trotman-Dickenson (*loc. cit.* [21]) attributes these differences to the varying number of hydrogen atoms available for hydrogen bonding in

[21] A. F. Trotman-Dickenson, *J. Chem. Soc.*, 1293 (1949).
[22] H. Goldschmidt and E. Mathiesen, *Z. physikal. Chem.*, **119**, 439 (1926).

the cations RHN_3^+, $R_2NH_2^+$, and R_3NH^+, and it is also possible that the hydrogen bonding of the amine molecules is a relevant factor. The part played by the chemical nature of the solvent in determining the relative strengths of primary, secondary, and tertiary amines is shown clearly by recent indicator measurements in a variety of solvents.[23]

The quantity K_r^∞ in Equation (3) was termed by Wynne-Jones (*loc. cit.* [19] the "intrinsic strength" (relative to the standard chosen) and corresponds to the intercepts in Figure 2. In principle it represents the relative strength divorced from external electrostatic effects, and it has been suggested that it should be used in discussing the effect of structure on acid-base strength. However, since Equation (3) applies only to water and the alcohols, it seems probable that K_r^∞ still contains a considerable measure of solute-solvent interaction, and it is doubtful whether it is better suited to structural interpretations than K_r measured in a given solvent.

So far it has been assumed that there is no ionic association in the solutions considered, and it is in fact only on this assumption that relative acidities have a unique meaning, even in a single solvent. The problem has been clearly stated by Kolthoff and Bruckenstein (*loc. cit.* [2]) in connection with investigations of acetic acid solutions. If an uncharged base B is in equilibrium with an acid HX, the possible equilibria are

$$HX + B \rightleftharpoons BH^+X^- \rightleftharpoons BH^+ + X^-$$

where BH^+X^- is an ion pair, and the following equilibrium constants can be written down;

$$K_i^{BHX} = \frac{[BH^+X^-]}{[B][HX]}, \qquad K_d^{BHX} = \frac{[BH^+][X^-]}{[BH^+X^-]}, \qquad (4)$$

$$K_D^{BHX} = K_i^{BHX} K_d^{BHX} = \frac{[BH^+][X^-]}{[B][HX]}.$$

The assumption which we have made so far is that the concentration of the ion pair is very small, so that K_i is very small, K_d very large, and K_D is measurable directly either by optical or electrical means. Under these conditions the relative strengths of two acids HX and HY, using BH^+ as the standard acid, are given by

$$\frac{K_D^{BHX}}{K_D^{BHY}} = \frac{[X^-][HY]}{[Y^-][HX]},$$

[23] R. G. Pearson and D. C. Vogelsong, *J. Am. Chem. Soc.*, **80**, 1038 (1958).

which is independent of B; i.e., in determining the relative strengths of two acids we may either compare them directly or compare them separately with any third system BH⁺—B and take the ratio of the strengths.

The position is different if the ion pair is almost undissociated, so that K_d and K_D are both very small and K_i is the quantity measured by an optical method. The relative strengths of the two acids HX and HY are now given by

$$\frac{K_i^{\mathrm{BHX}}}{K_i^{\mathrm{BHY}}} = \frac{[\mathrm{BH^+X^-}][\mathrm{HY}]}{[\mathrm{BH^+Y^-}][\mathrm{HX}]} = \frac{[\mathrm{X^-}][\mathrm{HY}]}{[\mathrm{Y^-}][\mathrm{HX}]} \cdot \frac{K_d^{\mathrm{BHY}}}{K_d^{\mathrm{BHX}}} .$$

This is no longer independent of B, since there is no reason to expect either that $K_d^{\mathrm{BHY}} = K_d^{\mathrm{BHX}}$ or that their ratio is independent of the nature of B. Similarly, we cannot directly investigate the equilibrium $\mathrm{HX} + \mathrm{Y^-} \rightleftharpoons \mathrm{HY} + \mathrm{X^-}$ without introducing some cation, say $\mathrm{Z^+}$; the equilibrium is then really $\mathrm{HX} + \mathrm{Z^+Y^-} \rightleftharpoons \mathrm{HY} + \mathrm{Z^+X^-}$ and its position will depend upon the nature of Z.

Similar considerations apply to acids of other charge types, and in general if investigations are made in a solvent where ions are associated *the apparent relative strength of two acids will depend upon the base used for comparison*, and also on the nature of other ions present in solution even when these have no acidic or basic properties. The above treatment applies to the investigation of equilibria by optical means (for example, by means of indicators), but the same conclusion holds if electrical methods are used for measuring the concentrations or activities of the free ions. For example, if we measure the concentrations of BH⁺ and X⁻ by conductivity measurements, the "dissociation constant" obtained will be

$$[\mathrm{BH^+}][\mathrm{X^-}]/([\mathrm{B}] + [\mathrm{BH^+X^-}])([\mathrm{HX}] + [\mathrm{BH^+X^-}]),$$

which is related to K_D through the constant K_d^{BHX}, and thus the relative strengths obtained will again depend upon the nature of B. This is essentially the same difficulty that arises in comparing the strengths of Lewis acids (electron acceptors), although, as we shall see, the deviations observed are much smaller.

These predictions are borne out by the indicator measurements of Kolthoff and Bruckenstein (*loc. cit.* [2]) in anhydrous acetic acid. This has a dielectric constant $\epsilon = 6.3$, and an electrostatic calculation[24] predicts that for ionic radii in the range 3 to 5 Å ion pairs will

[24] N. Bjerrum, *K. Danske Vid. Selsk, Math.-fys. Medd.*, **7**, no. 9 (1926); R. M. Fuoss and C. A. Kraus, *J. Am. Chem. Soc.*, **55**, 1919 (1933).

have dissociation constants in the range 10^{-5} to 10^{-7}, as is confirmed by conductivity measurements,[25] so that ionic association will be considerable over any convenient range of concentrations. Correspondingly, it is found that the relative strengths of acids depend upon the bases with which they are reacting. For example, for reaction with urea $K_i(\text{HCl}):K_i(p\text{-toluenesulfonic acid}):K_i(\text{HClO}_4) = 1:2.3:330$, while for reaction with the indicator p-naphtholbenzein the corresponding ratios are $1:2.8:1,500$. Kolthoff gives other examples of the same kind of behavior. The effect of concentration upon the equilibrium position will of course also depend upon whether the ions are associated. For example, if we add a small concentration c of a basic indicator to an excess of a weak acid HX, concentration a, then if $\text{BH}^+\cdot\text{X}^-$ is dissociated the equilibrium is governed by $cx^2/a(1-x)$ $= K$ (x dependent on c), while if $\text{BH}^+\cdot\text{X}^-$ is undissociated, $x/a(1-x)$ $= K$ (x independent of c).

There exist many measurements of acid strengths, mostly by indicator measurements, in solvents of low dielectric constant, for example in m-cresol ($\epsilon = 11.8$),[26] chlorobenzene ($\epsilon = 5.6$),[27] chloroform ($\epsilon = 4.8$),[28] anisole ($\epsilon = 4.3$)[29] and benzene ($\epsilon = 2.3$).[30] Ion-pair formation would be anticipated in all these solvents, and although the question has not always been investigated or considered explicitly the results are consistent with this view, and in the work of Davis and McDonald (*loc. cit.* [30]) the interaction between picric acid and tribenzylamine was shown to agree very accurately with the equilibrium $\text{HX} + \text{B} \rightleftharpoons \text{BH}^+\text{X}^-$. At higher concentrations there is undoubtedly further association to give ion triplets or dipole aggregates,[31] and this has been shown to cause complications in indicator measurements in acetic acid.[32] Further, carboxylic acids, which have been widely investigated, are dimerized

---

[25] E.g., Kolthoff and Willman, and also Smith and Elliott, *loc. cit.* (2).

[26] J. N. Brönsted, A. Delbanco, and A. Tovborg-Jensen, *Z. physikal. Chem.*, 169A, 361 (1934); D. C. Griffiths, *J. Chem. Soc.*, 815 (1938).

[27] Griffiths, *loc. cit.* (26), p. 818, R. P. Bell and J. W. Bayles, *J. Chem. Soc.*, 1518 (1952); J. W. Bayles and A. Chetwyn, *ibid.*, 2328 (1958).

[28] A. Hantzsch and W. Voigt, *Ber.*, 62B, 970 (1929).

[29] Bell and Bayles, *loc. cit.* (27).

[30] J. N. Brönsted, *Ber.*, 61B, 2049 (1928); V. K. LaMer and H. C. Downes, *J. Am. Chem. Soc.*, 53, 888 (1931); 55, 1840 (1933); M. M. Davis and P. J. Schuhmann, *J. Res. Nat. Bur. Stand.*, 39, 221 (1947); M. M. Davis and E. A. McDonald, *ibid.*, 42, 595 (1949); M. M. Davis and H. B. Hetzer, *ibid.*, 46, 496 (1951); 48, 381 (1952). For recent measurements in a number of solvents, see Pearson and Vogelsong, *loc. cit.* (23).

[31] See, e.g., R. M. Fuoss and C. A. Kraus, *J. Am. Chem. Soc.*, 55, 2387 (1933); 57, 1 (1935); R. M. Fuoss, *ibid.*, 56, 1027 (1934); F. M. Batson and C. A. Kraus, *ibid.*, 56, 2017 (1934); A. A. Maryott, *J. Res. Nat. Bur. Stand.*, 41, 1 (1948).

[32] Kolthoff and Bruckenstein, *loc. cit.* (2).

to a considerable extent in solvents such as benzene and chloroform,[33] and the same is probably true for some of the indicators used.

There are thus many reasons why acid strengths measured in solvents of low dielectric constant should be uncertain and not directly comparable with strengths in water and the lower alcohols. It is therefore remarkable that values obtained in such solvents do in fact correlate with values in water about as well as the data for solvents of

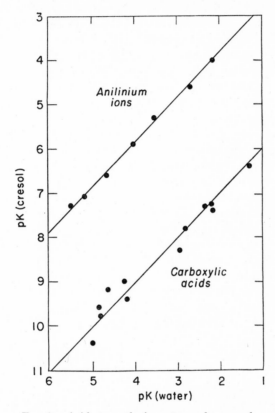

FIG. 3.—Acid strengths in water and *m*-cresol.

higher dielectric constant given in Tables 1–4. Two examples will be given to illustrate this. Figure 3 shows the conventional pK values for two classes of acid in water and *m*-cresol.[34] The measurements in

[33] For a review see G. Allen and E. F. Caldin, *Chem. Soc. Quart. Rev.*, **7,** 255 (1953).

[34] The values for cresol have been obtained from the indicator constants measured by Brönsted, Delbanco, and Tovborg-Jensen (*loc. cit.* [26]), using the value $pK_s = 14.7$ obtained by Griffiths (*loc. cit.* [26]). Although this value is uncertain, the relative strengths are not affected by the uncertainty.

m-cresol involved the use of several indicators of differing charge type
and the presence of various nonparticipating ions which could take
part in ion pairs.   In many cases the apparent indicator constants
varied considerably with the composition of the solution; this was
ascribed to a "salt effect" (though it was quite probably due to association of ions or molecules), and the constants reported refer to a particular ionic strength (0.01).   Nevertheless, for each type of acid the
ratio of the acid strengths in the two solvents is almost constant, as
shown by the lines of unit slope in the diagram.   Table 5 gives the

TABLE 5.—RELATIVE ACID STRENGTHS IN WATER AND CHLOROBENZENE
K_r = acid strength relative to 2,6-dinitrophenol

Acid	log $K_r(H_2O)$	log $K_r(C_6H_5Cl)$
Propionic	−1.07	−1.08
Acetic	−0.95	−1.00
Benzoic	−0.39	−0.58
Salicylic	0.82	0.74
Monochloroacetic	0.97	0.77
Dichloroacetic	2.50	2.52

relative acid strengths in chlorobenzene obtained by Griffiths (*loc.*
cit. [26]).   They were all measured relative to the same indicator
(2,6-dinitrophenol), and the cation present was $Me_2CH \cdot CH_2NH_3^+$;
however, the apparent constants again vary with the composition
of the solution, and the comparison between different acids was arbi-
trarily made between solutions in which $[RCO_2H] = [RCO_2^-]$.
Again the relative strengths of the acids are nearly the same in the
two solvents.

Our survey of the position in a wide range of solvents suggests the
generalization that *the relative strengths of acids of the same charge and*
chemical type are independent of the solvent.   This is nearly always true
to within a power of ten, and often to considerably better than this.
It is certainly invalid for acids of different charges, and the chemical
type must not vary to any considerable extent; for example, phenols
cannot usually be compared with carboxylic acids.   An even less allow-
able variation is between primary, secondary, and tertiary amines,
which involves a substitution on the atom carrying the proton.   Thus
if the data for *N*-methylaniline and *N*-dimethylaniline are plotted in
Figure 3, they fall far below the line for the primary anilines.   It seems
likely that these regularities extend to solvents of low dielectric constant because the formation of ion pairs reduces the individual inter-

actions between the ions and the solvent, thus counteracting the irregularities caused by the ion-pair formation itself.

Returning to solvents in which ions are not associated, it is of interest to express the effect of change of solvent in terms of activity coefficients. Within a given solvent activity coefficients are usually defined so that $f_i \rightarrow 1$ at infinite dilution in the solvent in question, and deviation of f_i from unity arise from the deviations from the laws of dilute solution, for example, because of interionic attraction. We shall suppose that all the equilibrium constants have been extrapolated to infinite dilution, so that this type of activity coefficient can be omitted. When we deal with changes of solvent, all activity coefficients must be referred to infinite dilution *in a given solvent*, which for our purposes is most conveniently taken as water. We can then define an activity coefficient for a species i in any solvent by the expression $\Delta G^\circ = RT \ln f_i^\circ$, where ΔG° is the free energy change involved in transferring one mole of i from a dilute solution in the solvent in question to a solution of equal concentration in the standard solvent (water).[35] This kind of activity coefficient has been termed a *degenerate activity coefficient*[36] and is equal to the distribution coefficient of the species i between water and the solvent concerned, assuming dilute solutions in each. If an acid-base equilibrium $A_1 + B_2 \rightleftharpoons A_2 + B_1$ has an equilibrium constant K° in water, its equilibrium constant K in any other solvent is given by

$$K/K^\circ = f_{A_1}^\circ f_{B_2}^\circ / f_{A_2}^\circ f_{B_1}^\circ. \tag{5}$$

Equation (5) expresses the relative strengths of A_1 and A_2 in water and in the solvent concerned, and the condition for these relative strengths to be the same is that the function $f_{A_1}^\circ f_{B_2}^\circ / f_{A_2}^\circ f_{B_1}^\circ$ shall be unity.

At least two of the species A_1, B_1, A_2, and B_2 must be ions, and the individual activity coefficients of these species will have no thermodynamic significance. However, the right-hand side of Equation 5 is always physically significant, and the same will be true for certain combinations involving ionic activity coefficients. Thus if A_1 and A_2 have positive charges z_1 and z_2 respectively, then if $z_1 = z_2$ the ratios $f_{B_1}^\circ / f_{B_2}^\circ$ and $f_{A_1}^\circ / f_{A_2}^\circ$ are physically significant, and if $z_1 + z_2 = 1$ the same is true of the products $f_{A_1}^\circ f_{B_2}^\circ$ and $f_{A_2}^\circ f_{B_1}^\circ$. On the other hand, it is never possible to attach a meaning to the ratios $f_{A_1}^\circ / f_{B_1}^\circ$ or $f_{A_2}^\circ / f_{B_2}^\circ$.

These points can be illustrated by taking particular cases. For the

[35] The definition of f_i° depends upon the concentration scale used, which must of course be the same as is used in defining the equilibrium constants. When dealing with more than one solvent, it is most convenient to use molarities (moles per liter).

[36] E. Grunwald and B. J. Berkowitz, *J. Am. Chem. Soc.*, **73**, 4939 (1951).

equilibrium $R_1CO_2H + R_2CO_2^- \rightleftharpoons R_2CO_2H + R_1CO_2^-$ the quantities $f^\circ(R_1CO_2H)$ and $f^\circ(R_2CO_2H)$ are separately determinable, and so is the ratio $f^\circ(R_1CO_2^-)/f^\circ(R_2CO_2^-)$. For example, the latter could be determined by measuring the solubilities of suitable sparingly soluble salts $R_1CO_2^- \cdot X^+$ and $R_2CO_2^- \cdot X^+$ in water and in the solvent considered. Similarly, for $R_1NH_3^+ + R_2NH_2 \rightleftharpoons R_2NH_3^+ + R_1NH_2$ the measurable quantities are $f^\circ(R_1NH_2)$, $f^\circ(R_2NH_2)$, and $f^\circ(R_1NH_3^+)/f^\circ(R_2NH_3^+)$, while for $R_1CO_2H + R_2NH_2 \rightleftharpoons R_2NH_3^+ + R_1CO_2^-$ we can determine $f^\circ(R_1CO_2H)$, $f^\circ(R_2NH_2)$, and the product $f^\circ(R_2NH_3^+)f^\circ(R_1CO_2^-)$.

Equation (5) does not at first sight apply to the effect of solvent upon conventional dissociation constants of the type $A + S \rightleftharpoons B + SH^+$, since it implies that both A_1—B_1 and A_2—B_2 exist in the same form in different solvents. We can, however, define a quantity $f_{H^+}^\circ$ (relative to dilute solutions in water) so that $RT \ln f_{H^+}$ represents the standard free energy change for the process H_3O^+ (in water) + SH (in SH) $\rightleftharpoons H_2O$ (in water) + SH_2^+ (in SH), i.e., for the transfer of a proton from one solvent to another. (A similar scheme would apply for the transfer of any ion if solvation were taken explicitly into account.) Further, since the solvent activities are conventionally put equal to unity in defining dissociation constants, we can write for the ratio of dissociation constants of an acid A in any solvent and in water,

$$K_d/K_d^\circ = f_A^\circ/f_{H^+}^\circ f_B^\circ. \tag{6}$$

For an uncharged acid f_A° is measurable, and so is the product $f_{H^+}^\circ f_B^\circ$.[37] Similarly, for the dissociation of a cation acid the measurable quantities are f_B° and $f_A^\circ{}^+/f_{H^+}^\circ$.

Various attempts have been made to split up Equations (5) and (6) still further, so as to obtain individual ionic activity coefficients.[38] However, such a procedure necessarily involves some extrathermodynamic assumptions, and since all the experimental results used or predicted involve the activity coefficients in thermodynamically acceptable combinations it seems that the values obtained for individual ions must be essentially arbitrary, though sometimes convenient.

If Equation (5) is applied to the relative strengths of two acids of similar structure and charge type, it seems likely that the whole of the right-hand side will deviate less from unity than will any of the combinations into which it can be dissected. For example, in the equilib-

[37] For example, $f_{H^+}^\circ f_{Cl^-}^\circ$ could be derived from the e.m.f. of the cell $H_2 | HCl |$ AgCl $\cdot$ Ag in the two solvents and $f_{B^-}^\circ/f_{Cl^-}^\circ$ from the solubilities of suitable salts Y^+B^- and Y^+Cl^-, whence $f_{H^+}^\circ f_{B^-}^\circ = f_{H^+}^\circ f_{Cl^-}^\circ \cdot f_{B^-}^\circ/f_{Cl^-}^\circ$.

[38] See particularly B. Gutbezahl and E. Grunwald, *J. Am. Chem. Soc.*, **75**, 559 (1953).

rium $R_1CO_2H + R_2CO_2^- \rightleftharpoons R_2CO_2H + R_1CO_2^-$ we may suppose that one of the radicals, R_1, contains a group which is absent in R_2 and which interacts very differently with water and with the solvent concerned. This means that each of the ratios $f^\circ(R_1CO_2H)/f^\circ(R_2CO_2H)$ and $f^\circ(R_1CO_2^-)/f^\circ(R_2CO_2^-)$ will deviate considerably from unity. On the other hand, their deviations are likely to be in the same direction and will tend to cancel out when we consider the ratio

$$f^\circ(R_1CO_2H)f^\circ(R_2CO_2^-)/f^\circ(R_2CO_2H)f^\circ(R_1CO_2^-).$$

This kind of cancellation probably accounts for the approximate constancy of relative strengths over a wide range of solvents, and we shall see that it is important when considering equilibria and kinetics in concentrated acid solutions.

A great deal of experimental work has been carried out on acid-base equilibria in *mixed solvents*, especially mixtures of water with the alcohols or dioxane. The presence of two solvent species introduces a number of complications. In the first place, there are now a number of different acidic and basic species derived from the solvent. Thus in aqueous alcohol we have as acids H_2O, $EtOH$, H_3O^+, and $EtOH_2^+$ and as bases H_2O, $EtOH$, OH^-, and EtO^-. In the second place, the composition of the solvent can now vary in the neighborhood of an ion (and to a smaller extent near an uncharged molecule) by a preferential solvation effect, so that the macroscopic properties of the solvent will be even less relevant than they are with pure solvents.[39] For these reasons the problem of mixed solvents will not be discussed here.

[39] It might be thought that the same problem is present in pure solvents, many of which are associated and can be thought of as mixtures of different polymerized molecules. However, these molecules are all in mobile equilibrium with one another so that the solvent behaves thermodynamically as a single species, thus differing from a mixture of two solvents.

CHAPTER V

Thermodynamic Functions Relating to Acid-Base Equilibria

So far we have dealt with equilibrium constants at a single temperature, and these are of course related to the standard free energy change by the equation

$$-RT \ln K = \Delta G°. \tag{7}$$

If values of K are available over a range of temperatures, we can deduce the enthalpy change ΔH from

$$\Delta H = -T^2 \frac{d}{dT}\left(\frac{\Delta G°}{T}\right) = RT^2 \frac{d \ln K}{dT}, \tag{8}$$

the standard entropy change from

$$\Delta S° = -d\Delta G°/dT = (\Delta H - \Delta G°)/T, \tag{9}$$

and the change in molar specific heat from

$$\Delta C_p = d\Delta H/dT = Td\Delta S°/dT = -Td^2\Delta G°/dT^2. \tag{10}$$

If it is assumed that ΔC_p remains constant over the temperature range investigated, the above equations can be integrated, giving

$$\Delta H = \Delta H_0 + \Delta C_p T, \qquad \Delta S° = \Delta S_0° + \Delta C_p \ln T,$$
$$\ln K = \frac{\Delta H_0}{RT} + \frac{\Delta C_p}{R} \ln T + \frac{(\Delta S_0° - \Delta C_p)}{R} \tag{11}$$

Equation (11) is a three-constant equation of the form $\ln K = A/T + B \ln T + C$, and the three constants can be evaluated if K is known with sufficient accuracy over a range of temperature, thus giving values of ΔH_0, $\Delta S_0°$, and ΔC_p, and hence also the values of ΔH and $\Delta S°$ at some standard temperature such as 25°C. The best method of treating the experimental data has been discussed by Everett and Wynne-Jones.[1] Several equations differing in form from (11) have been suggested to represent the variation of K with temperature.[2] Most of these are empirical, and the available data are not of sufficient accuracy to distinguish between them. The thermodynamic functions calculated from the various equations usually agree well in the experimental range of temperature, and many authors have used the equation $\ln K = A/T + B + CT$, suggested by Harned and Robinson (*loc. cit.* [2]), which is more convenient than (11) for numerical computation. This last equation corresponds to the assumption that ΔC_p is directly proportional to the absolute temperature, and over the range of accessible temperatures this is usually experimentally indistinguishable from a constant ΔC_p, as assumed in Equation (11). Feates and Ives[3] have deduced a temperature variation in ΔC_p (with a minimum near 25°C) on the basis of very accurate conductivity measurements with cyanoacetic acid, but this demands an accuracy of 0.03 percent in the determination of K, and either of the assumptions $\Delta C_p =$ constant or $\Delta C_p \propto T$ is adequate to reproduce most experimental data.

In principle it should be possible to determine ΔH and ΔC_p more directly from calorimetric measurements, but not much work of sufficient accuracy has been carried out,[4] and there are difficulties in extrapolating to infinite dilution. In practice, therefore, most of the reliable information about thermodynamic functions is derived from measurements of dissociation constants.

It is not easy to interpret directly the absolute values of thermodynamic functions for conventional acidity constants involving the solvent. As usually written, they have the dimensions of a concentration (e.g., $[X^-][H_3O^+]/[HX]$) so that the values of $\Delta G°$ and $\Delta S°$ are dependent upon the concentration units employed. If we include the solvent concentration, we then have the problem of interpreting the properties of the bulk solvent, which in the case of water is still a largely unsolved problem. It is more satisfactory to consider relative

[1] D. H. Everett and W. F. K. Wynne-Jones, *Trans. Faraday Soc.*, **35**, 1380 (1939); cf. K. S. Pitzer, *J. Am. Chem. Soc.*, **59**, 2365 (1937).

[2] For example, H. S. Harned and N. D. Embree, *J. Am. Chem. Soc.*, **56**, 1050 (1934); H. S. Harned and B. B. Owen, *Chem. Rev.*, **25**, 31 (1939); H. S. Harned and R. A. Robinson, *Trans. Faraday Soc.*, **36**, 973 (1940); J. F. J. Dippy and H. O. Jenkins, *ibid.*, **37**, 366 (1941); H. O. Jenkins, *ibid.*, **40**, 19 (1944).

[3] F. S. Feates and D. J. G. Ives, *J. Chem. Soc.*, 2798 (1956).

[4] T. W. Richards and B. J. Mair, *J. Am. Chem. Soc.*, **51**, 737 (1929); T. L. Cottrell, G. W. Drake, D. L. Levi, K. J. Tully, and J. H. Wolfenden, *J. Chem. Soc.*, 1016 (1948); W. J. Canady, H. M. Papée, and K. J. Laidler, *Trans. Faraday Soc.*, **54**, 502 (1958).

acidity constants, where the species in the equilibrium $A_1 + B_2$ $\rightleftharpoons A_2 + B_1$ are all in dilute solution. The values of all the thermodynamic functions are then all independent of the concentration scale and should be more readily interpreted. Such values can be obtained by subtraction from the published thermodynamic data for conventional acidity constants, and Table 6 gives the results of such a treatment, comparison with one standard system being made for each class of acid concerned. Care has been taken to include only accurate data obtained by modern methods, since the values of ΔS°, and even more of ΔC_p, are very sensitive to experimental error. The accuracy of the

TABLE 6.—THERMODYNAMIC DATA FOR ACID-BASE REACTIONS
IN WATER AT 25°C

Carboxylic acids—Reaction $RCO_2 + MeCO_2^- \rightleftharpoons RCO_2^- + MeCO_2H$.
(pK refers to $[RCO_2^-][H_3O^+]/[RCO_2H]$.)

| Acid | Reference | pK | kcal/mole | | | cal/mole/degree | |
			ΔG°	ΔH	$T\Delta S^\circ$	ΔS°	ΔC_p
Trimethylacetic	(1)	5.032	+0.37	−0.61	−0.98	−3.3	+3
Propionic	(1)	4.875	+0.16	−0.12	−0.28	−0.9	+1
Hexoic	(1)	4.857	+0.14	−0.59	−0.73	−2.5	+2
iso-Butyric	(1)	4.849	+0.12	−0.69	−0.80	−2.8	+5
iso-Hexoic	(1)	4.845	+0.12	−0.61	−0.73	−2.5	+4
Valeric	(1)	4.843	+0.12	−0.61	−0.73	−2.5	+4
Butyric	(2)	4.818	+0.08	−0.61	−0.69	−2.3	+2
iso-Valeric	(1)	4.781	+0.03	−1.11	−1.14	−3.9	+5
Acetic	(3)	4.756	0	0	0	0	0
Diethylacetic	(1)	4.736	−0.03	−1.92	−1.89	−6.4	+8
Succinic	(4)	4.207	−0.62	+0.87	+1.49	+5.4	+5
Lactic	(5)	3.860	−1.23	−0.06	+1.17	+3.9	−3
Glycollic	(6)	3.831	−1.27	+0.21	+1.06	+4.9	−3
Formic	(7)	3.752	−1.38	+0.07	+1.45	+4.8	−4
Iodoacetic	(8)	3.182	−2.16	−1.31	+0.85	+2.8	+4
Bromoacetic	(8)	2.902	−2.53	−1.13	+1.40	+4.7	−1
Chloroacetic	(8)	2.868	−2.58	−1.01	+1.57	+5.2	−9
Fluoroacetic	(8)	2.586	−2.96	−1.28	+1.68	+5.6	+4
Cyanoacetic	(9)	2.470	−3.12	−0.78	+2.34	+7.8	+1
p-Hydroxybenzoic	(10)	4.582	−0.24	+0.65	+0.89	+3.0	−8
Benzoic	(10)	4.213	−0.75	+0.53	+1.28	+4.2	−2
p-Bromobenzoic	(10)	4.002	−1.03	+0.22	+1.25	+4.2	+6
p-Chlorobenzoic	(10)	3.986	−1.06	+0.34	+1.40	+4.7	+14
m-Chlorobenzoic	(10)	3.827	−1.27	−0.07	+1.20	+4.0	−4
m-Bromobenzoic	(10)	3.809	−1.30	+0.05	+1.35	+4.5	+4
m-Cyanobenzoic	(10)	3.598	−1.58	+0.07	+1.65	+5.5	−10
p-Cyanobenzoic	(10)	3.551	−1.65	+0.14	+1.79	+6.0	−3
p-Nitrobenzoic	(10)	3.442	−1.80	+0.14	+1.94	+6.5	+6
$CO_2^- \cdot CO_2H$	(11)	4.266	−0.67	−1.55	−0.88	−2.9	−22
$CO_2^- \cdot CH_2CO_2H$	(12)	5.696	+1.43	−1.90	−2.33	−7.8	−24
$CO_2^- \cdot CH_2CH_2CO_2H$	(4)	5.638	+1.20	0.00	−1.20	−4.0	−15

TABLE 6.—(*Continued*)

Amine cations—Reaction $R_3NH^+ + NH_3 \rightleftharpoons R_3N + NH_4^+$

(pK refers to $[R_3N][H_3O^+]/[R_3NH^+]$)

Acid	Reference	pK	kcal/mole			cal/mole/degree	
			$\Delta G°$	ΔH	$T\Delta S°$	$\Delta S°$	ΔC_p
Ammonium	(13)	9.245	0	0	0	0	0
Methylammonium	(14)	10.624	+1.87	+0.69	−1.18	−3.9	+8
Ethylammonium	(15)	10.631	+1.91	+1.18	−0.83	−2.8	—
n-Propylammonium	(15)	10.530	+1.77	+1.45	−0.32	−1.1	—
n-Butylammonium	(15)	10.597	+1.85	+1.67	−0.18	−0.9	—
Hydroxyethylammonium	(16)	9.498	+0.34	−0.32	−0.64	−2.1	−1
Dimethylammonium	(14)	10.774	+2.11	−0.52	−2.63	−8.8	+20
Diethylammonium	(15)	10.933	+2.39	+0.37	−2.02	−6.7	—
Piperidinium	(17)	11.123	+2.53	+0.40	−2.13	−7.0	+21
Trimethylammonium	(14)	9.800	+0.77	−3.57	−4.34	−14.5	+41
Triethylammonium	(18)	10.867	+2.22	−0.19	−2.41	−8.0	—
Anilinium	(19)	4.596	−6.34	−5.29	+1.05	+3.5	0
o-Chloroanilinium	(20)	2.634	−9.02	−6.40	+2.62	+8.7	0
$NH_2(CH_2)_2NH_3^+$	(21)	9.928	+0.94	−0.58	−1.52	−5.1	+10
$NH_2(CH_2)_6NH_3^+$	(21)	10.930	+2.30	+1.51	−0.79	−2.6	+8
$\overset{+}{N}H_3(CH_2)_2\overset{+}{N}H_3$	(21)	6.848	−3.27	−1.53	+1.74	+5.8	+18
$\overset{+}{N}H_3(CH_2)_6\overset{+}{N}H_3$	(21)	9.830	+0.80	+1.42	+0.62	+2.1	+8

Values for acid dissociation of standard systems

	$\Delta G°$	ΔH	$T\Delta S°$	$\Delta S°$	ΔC_p
$CH_3CO_2H \rightleftharpoons CH_3CO_2^- + H^+$	6.49	−0.11	−6.60	−22.1	−37
$NH_4^+ \rightleftharpoons NH_3 + H^+$	12.61	12.40	−0.21	−0.7	0

1. D. H. Everett, D. A. Landsman, and B. R. W. Pinsent, *Proc. Roy. Soc.*, A, **215**, 403 (1952).
2. H. S. Harned and R. O. Sutherland, *J. Am. Chem. Soc.*, **56**, 2039 (1934); recalculated by Everett, Landsman, and Pinsent (*loc. cit.*).
3. H. S. Harned and B. B. Owen, *Physical Chemistry of Electrolyte Solutions* (New York. 1943), table 15-6-1A.
4. G. D. Pinching and R. G. Bates, *J. Res. Nat. Bur. Stand.*, **45**, 322, 444 (1950).
5. L. F. Nims and P. K. Smith, *J. Biol. Chem.*, **113**, 145 (1936).
6. L. F. Nims, *J. Am. Chem. Soc.*, **58**, 987 (1936).
7. H. S. Harned and N. D. Embree, *ibid.*, **56**, 1042 (1934).
8. D. J. G. Ives and J. H. Pryor, *J. Chem. Soc.*, 2104 (1955).
9. F. S. Feates and D. J. G. Ives, *ibid.*, 2798 (1956).
10. G. Briegleb and A. Bieber, *Z. Elektrochem.*, **55**, 250 (1951).
11. G. D. Pinching and R. G. Bates, *J. Res. Nat. Bur. Stand.*, **40**, 405 (1948).
12. W. J. Hamer, J. O. Burton, and S. F. Acree, *ibid.*, **24**, 269 (1940).
13. R. G. Bates and G. D. Pinching, *ibid.*, **42**, 419 (1949); *J. Am. Chem. Soc.*, **72**, 1393 (1950); D. H. Everett and D. A. Landsman, *Trans. Faraday Soc.*, **50**, 1221 (1954).
14. D. H. Everett and W. F. K. Wynne-Jones, *Proc. Roy. Soc.*, A, **177**, 499 (1941).
15. A. G. Evans and S. D. Hamann, *Trans. Faraday Soc.*, **47**, 34 (1951).
16. R. G. Bates and G. D. Pinching, *J. Res. Nat. Bur. Stand.*, **46**, 349 (1951).
17. R. G. Bates and N. E. Bower, *ibid.*, **57**, 153 (1956).
18. J. E. Ablard, D. S. McKinney, and J. C. Warner, *J. Am. Chem. Soc.*, **62**, 2181 (1940).
19. K. J. Pedersen, *Kgl. danske vid. Selsk. Skr.*, **14**, 9 (1937).
20. K. J. Pedersen, *ibid.*, **15**, 2 (1937).
21. D. H. Everett and B. R. W. Pinsent, *Proc. Roy. Soc.*, A, **215**, 416 (1952).

figures given will rarely exceed $\pm$ 0.1 kcal/mole in ΔH, $\pm$ 0.3 cal/mole degree in $\Delta S°$, and $\pm$ 1 cal/mole/degree in ΔC_p.

In a symmetrical reaction such as $R_1CO_2H + R_2CO_2^- \rightleftharpoons R_2CO_2H + R_1CO_2^-$ it is tempting to guess that the entropy change is close to zero, and hence $\Delta G°$ close to ΔH. Inspection of Table 6 shows that this is by no means the case, since the term $T\Delta S°$ is just as important as ΔH in determining the value of $\Delta G°$, and hence the equilibrium constant. Moreover, the separate contributions of ΔH and $T\Delta S°$ to $\Delta G°$ vary in an apparently erratic manner from one acid to another. Although such behavior is not unknown for nonionic equilibria and nonpolar solvents, the large effects observed suggest strongly that the entropy changes involve an interaction of the ions (and perhaps also the uncharged molecules) with the highly polar and associated aqueous medium. The same conclusion is reached by examining the values of ΔC_p, which is less sensitive than is $\Delta S°$ to changes in the types of motion executed by the system. Thus the complete freezing of an internal rotation corresponds to only $\frac{1}{2}R = 1$ cal/mole, and the changes of several units found in the last column of Table 6 must represent fairly drastic alterations in the system. This is particularly the case for the amine cations when we are comparing secondary and tertiary amines with ammonia or a primary amine.

One method of attempting to allow for the solvent interaction is to use an electrostatic picture. By combining equations (3) with (7) to (10), we obtain for the electrostatic contributions to $\Delta S°$ and ΔC_p

$$(\Delta S°)_e = \frac{\mathbf{N}e^2}{2}\left(\frac{1}{r_0} - \frac{1}{r}\right)\frac{d}{dT}\left(\frac{1}{\epsilon}\right) \tag{12}$$

$$(\Delta C_p)_e = \frac{\mathbf{N}e^2}{2}\left(\frac{1}{r_0} - \frac{1}{r}\right)T\frac{d^2}{dT^2}\left(\frac{1}{\epsilon}\right), \tag{13}$$

where $\mathbf{N}$ is the Avogadro number. The exact value of $d^2\epsilon/dT^2$ is uncertain, but if we use the table of values given by Harned and Owen[5] we find for water at 25°C

$$(\Delta S°)_e = 9.7\left(\frac{1}{r_0'} - \frac{1}{r'}\right) \text{ cal/mole/deg} \tag{14}$$

$$(\Delta C_p)_e = 5.7\left(\frac{1}{r_0'} - \frac{1}{r'}\right) \text{ cal/mole/deg} \tag{15}$$

where r_0' and r' are measured in Ångström units. Equations (14) and (15) might just be stretched to fit the experimental data for carboxylic

[5] H. S. Harned and B. B. Owen, *Physical Chemistry of Electrolyte Solutions,* (New York, 1940), table 5-1-3.

acids, though it is necessary to assume $r < 1\text{Å}$, which is hardly reasonable. They certainly fail to account for the large entropy and specific heat changes found for the amine cations; for example, the reaction $NMe_3H^+ + NH_3 \rightleftharpoons NMe_3 + NH_4^+$ has $\Delta S° = -14.5$, $\Delta C_p = +41$. Moreover, (14) and (15) predict $\Delta S° = 1.7\Delta C_p$. Table 6 shows no sign of any such regularity, there being in fact some tendency (for example, in the amine and fatty acid series) for $\Delta S°$ and ΔC_p to vary in opposite directions.

There is thus ample evidence that an electrostatic picture is inadequate to account for the solvent-ion interaction, though it has been used by many authors.[6] The same difficulty arises when we consider processes such as $R_1CO_2H + R_2NH_2 \rightleftharpoons R_1CO_2^- + R_2NH_3^+$. The thermodynamic functions for 420 such reactions can be derived by combining the first and second parts of Table 6, and although $\Delta S°$ and ΔC_p are both negative, in agreement with electrostatic calculation, their numerical values are frequently too high, and there is no sign of the predicted correlation between them ($\Delta S° = 1.7\Delta C_p$). To take an extreme example, the reaction $MeCO_2H + NMe_3 \rightleftharpoons MeCO_2^- + NHMe_3^+$ has $\Delta S° = -7$, $\Delta C_p = -78$.

The problem is of course not restricted to acid-base equilibria but arises whenever we wish to interpret the entropies or specific heats of ions in solution. The use of the dielectric constant is a crude macroscopic method of allowing for the orientation of the solvent molecules in the field of the ion, and there is no doubt that it is necessary to take a much more specific picture of the molecular interactions involved. A first step is to attempt a detailed analysis of the motions of the first shell of co-ordinated water molecules, and then to apply the electrostatic equations to the solvent outside this shell. This approach has been used both for entropies[7] and for specific heats[8] and is certainly an improvement on the Born equation. Unfortunately, however, there is now a great deal of evidence that the structure of water is influenced by ions even outside the first co-ordination shell. There is much support for the view[9] that for an ion of moderate size the inner co-ordination shell is surrounded by a region which is *less* ordered than

[6] See, e.g., R. W. Gurney, *J. Chem. Phys.*, **6**, 499 (1938); *Ionic Processes in Solution* (New York, 1953), chs. 7 and 8; E. C. Baughan, *J. Chem. Phys.*, **7**, 952 (1939).

[7] D. D. Eley and M. G. Evans, *Trans. Faraday Soc.*, **34**, 1093 (1938).

[8] D. H. Everett and C. A. Coulson, *Trans. Faraday Soc.*, **36**, 633 (1940).

[9] H. S. Frank and M. W. Evans, *J. Chem. Phys.*, **13**, 507 (1945). For a recent summary, with references, see H. S. Frank and Wen-Yang Wen, *Disc. Faraday Soc.*, **24**, 133 (1957). See also Feates and Ives, *loc. cit.* (3).

pure water (because of the competition between the two incompatible structures), the ordered structure of water returning at still greater distances. The balance between the ordering and disordering effects will determine the entropy of the ion, and in this way a plausible explanation can be given for many of the observed facts. Since the structure of pure water is still imperfectly understood, the explanation is essentially a qualitative one, and the position is further complicated by the fact that many nonpolar molecules (for example, the rare gases and the hydrocarbons) have large negative entropies of solution in water, i.e., they increase the order in the solvent.[10] Some authors have interpreted this effect in terms of definite cavity structures, such as are found in the solid clathrate hydrates of many gases,[11] and others regard it as a "freezing" of the normal water structure.

The above considerations have been applied mainly to ions and molecules which are spherical, or nearly so, and it is obvious that the problem will be much more difficult for unsymmetrical acid-base species such as those listed in Table 6.[12] A few individual explanations do emerge. For example, the reaction $NMe_3H^+ + NH_3 \rightleftharpoons NMe_3 + NH_4^+$ has $\Delta S° = -14.5$, and this can be attributed to the shielding action of the methyl groups, which hinder solvent orientation in the ion NMe_3H^+ and hence give it a higher entropy than NH_4^+. The same effect appears for a number of amines and has been variously described as hydrogen bonding by the H-atoms of the cation[13] or as solvent exclusion by the alkyl groups,[14] the two being equivalent. Unfortunately, however, the specific heat changes are in the opposite direction (for example, $\Delta C_p = +41$ for $NMe_3H^+ + NH_3 \rightarrow NMe_3 + NH_4^+$), and this is certainly unexpected, though explanations can be devised in terms of restricted rotation. There are undoubtedly many factors to be considered, as is well illustrated by the detailed discussions given recently

[10] D. D. Eley, *Trans. Faraday Soc.*, **35**, 1281, 1421 (1939); H. S. Frank, *J. Chem. Phys.*, **13**, 507 (1945); R. E. Powell and W. M. Latimer, *ibid.*, **19**, 1139 (1951); W. F. Claussen and M. F. Polglase, *J. Am. Chem. Soc.*, **74**, 4817 (1952).

[11] M. von Stackelberg and H. R. Muller, *Naturwiss.*, **38**, 456 (1951); **39**, 20 (1952).

[12] Table 6 lists equilibria which do not formally involve the solvent; this was done in the hope of avoiding difficulties connected with the structure of liquid water. Since this hope has proved a vain one, nothing is lost by considering the thermodynamic functions of equilibria such as $RCO_2H + H_2O \rightleftharpoons RCO_2^- + H_3O^+$ or $RNH_3^+ + H_2O \rightleftharpoons RNH_2 + H_3O^+$, as has been done by most authors. These can be derived from the entries in the table by using the values for the standard systems given at the end of it.

[13] A. F. Trotman-Dickenson, *J. Chem. Soc.*, 1293 (1949).

[14] A. G. Evans and R. D. Hamann, *Trans. Faraday Soc.*, **47**, 34 (1952).

by Everett, Landsman, and Pinsent[15] for the fatty acid series and by Feates and Ives (*loc. cit* [3]) for the series CH_2FCO_2H, CH_2ClCO_2H, CH_2BrCO_2H, CH_2ICO_2H, and CH_2CNCO_2H.

Although the values of $\Delta S°$ and ΔC_p are imperfectly understood, they are often of importance in interpreting acid-base equilibria in terms of molecular structure. The conventional dissociation equilibria of the carboxylic acids usually have small values of ΔH, and ΔC_p is in the neighborhood of -40 cal/degree (cf. Table 6). This means that the value of ΔH frequently changes sign near room temperature, corresponding to a maximum in the dissociation constant. This was first pointed out by Harned and Embree,[16] who showed that the experimental data could be represented closely by a parabolic expression of the form

$$\log K = \log K_m - p(T - T_m)^2 \qquad (16)$$

where K_m is the maximum value of K at the temperature T_m, p is a constant which does not vary much from one acid to another, while T_m varies considerably. Equation (16) is not exact and has no simple theoretical significance, but its form shows that the relative strengths of two acids will in general change with temperature, their order often being inverted either within the range studied experimentally, or not far outside it. This is illustrated for the fatty acid series by Table 7, taken from Everett, Landsman, and Pinsent (*loc. cit.* [15]). There is obviously no particular virtue in the standard temperature 25°C, and it is therefore dangerous to give structural interpretations of small differences in dissociation constants at this temperature, as has often been done.

This raises a question of general importance: What is the correct basis for comparing the predictions of a molecular model with the results of thermodynamic measurements? A molecular model, whether classical or quantal, essentially predicts energies (or effects on the energy) of molecules *in vacuo* at absolute zero, where there is of course no distinction between the enthalpy and the free energy. At a finite temperature these "model energies" are overlaid by a large amount of thermal energy, distributed between many degrees of freedom, and when a solvent is present there will be a considerable contribution from the effect of the system being studied upon the kinetic and potential energy of the solvent molecules. The quantities H and G represent, in

[15] D. H. Everett, D. A. Landsman, and B. R. W. Pinsent, *Proc. Roy. Soc.* A, **215**, 403 (1952).

[16] Harned and Embree, *loc. cit.* (2); cf. Harned and Owen, *loc. cit.* (2).

TABLE 7.—INVERSIONS OF RELATIVE STRENGTHS IN THE FATTY ACID SERIES

$K_1 > K_2$ above inversion temperature

(1)	(2)	Inversion temperature (C°)
Acetic	n-Hexoic	−34
Acetic	iso-Hexoic	−25
Acetic	iso-Valeric	16
Acetic	Diethylacetic	29
iso-Valeric	Diethylacetic	51
Propionic	n-Valeric	58
Propionic	iso-Butyric	46
Propionic	n-Butyric	90

effect, different ways of averaging the molecular energies,[17] and it is not at all obvious which of them is more directly comparable with the model. In the present problem there might seem to be some justification for using the quantity ΔH_0 in Equation (11), which has the formal appearance of an energy change at absolute zero and which is evaluated when fitting the experimental data to this equation. However, (11) implies that ΔC_p is independent of temperature, which may be a good approximation over a considerable temperature range but is certainly not valid down to absolute zero. Thus ΔH_0 is not likely to have any more fundamental significance than ΔH or $\Delta G°$ at 25°C; and it is certainly much less accurately known because it is highly dependent upon the value taken for ΔC_p and in effect involves a long extrapolation from the experimental data. Similarly, no physical significance can be attached to the quantity $\Delta S_0°$ in Equation (11).

In general it seems likely that free energies are more appropriate than are total energies for comparison with molecular models. This is clearly the case if our model attempts to allow for solvent effects by using the macroscopic dielectric constant, because electrostatic calculations (for example, the Born expression for the energy of an ion) always lead most directly to free energies, since they imply the use of reversible processes. Electrostatic expressions for the enthalpy will always involve not only the dielectric constant ϵ, but also $d\epsilon/dT$, as was

---

[17] If ϵ_i represents the energy of an individual molecular level, then the two types of averaging correspond to

$$H = \sum_i \epsilon_i e^{-\epsilon_i/kT} \bigg/ \sum_i e^{-\epsilon_i/kT}, \qquad e^{-G/kT} = \sum_i e^{-\epsilon_i/kT}$$

If all the systems are in the lowest state ϵ_0, then $H = G = \epsilon_0$.

first pointed out clearly by Bjerrum[18] in connection with the interionic attraction theory of strong electrolytes.

There are also more general reasons for believing that ΔG at finite temperatures approximates better than does ΔH to the behavior of the model. Suppose that we start with an ideal situation, a vacuum at absolute zero, and proceed to complicate the situation by raising the temperature and introducing a solvent. Considering first the temperature change, for a given reaction we have at absolute zero $\Delta H_0 = \Delta G_0$, $\Delta S_0 = 0$, and $\Delta C_p = 0$. At a finite temperature,

$$\Delta H = \Delta H_0 + \int_0^T \Delta C_p dT$$

$$\Delta G = \Delta H_0 + \int_0^T \Delta C_p dT - T \int_0^T \frac{\Delta C_p}{T} dT. \tag{17}$$

Suppose now that we modify the reaction slightly, for example by introducing a substituent, and indicate the corresponding small changes in ΔH_0, ΔC_p, and so forth, by $\delta \Delta H_0$, $\delta \Delta C_p$, and so forth. Then

$$\delta \Delta H - \delta \Delta H_0 = \int_0^T \delta \Delta C_p dT \tag{18a}$$

$$\delta \Delta G - \delta \Delta H_0 = \int_0^T \delta \Delta C_p dT - T \int_0^T \frac{\delta \Delta C_p}{T} dT. \tag{18b}$$

There are now good grounds for believing that (18b) will most commonly be numerically smaller than (18a), i.e., that $\delta \Delta G$ approximates more closely to $\delta \Delta H_0$ than does $\delta \Delta H$. No general proof of this can be given, and indeed it will not be universally true, but we may illustrate the point by writing $\delta \Delta C_p$ as a power series, beginning with a term in T^3 so as to give the correct behavior at absolute zero, i.e.,

$$\delta \Delta C_p = a_1 T^3 + a_2 T^4 + a_3 T^5 + \cdots . \tag{19}$$

This gives the result

$$\delta \Delta H - \delta \Delta H_0 = \frac{a_1}{4} T^4 + \frac{a_2}{5} T^5 + \frac{a_3}{6} T^6 + \cdots \tag{20a}$$

$$\delta \Delta G - \delta \Delta H_0 = - \frac{a_1}{3.4} T^4 - \frac{a_2}{4.5} T^5 - \frac{a_3}{5.6} T^6 - \cdots . \tag{20b}$$

[18] N. Bjerrum, *Z. physikal. Chem.*, **119**, 145 (1926).

We cannot make any general statements about the signs or magnitudes of a_1, a_2, a_3, $\cdots$, but it is clear that for random variations of these quantities there is a high probability that (20b) will be numerically smaller than (20a). This kind of consideration was first put forward by Evans and Polanyi,[19] using a somewhat different formulation. They applied the same treatment to kinetic problems, concluding that activation energies calculated from molecular models are better compared with measured reaction velocities (i.e., free energies of activation) than with measured activation energies (i.e., enthalpies of activation), and they also considered the effect of the solvent, to which we shall now turn.

The thermodynamic functions for a reaction in a solvent, $\delta\Delta H_s$, and so forth, can be expressed in terms of the corresponding quantities in the gas phase by the equations

$$\delta\Delta H_s - \delta\Delta H = \sum H^s \tag{21a}$$

$$\delta\Delta G_s - \delta\Delta G = \sum H^s - T \sum S^s \tag{21b}$$

where H^s and S^s are heats and entropies of solution and the summation is made over all the species involved in the reactions. There is good experimental evidence[20] that the heats and entropies of solution of a series of similar substances in a given solvent are approximately related by expressions of the form

$$TS^s = \alpha H^s + \beta \tag{22}$$

where α and β are constants characteristic of the solvent, α being always positive and usually between 0.4 and unity. Some theoretical interpretations have been given for these and analogous relationships.[21] If Equation (22) applies to the species concerned, it is clear that (21b) will be numerically smaller than (21a), i.e., the solvent will affect $\delta\Delta G$ less than it does $\delta\Delta H$, so that there is again some justification for using free energies rather than enthalpies for comparison with molecular models.

It is clear that caution must be exercised in the molecular interpretation of thermodynamic quantities relating to acid-base equilibria. If

[19] M. G. Evans and M. Polanyi, *Trans. Faraday Soc.*, **32**, 1333 (1936); cf. also J. A. V. Butler, *ibid.*, **33**, 169 (1937).

[20] J. A. V. Butler, *Trans. Faraday Soc.*, **33**, 229 (1937); R. P. Bell, *ibid.*, **33**, 496 (1937); I. M. Barclay and J. A. V. Butler, *ibid.*, **34**, 1445 (1938). For a summary see J. E. Leffler, *J. Org. Chem.*, **20**, 1202 (1955).

[21] H. S. Frank, *J. Chem. Phys.*, **13**, 478 (1945); H. S. Frank and M. W. Evans, *ibid.*, **13**, 507 (1945); O. K. Rice, *J. Chem. Phys.*, **15**, 875 (1947); J. A. Christiansen, *Acta Chem. Scand.*, **3**, 61 (1949).

large effects are concerned (for example, several powers of ten in a dissociation constant), semiquantitative conclusions can often be drawn, but it is dangerous to rely on small changes, which may even be reversed if the solvent or the temperature is changed. Moreover, as seen in the last chapter, not much is gained by attempting to eliminate the effect of the solvent either by using a nonpolar medium or by extrapolating to infinite dielectric constant. Dissociation constants in water at a standard temperature (i.e., values of $\Delta G°$) are likely to be somewhat better than enthalpy changes for correlating with structural effects, and this prediction is borne out in the few cases where both quantities are available. For example, in the series CMe_3CO_2H, CH_3CO_2H, HCO_2H, CH_2ICO_2H, CH_2BrCO_2H, CH_2ClCO_2H, and CH_2FCO_2H (cf. Table 6) the value of pK decreases steadily, as would be predicted by electronic theory, while ΔH behaves in an erratic manner.

In the majority of cases dissociation constants are available only at one temperature, and most comparisons have been made on this basis. It would be of great interest to have more extensive information about ΔH, $\Delta S°$, and ΔC_p, especially for a better understanding of solute-solvent interactions. Unfortunately, such information can only be obtained by making very accurate measurements over a considerable temperature range, and Table 6 contains almost all of the reliable values to date. Similar information is lacking for solvents other than water, except for a small amount of work in mixtures of water with dioxane and the lower alcohols.

CHAPTER VI

Concentrated Solutions of Acids and Bases

THE properties of concentrated solutions of acids often deviate considerably from what would be predicted by extrapolation from more dilute solutions. This is particularly true for acids which are completely dissociated in dilute solution, and it is a general feature that the "acidity" of the solution (as measured by its effect on indicators, its solvent power for weak bases, or its catalytic effect) increases much more rapidly than its concentration, the divergence often amounting to several powers of ten. Such behavior clearly cannot be explained in terms of incomplete dissociation, and it is of interest to see what generalizations can be made about these concentrated solutions, and whether their properties can be accounted for on a molecular basis.

The thermodynamic behavior of a solution of an acid HX can of course be expressed in terms of an activity coefficient, usually $f_{\pm} = (f_{H^+}f_{X^-})^{\frac{1}{2}}$, which can be determined by any of the standard methods, such as measurements of freezing points, vapor pressures, or e.m.f. It is found that the values for the strong acids HCl, HBr, HI, and HClO$_4$ are very similar to those for the corresponding lithium salts, i.e., they pass through a shallow minimum value of 0.7 to 0.8 in the region 0.2 to 0.4M, and then increase to values considerably greater than unity above 1M.[1] Although the comparison with lithium is of interest, as we shall see later, the interpretation of ionic activities in concentrated solutions is still imperfectly understood. The effect of the electrical forces between the ions can only be computed for dilute solutions, and there are certainly additional factors at higher concentrations, such as ion pairing, the hydration of the ions, and the change in the dielectric constant of the solvent.[2] Moreover, from the point of view of acidity, $f_{\pm}$ contains irrelevant information about the

---

[1] See, e.g., R. A. Robinson and R. H. Stokes, *Electrolyte Solutions* (London, 1955), p. 476, app. table 9.

[2] For a recent discussion see "Interactions in Ionic Solutions," *Disc. Faraday Soc.*, **24** (1957).

anion, which is not directly involved in the acidic behavior of the solution. As already stressed, there is no type of measurement by which $f_\pm$ can be split up into the separate activity coefficients f_{H^+} and f_{X^-}.

It might be thought that measurements of conductivity would be more revealing, since a large part of the conductivity is due to the hydrogen ions. There is, however, no simple way of interpreting these measurements. The calculation of the effect of interionic attraction is more complex for mobilities than for activities, and in addition to this solutions of strong acids show an abnormally great decrease in conductivity at concentrations above about 0.2M. This probably depends upon the "proton-jump" mechanism, to which the hydrogen ion in water owes its high mobility. This mechanism will be particularly sensitive to modifications in the water structure produced by high ionic concentrations.[3]

The most recent approach to the problem of concentrated acid solutions has been through the *acidity function*, first introduced by Hammett and Deyrup[4] and recently reviewed by Paul and Long.[5] The experimental method consists of adding to the acid solution a small amount of an uncharged base B (usually an indicator) and then determining the extent to which it is converted into the conjugate acid BH^+ by spectrophotometric measurements. Hammett then defines a quantity h_0 by means of the equation

$$h_0 \equiv K_{BH^+} \frac{[BH^+]}{[B]}, \tag{23}$$

where K_{BH^+} is the thermodynamic dissociation constant of BH^+, the standard state for activity coefficients being dilute aqueous solution. Equation (23) can be written in the logarithmic form

$$H_0 \equiv -\log h_0 \equiv pK_{BH^+} - \log \frac{[BH^+]}{[BH]}, \tag{24}$$

and it is the quantity H_0, defined by (24), which is usually termed the acidity function. In sufficiently dilute solutions of acids containing no added salt, $K_{BH^+} = [B][H^+]/[BH^+]$, so that h_0 and H_0 become respectively equal to $[H^+]$ and pH under these conditions. Since B is added in very low concentrations, it will not have any appreciable effect on the properties of the acid solution.

[3] L. Onsager, *Ann. N. Y. Acad. Sci.*, **46**, 265 (1945); Robinson and Stokes, *op. cit.* (1), p. 361.

[4] L. P. Hammett and A. J. Deyrup, *J. Am. Chem. Soc.*, **54**, 2721 (1932).

[5] M. A. Paul and F. A. Long, *Chem. Rev.*, **57**, 1 (1957). Much of the material in the present chapter is taken from this review.

In concentrated solutions h_0 differs considerably from $[H^+]$, and similarly H_0 from pH. For example, in 10-molal solutions of mineral acids h_0 is somewhat greater than 1,000. This can be represented formally by inserting activity coefficients in (24), giving

$$H_0 = -\log [H^+] + \log \frac{f_{BH^+}}{f_B f_{H^+}} . \tag{25}$$

Since we are now dealing with concentrated solutions, the choice of concentration scale becomes of importance; $[H^+]$ can be expressed in either molarities or molalities, with corresponding changes in the values of the activity coefficients.

The usefulness of the acidity function, as defined by Equations (24) and (25), depends upon the fact that *its value for a given acid solution is approximately independent of the base used.* It is difficult to test this statement directly, since the bases (indicators) which are of value for investigating concentrated acid solutions are so weak that it is difficult to determine pK_{BH^+} accurately. Since K_{BH^+} is a thermodynamic dissociation constant, its determination must involve extrapolation to infinite dilution at some stage. However, less direct tests can easily be made. For example, if a and b are any two acid solutions, which may differ in concentration and also in the nature of the acid, Equation (24) gives

$$(H_0)_a - (H_0)_b = -\left\{\log \frac{[BH^+]}{[B]}\right\}_a + \left\{\log \frac{[BH^+]}{[B]}\right\}_b . \tag{26}$$

The right-hand side of Equation (26) contains only measurable quantities and should be found to have the same value for different indicators if H_0 is independent of B. A convenient method of applying this test is to take a series of acid solutions of different concentrations and to measure $[BH^+]/[B]$ in each solution for a number of different indicators. If $\log [BH^+]/[B]$ is plotted against the acid concentration, (26) implies that different indicators will give a series of parallel curves (not necessarily straight lines). Figure 4 shows plots of this kind for fifteen indicators in sulfuric acid solutions covering the whole range of 0 to 100 percent H_2SO_4. Up to about 60 percent H_2SO_4(9M), covering seven indicators, the plots are satisfactorily parallel, but above this individual differences begin to appear. The data in Figure 4 are mainly from Hammett's original measurements, which employed a visual colorimeter without temperature control and are not of high accuracy. Figure 5 shows recent measurements[6] for three indicators

[6] K. N. Bascombe and R. P. Bell, *J. Chem. Soc.*, 1096 (1959).

in sulfuric acid (0–5M) at 25°C, using a photoelectric spectrophotometer; the plots here are accurately parallel.

Results of this kind serve to confirm Equation (26) and thus to indicate that the acidity function is approximately independent of the base chosen. It must be admitted, however, that this has not been demonstrated for many systems and that the indicators used are all closely similar, being almost all nitroanilines. The application of acidity functions to kinetic problems suggests that the same regularity

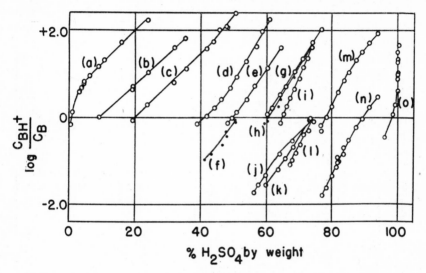

Fig. 4.—Indicator ratios in sulfuric acid–water mixtures. (a) *p*-Nitroaniline. (b) *o*-Nitroaniline. (c) 4-Chloro-2-nitroaniline. (d) *p*-Nitrodiphenylamine. (e) 2,4-Dichloro-6-nitroaniline. (f) *p*-Nitroazobenzene. (g) 2,6-Dinitro-4-methylaniline. (h) 2,4-Dinitroaniline. (i) N,N-Dimethyl-2,4,6-trinitroaniline. (j) Benzalacetophenone. (k) β-Benzoylnaphthalene. (l) *p*-Benzoyldiphenyl. (m) 6-Bromo-2,4-dinitroaniline. (n) Anthraquinone. (o) 2,4,6-Trinitroaniline.

extends to a much wider range of basic molecules, but it would certainly be desirable to have direct confirmation of this, especially for oxygen bases and for molecules which are smaller than the aromatic bases commonly used.

In order to obtain numerical values for H_0 it is necessary to know the value of pK_{BH^+} in Equation (24). For indicators which are moderately strong bases ($pK > 1$) this can be done by making measurements in dilute solutions of strong acids (< 0.05M). In these solutions [H⁺] can be taken equal to the acid concentration c and the factor $f_{BH^+}/f_B f_{H^+}$ will differ inappreciably from unity; hence $H_0 = -\log c$ and Equation (24) then gives pK_{BH^+}. For somewhat weaker bases

(pK between $+1$ and zero) this procedure is no longer applicable, but it is found empirically that the quantity $\log [BH^+]/[B] - \log [H^+]$ is a linear function of c for solutions of a strong acid up to about 2M, so that pK_{BH^+} can be obtained as the intercept of such a linear plot at $c = 0$. This implies that $\log f_{BH^+}/f_B f_{H^+}$ is a linear function of c; the slope of the plot will depend upon the acid chosen, but the intercept should be the same for all acids. Little work has been done to test whether this is so.

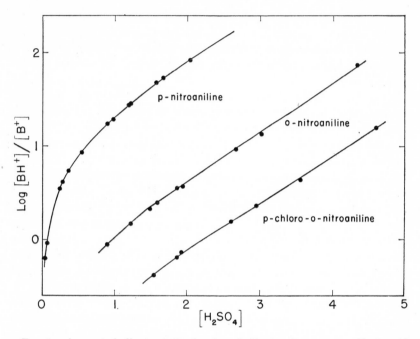

Fig. 5.—Accurate indicator ratios for three indicators in aqueous sulfuric acid.

For weaker bases such as must be used for concentrated acids (pK negative) neither of these methods is applicable, and pK must be obtained by a stepwise procedure, each indicator being compared in turn with one of higher pK. For any two indicators B_1 and B_2 the observed ratios in a given solution are given by

$$\log \frac{[B_1H^+]}{[B_1]} - \log \frac{[B_2H^+]}{[B_2]} = pK_1 - pK_2, \qquad (27)$$

so that if pK_1 is known pK_2 can be determined. $pK_1 - pK_2$ is in fact the vertical distance between the parallel lines in Figures 4 and 5, or in the analogous plots of log $[BH^+]/[B]$ − log $[H^+]$ against c, and the same value should be obtained using solutions of different acids. This last point has been tested for only a few indicators, but for these the agreement is fairly good (about ± 0.05 in pK). In this way a series of indicators has been established with pK down to about − 4.5,[7] though the stepwise procedure used may involve cumulative errors, and it is difficult to judge the reliability of the lower values. Values for pK have been given for even weaker bases, down to 2,4-dinitrotoluene, with pK = − 12.8, but these rest entirely on measurements in sulfuric acid in the range of 70 to 100 percent and in fuming sulfuric acid, so that it is uncertain whether they are of general validity.

Certain difficulties arise in interpreting optical measurements in concentrated solutions, since the extinction coefficients of a given species may no longer be independent of composition, and if measurements are confined to a single wavelength there is no independent method of checking this in the indicator systems with which we are concerned here. However, if measurements at a number of different wavelengths give the same value of $[BH^+]/[B]$, it is unlikely that the extinction coefficient is appreciably affected by change of medium. Measurements by Bell and Bascombe (*loc. cit.* [6]) show that this is the case up to moderate concentrations of most acids (usually about 6M) but that at higher concentrations there are invariably changes in absorption spectrum with composition, leading to inconsistencies in values of H_0 measured at different wavelengths. In some instances the changes in absorption spectrum are so radical as to suggest the formation of different indicator species as the pure anhydrous acid is approached. An analogous difficulty is met with in evaluating the extinction coefficients of BH^+, which are usually much smaller than those for B but not always negligible. For a very weak base the concentration of acid necessary to convert it completely to BH^+ is so high that the medium effects on the extinction coefficients are bound to be considerable. Various methods have been devised for overcoming these difficulties,[8] but they necessarily involve some degree of arbitrary assumption.

In spite of the above qualifications, there is no doubt that the acidity function is a well-defined quantity for aqueous solutions of many acids up to about 8-molar, giving a measure of the tendency of the solution to protonate an uncharged base. This means that the quantity $f_{BH^+}/f_B f_{H^+}$ in Equation (25) is independent of the nature of B;

---

[7] See Paul and Long. *loc. cit.* (5), table 1.

[8] L. A. Flexser, L. P. Hammett, and A. Dingwall, *J. Am. Chem. Soc.*, **57**, 2103 (1935); C. T. Davis and D. A. Geissman, *ibid.*, **76**, 3507 (1954).

i.e., for two bases B_1 and B_2 in the same acid solution $f_{B_1H^+}f_{B_2}/f_{B_2H^+}f_{B_1} = 1$. This is exactly the same function of activity coefficients which arose in the discussion of the relative strengths of acids in different solvents (Chapter IV, Equation 5), where it was shown that the whole function might be close to unity even when its constituent parts were not. The

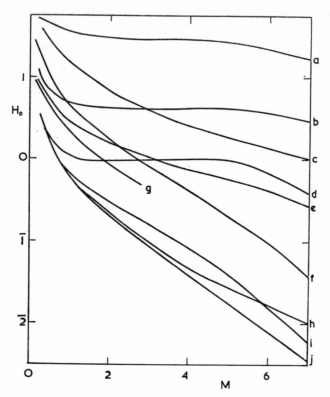

Fig. 6.—Acidity functions for aqueous acids. (a) CH_2ClCO_2H. (b) $CHCl_2CO_2H$. (c) HF. (d) CCl_3CO_2H. (e) H_3PO_3. (f) H_3PO_4. (g) $KHSO_4$. (h) HNO_3. (i) $MeSO_3H$. (j) HCl.

same clearly applies in the present problem, where we are dealing with changes of environment less drastic than a change from one pure solvent to another.

Figure 6 shows the experimental results for a number of acids, **the** values given by Paul and Long being supplemented by measurements by Bascombe and Bell (*loc. cit.* [6]). They show a general gradation according to acid strength, though a few weak acids behave anomalously, notably HF and H_3PO_4. The curves for the strong acids HCl, HBr, $HClO_4$, and H_2SO_4 are grouped closely together, and we shall first consider the interpretation of these.[9] If the concentrations are expressed as molalities (rather than molarities, as in Figure 6), the curves for the four strong acids fall very closely together. This is illustrated by the figures in columns 2 to 5 of Table 8. Up to $m = 8$ it is doubtful whether the differences exceed the experimental error. The sixth column gives the mean values for the four acids. This shows that H_0 is independent of the nature of the anion, being determined essentially by the ratio of hydrogen ions to water molecules and thus suggesting that the rise of acidity with concentration is due to a stoichiometric interaction between the ions and the water. We have so far written

TABLE 8.—MEAN VALUES OF $-H_0$ FOR AQUEOUS SOLUTIONS OF STRONG ACIDS

Molality	HCl	HBr	HClO$_4$	H$_2$SO$_4$	Mean	Calculated
1.00	0.19	0.18	0.19	0.24	0.20	0.17
2.00	0.64	0.67	0.64	0.76	0.68	0.64
4.00	1.30	1.35	1.29	1.42	1.34	1.37
6.00	1.89	2.01	2.00	1.99	1.99	1.99
8.00	2.43	2.67	2.67	2.70	2.62	2.69
10.00	2.97	3.31	3.41	3.18	3.22	3.57

the hydrogen ion in water as H_3O^+, but there is no doubt that it will hold a further number of water molecules fairly firmly. If the proton is associated with a total of h water molecules to form a species H_h^+, the reaction with a base can be written as $H_h^+ + B \rightleftharpoons BH_h^+ + hH_2O$, neglecting the hydration of the other species concerned. In concentrated acid solutions the activity of free water will be considerably reduced, and this will shift the above equilibrium to the right, corresponding to an increased acidity of the solution. We can write

$$H_0 = \log\left[H_h^+\right] - h \log a_{H_2O} + \log\left(f_B f_{H_h^+}/f_{BH_h^+}\right) \quad (28)$$

since H_0 must reduce to $\log\left[H_h^+\right]$ in dilute solutions, where $a_{H_2O} \to 1$ and the last term tends to zero. At fairly high concentrations the second term will be the most important (assuming that h is in the range 3 to 6), and, as pointed out by Wyatt,[10] it is a striking fact that H_0 for stronger acids is a unique function of the water activity over a very wide range of concentration.

We shall now show that the assumption of a constant hydration number $h = 4$ goes a long way toward explaining the facts. According to (28) $\log\left(f_B f_{H_h^+}/f_{BH^+}\right) = -H_0 - \log c + 4 \log a_{H_2O}$, where c is the concentration of the strong acid, and if this quantity is plotted

[9] R. P. Bell and K. N. Bascombe, *Disc. Faraday Soc.*, **34**, 158 (1957).

[10] P. A. H. Wyatt, *Disc. Faraday Soc.*, **24**, 162 (1957).

against c we obtain straight lines with slopes of about 0.1.   Now it is
well known that the activity coefficients of uncharged molecules in salt
solutions can be represented by equations of the type $\log f_B = Ac$,
with A in the neighborhood of 0.1.[11]   This is consonant with the assumption $f_{B_h^+} \simeq f_{BH^+}$, which is reasonable for two ions of the same
charge and similar size.

The problem can also be treated without having recourse to the
measured water activities.   Equation (28) can be rewritten in the form

$$-H_0 = \log [H_h^+] - 4 \log [H_2O] + \log \frac{f_B f_{H_h^+}}{f_{H_2O}^h f_{BH^+}} \cdot \tag{29}$$

We shall now investigate the effect of assuming that the last term in
(29) is zero.   This assumption is not unreasonable, since the molecule
B is several times larger than a water molecule, but it can only be
justified by its consequences.   So far the concentration units in (29)
have not been specified. $[H_h^+]$ must reduce to either the molality or
the molarity in dilute solution, and the choice has little effect on the
value predicted for H_0 in concentrated solutions.   We shall choose the
molarity c, since volume concentrations seem more appropriate in considering the reactivity of the solution towards a base present in small
amount.   It is more difficult to decide how to express $[H_2O]$.   The
effect of hydration is to reduce the amount of free water by the factor
$(1 - 4 \ m/55.5) = (1 - 0.072 \ m)$.   It would be possible to use the
mole fraction of free water, which is $(1 - 0.072 \ m)/(1 - 0.036 \ m)$, but
this is not likely to have much significance in an associated system of
diverse components.   We have preferred to express the concentration
$[H_2O]$ as (number of formula weights of H_2O per liter)/55.5, when
(29) becomes

$$-H_0 = \log c - 4 \log \left\{ \frac{c}{m} (1 - 0.072 \ m) \right\} . \tag{30}$$

The ratio c/m depends upon the density of the solution, which differs
from one acid to another, but to a fair approximation the relation
$m/c = 1 + 0.032 \ m$ applies to the four acids considered.[12]   Inserting
this in (30), we obtain finally

[11] F. A. Long and W. F. McDevit, *Chem. Rev.*, **51**, 119 (1952).

[12] In the paper by Bascombe and Bell (*loc. cit.* [9]) different relations were
used for the four acids, slightly improving the individual agreements.   The
present treatment might seem to imply that H_0 is a unique function of c as well
as of m, in contradiction to experiment.   This is not so, however, since we are
using the approximate relation $m/c = 1 + 0.032m$ only in the less sensitive
parts of the expression and are retaining the exact form in the sensitive term
$1 - 0.072m$.

$$- H_0 = \log m - 4 \log (1 - 0.072\, m) + 3 \log (1 + 0.032\, m). \quad (31)$$

Equation (31) contains no adjustable constants, and the values calculated from it (given in the last column of Table 8) are in excellent agreement with experiment up to $m = 8$. It must obviously break down at higher concentrations, since when $m = 13.8$ there are not enough water molecules in the solution to provide four for each proton. In fact, the divergence is appreciable at $m = 10$ and increases rapidly above this. In any case the calculation must not be taken too seriously, since it involves a number of assumptions which are highly questionable, for example, that the anion and BH^+ are not hydrated and that a volume concentration may be used to represent $[H_2O]$. Nevertheless, the agreement with experiment confirms the view that the rise of acidity is essentially due to hydration of hydrogen ions, and no integral hydration number other than four gives a satisfactory account of the results.

The assumption $h = 4$ receives independent support from other sources. Glueckauf,[13] in accounting for the mean activity coefficients of concentrated electrolytes, arrives at the same number, in agreement with the amount of water taken up by acidic ion exchange resins.[14] It is also found[15] that when strong acids are extracted from water by means of organic solvents they frequently take with them four molecules of water per acid molecule. The same number was deduced from the specific heats and other properties of aqueous acids by Wicke, Eigen, and Ackermann,[16] who also point out that it receives a natural explanation in terms of the structure

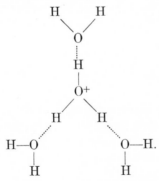

[13] E. Glueckauf, *Trans. Faraday Soc.*, **51**, 1235 (1955).

[14] E. Glueckauf and G. P. Kitt, *Proc. Roy. Soc.*, A, **228**, 322 (1955).

[15] D. G. Tuck and R. M. Diamond, *Proc. Chem. Soc.*, 236 (1958); cf. also A. H. Laurene, D. E. Campbell, S. E. Wiberley, and H. M. Clark, *J. Phys. Chem.*, **60**, 901 (1956).

[16] E. Wicke, M. Eigen, and T. Ackermann, *Z. physik. Chem.* (Frankfurt), **1**, 340 (1954).

We have already seen (Chapter III) that the hydration energy of H_3O^+ amounts to about 100 kcal/mole, and if a considerable proportion of this is located in the three hydrogen bonds in the above diagram these bonds will be much stronger than the normal hydrogen bonds in water (ca. 6 kcal/mole), thus making it reasonable to regard $H^+(H_2O)_4$ as a stable species. The assumption of stoichiometric hydration seems particularly appropriate to H_3O^+, since, unlike spherical monatomic ions, it has definite points of attachment for water molecules.

In extremely concentrated solutions the hydration number must be less than four, and it has been shown by Wyatt (*loc. cit* [10]) that acidity functions and other properties of 70 to 90 percent sulfuric acid can be explained in terms of the species $H^+(H_2O)_2$. There will certainly be an intermediate range in which the average hydration number is decreasing from four to two, and the treatment given above suggests that this range is approximately 10 to 20 molal (e.g., 50 to 70 percent sulfuric acid).

As pointed out by Wyatt (*loc. cit.* [10]), the degree of dissociation of acids in very concentrated solutions will also be dependent upon hydration effects. For example, measurements of the degree of dissociation of perchloric acid from Raman spectra and nuclear magnetic resonance[17] lead to a thermodynamic dissociation constant $K = 40$, which seems extremely low, in view of other evidence that perchloric acid is one of the strongest acids known and might be expected to have $K > 10^7$. However, the amount of undissociated $HClO_4$ cannot be stated with any certainty at concentrations below about $m = 11$, where the amount of free water is very low; hence the behavior in more dilute solutions may bear little relation to the degrees of dissociation observed under these conditions. In fact, the extrapolation made by Hood, Redlich, and Reilly (*loc. cit.* [17]) is highly arbitrary, and their results are not inconsistent with a much higher thermodynamic dissociation constant.

The values of H_0 for nitric acid (cf. Figure 6) show acidities considerably less than those for the four strong acids, and this can be related to its incomplete dissociation. The most accurate values for the degree of dissociation are from the Raman measurements of Young and Krawetz.[18] If we assume that the treatment already given applies to the dissociated part of the nitric acid, Equation (31) becomes

[17] O. Redlich, E. K. Holt, and J. Bigeleisen, *J. Am. Chem. Soc.*, **66**, 13 (1944); G. C. Hood, O. Redlich, and C. A. Reilly, *J. Chem. Phys.*, **22**, 2067 (1954); Y. Masuda and T. Kanda, *J. Phys. Soc. Japan*, **9**, 82 (1954); O. Redlich and G. C. Hood, *Disc. Faraday Soc.*, **24**, 87 (1957).

[18] T. F. Young and A. A. Krawetz, quoted by H. A. C. McKay, *Trans. Faraday Soc.*, **52**, 1568 (1956). Cf. also Hood, Redlich, and Reilly, *loc. cit.*

$$-H_0 = \log \alpha m - 4 \log (1 - 0.072\ \alpha m) + 3 \log (1 + 0.032\ m) \quad (32)$$

where α, the degree of dissociation, varies from unity to 0.72 in the range 0 to 8 molal for which acidity function measurements are available. Equation (32) does in fact represent the experimental data within 0.1 logarithmic units. Figure 6 shows that methanesulfonic acid is a somewhat weaker acid than nitric, but in this case there are no independent estimates of the degree of dissociation. However, by assuming that (32) still applies, we can use the experimental H_0 values to estimate α, and hence arrive at $K_c \simeq 4$ for this acid.

The solutions of the weak acids CH_2ClCO_2H, $CHCl_2CO_2H$, and CCl_3CO_2H (cf. Figure 6) never reach high acidities and show little change in H_0 in the range $c = 2$ to $c = 6$. This is what might be anticipated, since, when $c \gg K_c$, the hydrogen ion concentration is given by $[H^+] = (K_c c)^{\frac{1}{2}}$, and, if $K < 0.1$, $[H^+]$ will never exceed unity in the concentration range studied. When $[H^+] < 1$, the hydration effect is small so that high acidities are never reached, and the variation of H_0 with c is mainly determined by $\frac{1}{2}\log c$, which varies by only 0.2 in the range considered.

Different behavior is found for the weak acids HF, H_3PO_3, HSO_4^-, and H_3PO_4, which show a steady increase of acidity with concentration, reaching H_0 values in concentrated solution which are much more negative than would be expected from their dissociation constants. In the case of HF there is little doubt that this behavior depends upon the formation of the ions HF_2^-, $H_2F_3^-$, $H_3F_4^-$, and so forth.[19] These are the anions of strong acids (in the sense that there is no evidence for the existence of H_2F_2, H_3F_3, etc., in aqueous solution), and the system therefore behaves like a solution of a strong acid of concentration c/n, where n is the average value in the ion $H_{n-1}F_n^-$. As with sulfuric acid, the increase in acidity continues all the way up to 100 percent HF, values of $-H_0 = 9$ to 10 being reached,[20] though other factors must obviously be taken into account at this end of the scale. It has been suggested that the behavior of phosphoric and phosphorous acids depends upon some similar formation of polymeric ions, for example $H_{n+1}P_nO_{3n+1}^-$, but the Raman spectra of concentrated phosphoric acid

---

(17). Because of incomplete dissociation the hydrogen ion concentrations never exceed about $m = 6$, so that the amount of water present is always adequate for hydration; hence the extrapolation to give $K = 23$ is reasonably accurate for this acid.

[19] R. P. Bell, K. N. Bascombe, and J. C. McCoubrey, *J. Chem. Soc.*, 1286 (1956).

[20] H. H. Hyman, M. Kilpatrick, and J. J. Katz, *J. Am. Chem. Soc.*, **79**, 3668 (1957).

solutions show no indications of such polymerization,[21] and this type of explanation is not applicable to HSO_4^-. It is possible that the difference between the organic and the inorganic acids is due in part to different salting-out effects on the undissociated molecules.

We have seen that measurements of H_0 can be used to estimate the dissociation constants of "strong" acids such as nitric, methanesulfonic, and trifluoroacetic acids. A more common use is to determine pK values for very weak bases. If the protonation of the base is accompanied by a change in absorption spectrum, the procedure is identical with that already described for determining the pK values of basic indicators, the base being added in small amount to a concentrated acid solution of known H_0. If no spectral shift is observed, it is necessary to add base in concentrations comparable with that of the acid and to observe the change in acidity by means of an added indicator. Examples of both kinds of procedure are given by Paul and Long (*loc. cit.* [5], table 10).

There are many other aspects of acidity functions which we have not considered, for example, the functions H_- and J_0 (corresponding respectively to equilibria of the type $B^- + H^+ \rightleftharpoons BH$ and $ROH + H^+ \rightleftharpoons R^+ + H_2O$), the properties of concentrated solutions of alkalis, and acidity functions in nonaqueous and mixed solvents. All these topics are dealt with in the review by Paul and Long. It may be noted here that the usefulness of acidity functions in nonaqueous and mixed solvents is more limited than it is in water, because they often vary considerably with the nature of the base used.

[21] A. Simon and G. Schulze, *Z. anorg. Chem.*, **242**, 313 (1939).

CHAPTER VII

Acid-Base Strength and Molecular Structure

MANY detailed discussions have been published on the effects of substituents on the strengths of organic acids and bases.[1] We have seen that caution is necessary in interpreting small differences in dissociation constants in terms of molecular models, and this chapter will deal only with a few of the more striking effects, with special reference to some which are of interest in reaction kinetics. We shall consider first the strengths of hydrides and oxyacids of different elements.

TABLE 9.—APPROXIMATE pK VALUES FOR SIMPLE HYDRIDES

CH_4	58	NH_3	35	OH_2	16	FH	3
		PH_3	27	SH_2	7	ClH	-7
				SeH_2	4	BrH	-9
				TeH_2	3	IH	-10

Table 9 gives approximate pK values for a number of simple hydrides, some of which need special comment. $pK(CH_4) = 58$ derives from an argument due to Schwarzenbach,[2] who assumes that

$$pK(CH_4) - pK(\overset{+}{N}H_4) = pK(NH_3) - pK(\overset{+}{O}H_3),$$

the values for the second pair being known experimentally. He gives $pK(CH_4) = 34$, but he used an incorrect value for $pK(NH_3)$, and his argument implies that all the bond energies concerned are the same. The value in the table takes into account the different bond energies

---

[1] For recent articles see, C. K. Ingold, *Structure and Mechanism in Organic Chemistry* (Ithaca, N. Y., 1953), ch. xiii; H. C. Brown, D. H. McDaniel, and O. Häfliger, article in *The Determination of Organic Structures by Physical Methods*, ed. E. A. Braude and F. C. Nachod (New York, 1955); G. W. Wheland, *The Theory of Resonance in Organic Chemistry* (New York, 1955), ch. vii.

[2] G. Schwarzenbach, *Z. physikal Chem.*, **176A**, 133 (1936).

(C—H = 105 kcal, N—H = 104 kcal, O—H = 120 kcal). All that can be said with certainty is that methane is a very much weaker acid than any of the others in the table. $pK(\text{NH}_3) = 35$ depends upon the ionic product of liquid ammonia, for which the most reliable value is $[\text{NH}_4^+][\text{NH}_2^-] = 10^{-33}$ at $-50°\text{C}$, obtained by e.m.f. measurements.[3] By use of the measured heat of the reaction $\text{NH}_4^+ + \text{NH}_2^- \rightarrow 2\text{NH}_3$, it has been estimated[4] that the corresponding value at $25°\text{C}$ is 10^{-28}, giving 10^{-31} for the constant $[\text{NH}_4^+][\text{NH}_2^-]/[\text{NH}_3]^2$. This must be increased to allow for the change from liquid ammonia ($\epsilon = 22$) to water ($\epsilon = 78$), since we are basing our comparisons on the latter solvent, and our previous discussion (Chapter IV) on the effect of changing the solvent suggests a factor of about 10^5, giving

$$[\text{NH}_4^+][\text{NH}_2^-]/[\text{NH}_3]^2 = 10^{-26}$$

for aqueous solutions at $25°\text{C}$. In these solutions we have

$$[\text{NH}_3][\text{H}_3\text{O}^+]/[\text{NH}_4^+] = 10^{-9},$$

and hence finally

$$\frac{[\text{NH}_2^-][\text{H}_3\text{O}^+]}{[\text{NH}_3]} = \frac{[\text{NH}_4^+][\text{NH}_2^-]}{[\text{NH}_3]^2} \cdot \frac{[\text{NH}_3][\text{H}_3\text{O}^+]}{[\text{NH}_4^+]} = 10^{-35}.$$

A closely similar value (10^{-36}) has recently been obtained by Wooding and Higginson.[5]

The corresponding value $pK(\text{PH}_3) = 27$ was derived from kinetic measurements of deuterium exchange.[6] These gave values for the velocity constant of the reaction $\text{PH}_3 + \text{OH}^- \rightarrow \text{PH}_2^- + \text{H}_2\text{O}$, and the equilibrium constant was estimated by assuming that the reverse reaction took place on every collision.

In the series of hydrogen halides $pK(\text{HF}) = 3$ can be measured directly,[7] though some correction is necessary for the formation of bifluoride ion. The acid strength of HCl has been estimated in a number of ways, all of which involve the measured vapor pressure of HCl over concentrated aqueous solutions. This can be used to calcu-

[3] V. A. Pleskov and A. M. Monoszon, *Acta Physicochim. U.R.S.S.*, 1, 725 (1935). The value of 10^{-22}, which is frequently quoted, is derived from the measured conductivity of liquid ammonia and is certainly too high.

[4] W. L. Jolly, *Chem. Rev.* 50, 351 (1951); cf. H. D. Mulder and F. C. Schmidt, *J. Am. Chem. Soc.*, 73, 5575 (1951); W. M. Latimer and W. L. Jolly, *ibid.*, 75, 4147 (1953).

[5] N. S. Wooding and W. C. E. Higginson, *J. Chem. Soc.*, 774 (1952).

[6] R. E. Weston and J. Bigeleisen, *J. Am. Chem. Soc.*, 76, 3074 (1955).

[7] H. H. Broene and T. de Vries, *J. Am. Chem. Soc.*, 69, 1644 (1947).

late the concentration of undissociated HCl in solution provided that a value is assumed for the Henry's law constant of this species (i.e., its distribution coefficient between aqueous solutions and the vapor phase), and the problem is mainly one of estimating this constant. Wynne-Jones[8] assumed that Raoult's law applied to the system H_2O + HCl (undissociated), and by using the vapor pressure of liquid HCl at room temperature arrived at $pK(HCl) = -7$. This value represents K_c rather than the thermodynamic K, and Robinson[9] used the same data in conjunction with the measured activity coefficients to extrapolate to infinite dilution, obtaining $pK(HCl) = -6$ at 25°C; he also calculated K over the temperature range 0° to 50°C and concluded that the reaction $HCl + H_2O \rightarrow H_3O^+ + Cl^-$ was exothermic, with $\Delta H = -18$ kcal/mole. The application of Raoult's law is open to criticism, and a different assumption about the Henry's law constant was made by Ebert,[10] who regarded HCl as the first member of the series HCl, CH_3Cl, C_2H_5Cl, and so forth and extrapolated the measured solubilities of the alkyl halides, thus obtaining $pK(HCl) = -7$. An alternative assumption is to suppose that the HCl molecule will behave in the same way as HCN, which is similar in size and polarity but is almost undissociated in aqueous solution; this leads also to $pK(HCl) = -7$. Thus although each of the methods employed is open to some criticism, their agreement makes it unlikely that the value $K = 10^{+7}$ is in error by more than a power of ten.

There is less abundant information about HBr and HI, but if we apply Robinson's treatment to the vapor pressure data[11] we find $pK(HBr) = -8$, $pK(HI) = -9$, compared with $pK(HCl) = -6$, suggesting that the strengths of the three acids are approximately in the ratio $1:10^2:10^3$. There is confirmatory evidence that HBr is a considerably stronger acid than HCl, for example, from the conductivities, titration curves, and behavior toward indicators in glacial acetic acid.[12] It is also frequently found that HBr is a much more effective acid catalyst than HCl under conditions where both acids are undissociated.[13] The values in Table 9 are likely to be correct to within about a power of ten.

[8] W. F. K. Wynne-Jones, *J. Chem. Soc.*, 1064 (1930).

[9] R. A. Robinson, *Trans. Faraday Soc.*, **32**, 743 (1936).

[10] L. Ebert, *Naturwiss.*, **13**, 393 (1925).

[11] S. J. Bates and H. D. Kirschman, *J. Am. Chem. Soc.*, **41**, 1991 (1919).

[12] For references see Chapter IV.

[13] A. Hantzsch, *Z. physikal. Chem.*, **134**, 406 (1928); R. P. Bell and R. le G. Burnett, *Trans. Faraday Soc.*, **35**, 324 (1939); P. B. D. De La Mare and P. W. Robertson, *J. Chem. Soc.*, 888 (1945).

Table 9 shows obvious trends, and the large increases in acidity from left to right are certainly mainly due to an increase in the electronegativity (electron affinity) of the elements. However, the increase in acidity in going down a group of the periodic table is not so easily explained. For example, in the series HF, HCl, HBr, and HI the dipole moment and "ionic character" of the bond decreases. This might have been expected to lead to a decrease in acidity, whereas the reverse is actually the case. It is possible to carry out a detailed analysis for the hydrogen halides, which serves to illustrate the variety of factors involved in determining dissociation constants in solution, even for the simplest compounds. The details of the calculation have been given by McCoubrey,[14] and only an outline will be given here.

Consider first the reaction in the gas phase, $HX \rightarrow H^+ + X^-$. This can be split up into a number of steps as follows:

$$HX \rightarrow H + X, \qquad D_e$$
$$H \rightarrow H^+ + \epsilon, \qquad I$$
$$X + \epsilon \rightarrow X^-, \qquad E$$
$$HX \rightarrow H^+ + X^-, \qquad \Delta H_g = D_e + I - E.$$

I, the ionization energy of hydrogen, has the same value (315 kcal/mole) for all the hydrogen halides, but both D_e (the bond energy) and E (the electron affinity of the halogen) vary from one halogen to another. The first part of Table 10 gives the values for these quantities. It is a simple matter to calculate from statistical mechanics the standard entropy change in the gas reactions, and this varies very little along the series. The large positive values of ΔG_g° show that no detectable ionic dissociation can occur in the gas phase, but their trend indicates an increase in acidity with increasing molecular weight, with a particularly large change in going from HF to HCl. The differences are due almost entirely to the different bond energies, the electron affinity of the halogen playing only a minor role.

In proceeding from dissociation in the gas phase to dissociation in aqueous solution, we need to know the energies and entropies of hydration of the species H^+, X^-, and HX. These are accessible from experiment for $H^+ + X^-$ (though their division into separate contributions for H^+ and X^- is an arbitrary one), but for the undissociated molecule HX values must be estimated from data for molecules of similar size and polarity.[15] The hydration terms are given in the second part

[14] J. C. McCoubrey, *Trans. Faraday Soc.*, **51**, 743 (1955).

[15] In computing the entropies of hydration it is important to take into account the difference in the standard states for the gas (1 atmosphere) and in solution (1 mole/liter).

TABLE 10.—IONIC DISSOCIATION OF THE HYDROGEN HALIDES AT 25°C

All values of ΔH, $T\Delta S°$, and $\Delta G°$ are given in kcal/mole, rounded off to the nearest unit, and relate to the process $HX \rightarrow H^+ + X^-$ unless otherwise stated

	HF	HCl	HBr	HI
Gas phase dissociation				
D_e	135	103	88	71
E	82	87	82	76
ΔH_e	367	331	321	311
$T\Delta S_g$	7	7	7	7
ΔG_g	360	324	314	304
Hydration terms				
ΔH (hydration of HX)	−12	−4	−5	−6
ΔH (hydration of $H^+ + X^-$)	−382	−349	−341	−330
$T\Delta S°$ (hydration of HX)	7	5	6	6
$T\Delta S°$ (hydration of $H^+ + X^-$)	−20	−16	−15	−14
Dissociation in aqueous solution				
ΔH_{aq}	−3	−14	−15	−14
$T\Delta S_{aq}$	−6	−4	−3	−1
ΔG_{aq}	3	−10	−12	−13
pK (calc.)	2	−7	−9	−10
pK (obs.)	3	−7	−9	−10

of Table 10, and finally the calculated thermodynamic functions and pK values for dissociation in aqueous solution.

The excellent agreement between the observed and calculated pK values in Table 10 is no doubt partly fortuitous, but it is worth emphasizing that the calculated values for HCl, HBr, and HI do not make use of the vapor pressure measurements which were used to estimate the "observed" acid strengths; hence the present calculations serve to confirm these estimates, which involved some rather doubtful assumptions. It is clear from the table that the dissociation constants in water are governed by the interplay of a number of different factors, no one of which is dominant in determining the acid strengths as usually defined. Comparing $\Delta G_{aq}°$ with $\Delta G_g°$, we see that the considerable difference between HF and HCl is preserved, though it has been reduced from 36 to 13 kcal, largely because the hydration enthalpies of F⁻ and Cl⁻ operate so as to produce a difference in the opposite direction. In fact, if the ionic enthalpies were the only quantities involved, there would be an even smaller difference in the strengths of HF and HCl, the final value depending significantly both on the hydration entropies of the ions and on the hydration enthalpies of the undissociated molecules. Similar remarks apply, a fortiori, to the smaller differences between HCl, HBr, and HI. It is still roughly true to say that the anomalous weakness of HF in this series is associated with its high bond strength, but it appears little more than a coincidence that the other three acids preserve the same order in solution as in the gas phase. This is one of many instances in which dissociation constants in water appear to reflect molecular regularities more faithfully than might be anticipated.

There is no other series of acids for which a complete analysis can be attempted, but there are two cases in which some theoretical interpretation can be given. The first of these deals with the *effect of charge*, as illustrated by the *pK* values in Table 11.

TABLE 11.—EFFECT OF CHARGE UPON ACID STRENGTH

H_3O^+	-1.7	H_2O	15.7	OH^-	25
NH_4^+	9.5	NH_3	35		
		H_2S	7.1	HS^-	14.7

In each case an increase of positive charge or a decrease of negative charge is accompanied by a large increase of acid strength. This effect is qualitatively what would be expected, but it cannot be interpreted on a simple electrostatic basis, since it depends on the electron affinities of species such as H_2O^+, OH, and O^-, which are not known.

Significant regularities exist in the strengths of the *inorganic oxyacids*, as shown in Table 12. This has been pointed out by a number of authors,[16] though their interpretations differ. As shown in the table, the acids fall into four groups, according to the value of n in the general formula $XO_n(OH)_m$. The strength of the acid increases with increasing n and does not depend significantly upon the value of m.

It is convenient first to consider some of the individual acids. A number of these fall into the appropriate group only if given the correct structural formula. Thus phosphorous and hypophosphorous acids cannot be $P(OH)_3$ and $HP(OH)_2$ respectively, and there is of course independent evidence that the formulas given in the table are the correct ones. Similarly telluric acid must be $Te(OH)_6$ (not $TeO_2(OH)_2$ or $Te(OH)_4$), and periodic acid $IO(OH)_5$ (not $IO_3(OH)$ or $IO_2(OH)_3$). It is perhaps remarkable that boric acid fits well into the class of very weak acids, since (as already mentioned in Chapter

[16] A. Kossiakoff and D. Harker, *J. Am. Chem. Soc.*, **60**, 2047 (1938); L. Pauling, *General Chemistry* (San Francisco, 1947), p. 394; J. E. Ricci, *J. Am. Chem. Soc.*, **70**, 109 (1948); R. J. Gillespie, *J. Chem. Soc.*, 2537 (1950).

II) there is good evidence that the borate ion in solution is $B(OH)_4^-$ rather than $^-OB(OH)_2$, so that the dissociation of boric acid would involve the addition of OH^- rather than the loss of H^+.[17] The boric acid molecule, however, may well exist in aqueous solution as $H_2\overset{+}{O}$—$\overset{-}{B}(OH)_3$, in which case its dissociation is more closely analogous to that of the other acids $X(OH)_m$.

The value $pK = 3.9$ given for carbonic acid is of course the true value for H_2CO_3, taking into account the fact that only 0.4 percent of the dissolved carbon dioxide is in this form.[18] The conventional value for carbonic acid, $pK = 6.5$ (not distinguishing between CO_2 and

TABLE 12.—pK VALUES FOR INORGANIC OXYACIDS

$X(OH)_m$		$XO(OH)_m$		$XO_2(OH)_m$		$XO_3(OH)_m$	
(very weak)		(weak)		(strong)		(very strong)	
$Cl(OH)$	7.2	$NO(OH)$	3.3	$NO_2(OH)$	-1.4	$ClO_3(OH)$	(-10)
$Br(OH)$	8.7	$ClO(OH)$	2.0	$ClO_2(OH)$	-1	$MnO_3(OH)$	—
$I(OH)$	10.0	$CO(OH)_2$	3.9	$IO_2(OH)$	0.8		
$B(OH)_3$	9.2	$SO(OH)_2$	1.9	$SO_2(OH)_2$	(-3)		
$As(OH)_3$	9.2	$SeO(OH)_2$	2.6	$SeO_2(OH)_2$	(-3)		
$Sb(OH)_3$	11.0	$TeO(OH)_2$	2.7				
$Si(OH)_4$	10.0	$PO(OH)_3$	2.1				
$Ge(OH)_4$	8.6	$AsO(OH)_3$	2.3				
$Te(OH)_6$	8.8	$IO(OH)_5$	1.6				
		$HPO(OH)_2$	1.8				
		$H_2PO(OH)$	2.0				

H_2CO_3), would not fit into the above table. It is interesting to note that the conventional value for sulfurous acid does fall into line with the other acids of formulas $XO(OH)_m$, thus suggesting that sulfur dioxide in aqueous solution is much more strongly hydrated than is carbon dioxide. There is no direct evidence on this point, but it is in accord with the solubility of sulfur dioxide in water, which is much higher than that of most molecules of similar size and polarity.

The explanations given for the regularities in Table 12 all depend upon the number of several equivalent oxygen atoms in the acid anion, which increases from one for the very weak acids $X(OH)_m$ to four for the very strong acids $XO_3(OH)_m$. The effect of this factor

[17] J. O. Edwards, G. C. Morrison, V. F. Ross, and J. W. Schulz, *J. Am. Chem. Soc.*, **77**, 266 (1955).

[18] Cf. Chapter III, pp. 29–31.

on the strength of the acid is usually expressed in terms of resonance or mesomerism in the ion. For example, the ion Cl—O$^-$ has only one reasonable valency structure, while the chlorite ion ClO_2^- can be written in two equivalent forms $^-$O—Cl=O and O=Cl—O$^-$, resonance between which serves to stabilize the ion and increase the strength of the acid. The number of equivalent structures, and hence the resonance energy, increases as we increase n in the formula $XO_n(OH)_m$. The stabilization of the anion can also be attributed, however, to an electrostatic effect, since the negative charge in the anion is distributed between $(n + 1)$ oxygen atoms and will therefore have a lower electrostatic energy than if it were concentrated in a single atom. In terms of a simple model, the free energy of a charge e on a single sphere of radius r is $e^2/\epsilon r$ (ϵ = dielectric constant of surrounding medium), whereas if it is distributed between $(n + 1)$ spheres of the same radius the free energy falls to $(n + 1)e^2/(n + 1)^2\epsilon r = e^2/(n + 1)\epsilon r$. This model exaggerates the effect, since it neglects the repulsion between the charges on the separate oxygen atoms, which will raise the energy somewhat. An alternative model, which is particularly appropriate to tetrahedral ions like XO_4^-, is to consider that the charge is situated on a sphere of volume $(n + 1)$ times that of a single oxygen atom; this gives a free energy of $e^2/(n + 1)^{\frac{1}{3}}\epsilon r$.

It is possible that the strengths of the oxyacids are mainly determined by the spread of charge, as suggested above. The electrostatic expressions are adequate to explain the facts only if the dielectric constant is taken to have a value of 15 to 20 instead of the macroscopic value $\epsilon = 78$, but this is not surprising, since there is ample evidence that the macroscopic dielectric constant underestimates the electrostatic energy of ions in solution. The relevance of the alternative explanation in terms of a change in the X—O binding depends on the view which is taken of the nature of these bonds. Thus for chlorous acid the dissociation process could be written in the following two ways:

(a) $\qquad\qquad$ O=Cl—OH → $^{\frac{1}{2}-}$O═Cl═O$^{\frac{1}{2}-}$ + H$^+$

(b) $\qquad\qquad$ $\overset{-}{O}$—$\overset{+}{Cl}$—OH → $\overset{-}{O}$—$\overset{+}{Cl}$—$\overset{-}{O}$ + H$^+$.

In (a) the double bond and single bond in the acid are converted into two mesomeric bonds in the anion, giving stabilization by resonance, and the chlorine atom has 10 valency electrons throughout. In (b) the chlorine and oxygen are united by semipolar bonds, giving octet structures throughout, and there is no change in binding on ionization.

Similar formulations apply to the other types of oxyacid, frequently with several intermediate possibilities, e.g., for perchloric acid,

$$O{=}\overset{\displaystyle O}{\underset{\displaystyle O}{\overset{\|}{Cl}}}{-}OH \;\rightarrow\; {}^{\frac{1}{2}-}O{-}\overset{\displaystyle O^{\frac{1}{2}-}}{\underset{\displaystyle O^{\frac{1}{2}-}}{\overset{\|}{Cl}}}{=}O^{\frac{1}{2}-} \;+\; H^-$$

$$^{\frac{1}{3}-}O{-}\overset{\displaystyle O^{\frac{1}{3}-}}{\underset{\displaystyle O^{\frac{1}{3}-}}{\overset{\|}{Cl}}}{^{1+}}{-}OH \;\rightarrow\; {}^{\frac{1}{2}-}O{-}\overset{\displaystyle O^{\frac{1}{2}-}}{\underset{\displaystyle O^{\frac{1}{2}-}}{\overset{\|}{Cl}}}{=}O^{\frac{1}{2}-} \;+\; H^+$$

$$^{\frac{2}{3}-}O{-}\overset{\displaystyle O^{\frac{2}{3}-}}{\underset{\displaystyle O^{\frac{2}{3}-}}{\overset{\|}{Cl}}}{^{2+}}{-}OH \;\rightarrow\; {}^{\frac{3}{4}-}O{-}\overset{\displaystyle O^{\frac{3}{4}-}}{\underset{\displaystyle O^{\frac{3}{4}-}}{\overset{\|}{Cl}}}{^{2+}}{=}O^{\frac{3}{4}-} \;+\; H^+$$

$$^{-}O{-}\overset{\displaystyle O^{-}}{\underset{\displaystyle O^{-}}{\overset{|}{Cl}}}{^{3+}}{-}OH \;\rightarrow\; {}^{-}O{-}\overset{\displaystyle O^{-}}{\underset{\displaystyle O^{-}}{\overset{|}{Cl}}}{^{3+}}{-}O^{-} \;+\; H^+$$

where the effect of resonance stabilization presumably decreases down the series, becoming zero in the last formulation.

Unfortunately, there is no agreement as to the nature of the bonds in these molecules and ions. It has been maintained[19] that bond lengths indicate predominantly doubly bonded structures, but other authors[20] have criticized these conclusions and have used the same data as evidence for octet structures with semipolar bonds. As shown later in this chapter, the latter view receives some support from the effect of the group —SO_3^- on the strengths of organic acids, but the question is still an open one. The resonance explanation of the data in Table 12 demands at least some degree of double-bond character, but the explanation in terms of charge spread is largely independent of the valency structure assumed; for example, all the formulations of the perchlorate ion given above will have essentially the same electrostatic energy, corresponding to that of a negative charge at the center of a sphere if radius about 2.5 Å. It thus seems certain that the electrostatic con-

[19] G. M. Phillips, J. S. Hunter, and L. E. Sutton, *J. Chem. Soc.*, 146 (1945).
[20] A. F. Wells. *J. Chem. Soc.*, 55 (1949).

tribution is an important one, and it may represent the whole explanation of the observed effects.

Most of the work on structure and acidity has dealt with the effect
of substituents upon the strength of organic acids and bases. We shall
consider first a few of the simpler effects in aliphatic compounds and
then the strengths of acids containing the group C—H, which are of
importance in kinetic problems.

Most information about substituent effects relates to carboxylic
acids, all of which are much stronger than alcohols. This recalls the
behavior of the inorganic oxyacids and can be related to the structure
of the carboxylate anions,

$$R-C \begin{array}{c} O^{\frac{1}{2}-} \\ \\ O^{\frac{1}{2}-} \end{array} \quad ,$$

it again being an open question whether the stability of the anion is
due to its bond resonance or to the division of the negative charge
between two oxygen atoms. An analogous situation exists in the
amidines,

$$R \cdot C \begin{array}{c} NH_2 \\ \\ NH \end{array} \quad ,$$

which are much stronger than the amines because the cation has the
structure

$$R \cdot C \begin{array}{c} \overset{\frac{1}{2}+}{NH_2} \\ \\ \overset{\frac{1}{2}+}{NH_2} \end{array} \quad ,$$

and the same effect operates to an even greater extent in guanidine,
$NH{=}C(NH_2)_2$, with the corresponding cation

$$C({=}\overset{\frac{1}{2}+}{NH_2})_3 \, .$$

The simplest class of effects is due to the presence in the molecule
of a group (charged or dipolar) whose charge distribution is not appreciably changed during the interconversion of the acid-base pair.
It is possible to picture the action of such a group kinetically, according

to whether it helps or hinders the loss of a proton, but since we are considering equilibrium phenomena it is then also necessary to consider the effect of the group upon the reverse process. For quantitative purposes it is more satisfactory to examine the charge distribution in the initial and final states of the acid-base reaction, and thus to calculate the effect of the substituent upon the over-all change in free energy.

The largest effects are encountered with groups bearing a net charge, and the best-known example deals with the *first and second dissociation constants of dicarboxylic acids*. In an acid $CO_2H \cdot (CH_2)_n \cdot CO_2H$ the free energy of the ion $CO_2^- \cdot (CH_2)_n \cdot CO_2^-$ will be increased by the mutual repulsion of the two negative charges, an effect which is absent both in the original molecule and in the singly charged ion $CO_2H \cdot (CH_2)_n \cdot CO_2^-$. This should cause the second dissociation constant to be smaller than

TABLE 13.—THE SUCCESSIVE DISSOCIATIONS OF DICARBOXYLIC ACIDS

Acid	$n(CH_2)$	pK_1	pK_2	ΔpK	r (calc.) Å			Model
					(a)	(b)	(c)	
Oxalic	0	1.23	4.19	2.96	0.91	3.85	3.37	3.50– 4.44
Malonic	1	2.83	5.69	2.86	1.36	4.10	3.43	4.12– 4.87
Succinic	2	4.19	5.48	1.29	3.65	5.75	5.58	4.66– 6.66
Adipic	4	4.42	5.41	0.99	8.11	7.75	8.22	5.59– 9.02
Azelaic	7	4.55	5.41	0.86	11.9	9.85	12.03	6.74–12.42

the first one, and the effect should decrease with increasing distance between the two carboxylic groups, and hence with the number of of CH_2 groups. This is illustrated by the values in the first five columns of Table 13, which are taken from the compilation by Brown, McDaniel, and Häfliger (*loc. cit.* [1]).[21] The first attempt to treat this problem quantitatively was due to Bjerrum,[22] who showed that on a simple electrostatic model the ratio of the successive dissociation constants should be given by

$$K_1/4K_2 = \exp\left(e^2/\epsilon r kT\right) \qquad (33)$$

where r is the distance between the two carboxyl groups. The factor 4 in Equation (33) represents the statistical effect, which occurs in various forms in both equilibrium and kinetic problems and is conveniently considered now. In the present instance it implies that $K_1 = 4K_2$

[21] Unless otherwise stated, all values of pK in the remainder of this chapter are taken from the same compilation.

[22] N. Bjerrum, *Z. physikal. Chem.*, **106**, 219 (1923).

even when r is so great that the electrostatic effect is negligible.   This may be seen by considering the two processes

(1) $CO_2H \cdot (CH_2)_n \cdot CO_2H \rightleftharpoons CO_2H \cdot (CH_2)_n \cdot CO_2^- + H^+$

                (i)   (ii)

(2) $CO_2H \cdot (CH_2)_n \cdot CO_2^- \rightleftharpoons CO_2^- \cdot (CH_2)_n \cdot CO_2^- + H^+$

                (ii)   (iii)

where n is so great that the tendency of the carboxyl group to lose a proton is the same in all the species concerned, while the same is true for the tendency of the group $—CO_2^-$ to accept a proton.   Comparison of the species (i) and (ii) as acids reveals that (i) will dissociate twice as fast as (ii), because of its two equivalent $—CO_2H$ groups, and this would make $K_1/K_2 = 2$.   Similarly, comparison of (ii) and (iii) as bases shows that (iii) will pick up protons twice as fast as (ii), because of its two equivalent $—CO_2^-$ groups, again giving $K_1/K_2 = 2$, and the total statistical effect will be $K_1/K_2 = 2 \times 2 = 4$.   This naïve kinetic argument can be replaced by a more sophisticated one which invokes the symmetry numbers of the species (i), (ii), and (iii), which are respectively 2, 1, and 2, but the result is the same.

Returning to Bjerrum's equation, column (a) of Table 13 gives the values of r obtained by substituting the experimental values of K_1/K_2 in (33), taking the dielectric constant $\epsilon = 78$.   They are of the right order of magnitude but are definitely too low for the earlier members of the series.   This is best seen by comparison with the last column of the table, which contains the range of distances predicted by a molecular model, the variation corresponding to different conformations of the flexible chain.   We have already seen that because of saturation effects $\epsilon = 78$ is certainly too high a value to take for calculations on a molecular scale.   An additional difficulty arises in dealing with interactions within the same molecule, since part of the space between the two charges is now occupied by the molecule itself, having an effective dielectric constant very much less than that of the solvent.   Various methods have been proposed for improving Bjerrum's calculation so as to allow for these effects.   Thus Kirkwood and Westheimer[23] use a model in which the charges are embedded in an ellipsoid of low dielectric constant, giving values of r in column (b) of Table 13.   Similarly, Gane and Ingold[24] attempt to allow individually for the polarizability

    [23] J. G. Kirkwood and F. H. Westheimer, *J. Chem. Phys.*, 6, 506 (1938); *J. Am. Chem. Soc.*, 61, 555 (1939); F. H. Westheimer and J. G. Kirkwood, *J. Chem. Phys.*, 6, 513 (1938).
    [24] R. Gane and C. K. Ingold, *J. Chem. Soc.*, 2153 (1931).

of the different groups in the molecule and for the saturation of the solvent dielectric, leading to the values of r in column (c) of the table. Both treatments (especially the former) lead to distances between the carboxyl groups which agree better with molecular models, but both methods of treatment involve parameters which are either adjustable or not known with certainty, so that exact quantitative agreement would be illusory.

The acid-base properties of the amino acids offer many examples of the interactions between oppositely charged groups, since they frequently exist in the zwitterion form $\overset{+}{N}H_3\text{----}CO_2^-$. As with the dicarboxylic acids both of the groups concerned have acid-base properties, and a simpler situation exists when the positive charge resides on a group such as $-\overset{+}{N}Me_3$, which has no proton to lose. For example, $\overset{+}{N}Me_3 \cdot CH_2 \cdot CO_2H$ has $pK = 1.83$, as against $pK(CH_3CO_2H) = 4.75$, and this large increase of strength can be reasonably attributed to stabilization of the species $\overset{+}{N}Me_3 \cdot CH_2CO_2^-$ by the attraction between the opposite charges.

It would be interesting to consider a negatively charged substituent lacking the markedly basic properties of $-CO_2^-$, and it might appear that the sulfonate group $-SO_3^-$ would be suitable for this purpose, since the alkyl sulfonic acids are strong acids with $pK \simeq 0$.[25] The effect of this substituent, however, is at first sight surprising, since $SO_3^- \cdot CH_2COOH$ has $pK = 4.05$; i.e., it is about five times as strong as acetic acid, instead of being much weaker. An even larger effect is shown in the pair $pK(CH_3\overset{+}{N}H_3) = 10.64$, $pK(SO_3^- \cdot CH_2\overset{+}{N}H_3) = 5.75$, in which the substituent is closer to the acidic proton. Again the order of strength is the reverse of what might be expected.

This behavior can be explained in terms of the electronic structure of the sulfonic acid group. As already discussed in connection with the strengths of the inorganic acids, the group $-SO_3^-$ can be written in a number of ways, of which the extreme forms are

(i)   and   (ii)

Substitution by structure (i) should certainly make an acid weaker, but this is not necessarily true for structure (ii), since if the acidic

[25] K. N. Bascombe and R. P. Bell, *J. Chem. Soc.*, 1096 (1959).

proton is close to the —SO$_3^-$ group the effect of the double positive charge on the sulfur atom may well outweigh that of the three negatively charged oxygen atoms. The evidence of the acid strengths thus supports the singly bonded octet structures for the sulfur oxyacids and makes it doubtful whether the concept of bond resonance is necessary to explain their strengths (cf. p. 95). There are two other pieces of experimental evidence which confirm the presence of a large positive charge on the sulfur atom in the group —SO$_3^-$. In the first place, kinetic measurements on the hydrolysis of the ester group in the species SO$_3^-$·CH$_2$CO$_2$Et show that in alkaline hydrolysis this group reacts more rapidly than ethyl acetate, whereas in acid hydrolysis the reverse is the case.[26] In the second place, the group —SO$_3^-$ acts as a weakly *meta*-directing group in benzene substitution, in contrast to the other negatively charged groups.[27] Both of these observations are consistent with structure (ii), but not with structure (i).

The point may be further illustrated by a simple calculation of the potential at a distance R from the charge distributions shown below, the second of which corresponds to structure (ii) for the sulfonate group.

$$-2e \qquad +e \qquad\qquad\qquad -3e \qquad +2e$$

$$\longleftarrow r \longrightarrow \longleftarrow R \longrightarrow \qquad \longleftarrow r \longrightarrow \longleftarrow R \longrightarrow$$

The two potentials are given by

$$V_b = \frac{e}{\epsilon}\left(\frac{1}{R} - \frac{2}{r+R}\right) = -\frac{e}{\epsilon r}\,\phi_b\left(\frac{R}{r}\right)$$

$$V_c = \frac{e}{\epsilon}\left(\frac{2}{R} - \frac{3}{r+R}\right) = -\frac{e}{\epsilon r}\,\phi_c\left(\frac{R}{r}\right)$$

and the two functions $\phi_b(R/r)$ and $\phi_c(R/r)$ are plotted in Figure 7, the curve (a) representing a simple Coulomb curve, i.e.,

$$V_a = -\frac{e}{\epsilon}\left(\frac{1}{r+R}\right) = -\frac{e}{\epsilon r}\,\phi_a\left(\frac{R}{r}\right).$$

It will be seen that ϕ_b and ϕ_c are initially opposite in sign to ϕ_a and that their deviations from a simple Coulomb potential are considerable even at large values of R/r.

Figure 7 suggests that as the distance of the group —SO$_3^-$ from the

[26] R. P. Bell and D. A. Rawlinson, *J. Chem. Soc.*, 4387 (1958).
[27] Ingold, *op. cit.* (1), p. 235.

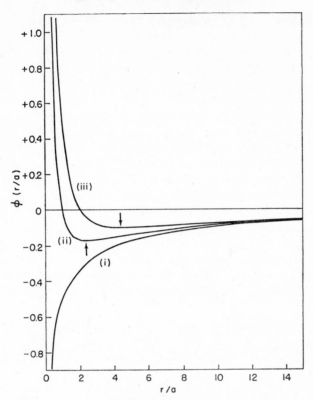

Fɪɢ. 7.—Variation of potential with distance for different charge distributions.

acidic proton is increased, its effect upon pK should successively diminish, change sign, and then decrease to zero. There appear to be no measurements for the series $SO_3^- \cdot (CH_2)_n CO_2H$, but data are available for a number of substances of the formula $SO_3^- \cdot (CH_2)_n \overset{+}{N}H_3$ and are given in Table 14.[28] Amine cations of the formula $CH_3(CH_2)_n \overset{+}{N}H_3$ ($n = 0$ to $n = 10$) all have $pK = 10.63 \pm 0.05$, and ΔpK in the table represents $pK - 10.63$. ΔpK diminishes and changes sign as expected, but it appears strange that the effect is still increasing between $n = 5$ and $n = 10$. The carbon chain, however, is flexible, and its ends will be drawn together by their opposite charges, so that their mean distance apart may well decrease rather than increase for values of n greater than 5.

[28] P. Rumpf, *Bull. Soc. chim. France*, [5], **5**, 871 (1938).

TABLE 14.—ACID STRENGTHS IN THE SERIES $SO_3^- \cdot (CH_2)_n \overset{+}{N}H_3$

$n =$	1	2	3	4	5	10
$pK =$	5.75	9.20	10.05	10.65	10.95	11.35
$\Delta pK =$	−4.88	−1.43	−0.58	+0.02	+0.32	+0.72

Curve (b) in Figure 7 corresponds to a group such as $-SeO_2^-$ if we again adopt the structure

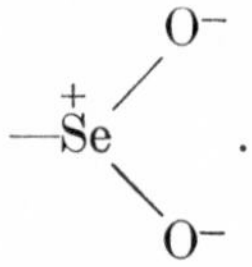

$$-\overset{+}{Se}\underset{\diagdown O^-}{\overset{\diagup O^-}{}} \quad .$$

The figure suggests that this will act as a proton-repelling group only at very short distances, and this is borne out by the following values:[29]

$$pK(CH_3CO_2H) = 4.75, \qquad pK(SeO_2^- \cdot CH_2CO_2H) = 5.43$$

$$pK(SeO_2^- \cdot CH_2CH_2CO_2H) = 5.99.$$

The effect of $-SeO_2^-$ in $SeO_2^- \cdot CH_2CO_2H$ is much smaller than that of $-CO_2^-$ in $CO_2^- \cdot CH_2CO_2H$ (cf. Table 13) and increases when we go to $SeO_2^- \cdot (CH_2)_2CO_2H$. This is qualitatively consistent with Figure 7, and the argument is not likely to be vitiated by the flexibility of the chain, since an extended position will be favored by the repulsion between the two negative charges.

Similar electrostatic explanations can be advanced to explain the effect of dipolar groups such as

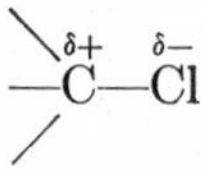

$$-\overset{\diagdown}{\underset{\diagup}{C}}\overset{\delta+ \quad \delta-}{-Cl}$$

in increasing the strength of acids. Quantitative calculations can again be made on the basis of models,[30] but the problem is more difficult than in the case of charged substituents, since the calculation demands a detailed knowledge of the charge distribution in the dipole, and the effect falls off more rapidly with distance, so that the results are sensitive to the assumptions made about molecular dimensions and local dielectric constants. It may be doubted, therefore, whether such calculations are of much value. One particular point may be mentioned,

---

[29] H. J. Backer and W. van Dam, *Rec. trav. Chim.*, **49**, 482 (1930).
[30] See, e.g., Westheimer and Kirkwood, *loc. cit.* (23).

namely, the effect of several dipolar groups attached to the same carbon atom, for example, in the series CH_3CO_2H ($pK = 4.75$), CH_2ClCO_2H ($pK = 2.76$), $CHCl_2CO_2H$ ($pK = 1.30$), and CCl_3CO_2H ($pK = 0.7$). It is sometimes argued that the effect of the group —CCl_3 should be about the same as that of —CH_2Cl, since the dipole moments of $CHCl_3$ and CH_3Cl are approximately equal. However, this argument neglects two points. Firstly, the angle which the dipole makes with the C—C bond is different in the two cases, though it is difficult to judge the importance of this, since the —CO_2H group is itself an angular group which can vary its orientation with respect to the C—C bond. Secondly (and more significantly), the resultant dipole is directly relevant only if we are considering the potential at a distance which is great compared with the charge separation in the dipole. The effect on a neighboring group will be more closely related to the charge on the carbon atom, and there is no doubt that this will be greater in —CCl_3 than in —CH_2Cl.

Many of the largest substituent effects upon acid-base properties arise when there is a large difference in electronic structure between the acid and its corresponding base, and these are commonly described as *resonance* or *mesomeric* effects. They have been treated in detail by many authors, especially for aromatic systems, and no general account will be attempted here. We shall, however, give some account of *carbon acids* (i.e., acids in which the proton is originally attached to carbon), since they are of particular interest in kinetic problems.

The paraffin hydrocarbons have no detectable acidic properties, and we have seen that $pK(CH_4)$ can be estimated to be about 58. The acidity is greatly increased by halogen substitution, and compounds CHX_3 (X = halogen) exchange hydrogen at a measurable rate in alkaline solution, as shown by experiments with deuterium or tritium,[31] but no estimates appear to have been made of their acid strength. In the absence of polar substituents hydrocarbons can show measurable acidity when they contain certain aromatic systems, and a number of pK values were obtained by McEwen,[32] using a stepwise procedure in which equilibria of the type $HX + Y^- \rightleftharpoons HY + X^-$ were investigated in ether solution. The results are only approximate, but they certainly demonstrate acidities considerably greater than those for the simple hydrocarbons; for example, he finds pK (triphenylmethane) = 33, and pK (indene) = 21. In these and similar cases

[31] J. Hine, R. C. Peck, and B. D. Oakes, *J. Am. Chem. Soc.*, **76**, 827 (1954); J. Hine and N. W. Burske, *ibid*, **78**, 3337 (1956); J. Hine, N. W. Burske, M. Hine, and P. B. Langford, *ibid.*, **79**, 1406 (1957).

[32] W. K. McEwen, *J. Am. Chem. Soc.*, **58**, 1124 (1936).

we may consider that the anion is stabilized by a distribution of the negative charge over a number of atoms, which can be formally represented by writing a number of resonance structures. Thus for the anion of triphenylmethane we can write

and seven other similar structures, while for indene there are twelve structures such as

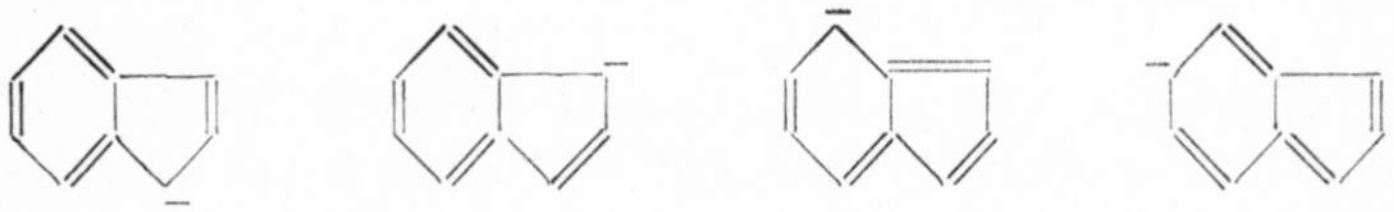

etc

It might seem strange that indene is so much stronger than triphenylmethane, but this is because the unionized triphenylmethane molecule has eight "normal" Kekulé structures, whereas indene has only the two,

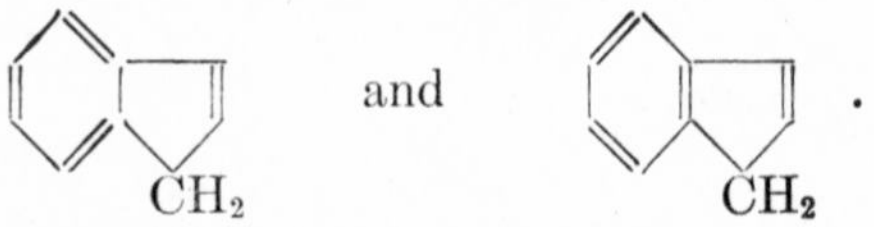

and

An extreme case of this kind of behavior has recently been reported.[33] The hydrocarbon fluoradene,

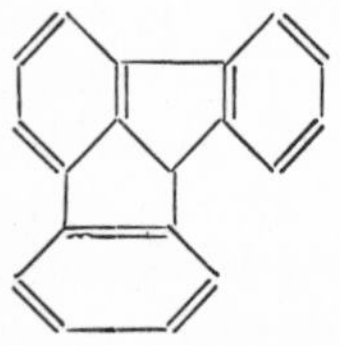

has $pK = 11 \pm 0.5$, and in this case the molecule has 8 normal structures while the anion has 62. An enhanced acidity is also shown by acetylenic compounds, which exchange hydrogen with deuterium oxide in alkaline solution. Measurements in liquid ammonia[34] give a pK of approximately 26 for acetylene itself, compared with our estimate of 58 for methane.

Much higher acidities occur in carbon acids where the negative charge can be transferred to an oxygen atom, which has a much

[33] H. Rapoport and G. Smolinsky, *J. Am. Chem. Soc.*, **80**, 2910 (1958).
[34] Wooding and Higginson, *loc. cit.* (5).

higher electron affinity than carbon. This occurs in compounds containing the group

$$\diagdown\!\!\text{CH} \cdot \text{C}\!\!-\!\!, \atop \diagup \quad \overset{\|}{\text{O}}$$

which becomes

$$\diagdown\!\!\text{C}\!\!=\!\!\text{C}\!\!-\!\! \atop \diagup \qquad | \atop \quad\;\; \text{O}^-$$

on losing a proton. Thus acetophenone, $C_6H_5COCH_3$, was found by McEwen (*loc. cit.* [32]) to have $pK = 19$, while it has been deduced from kinetic data[35] that pK (acetone) $= 20$. The β-diketones and β-keto esters are even stronger acids, e.g., $pK(CH_3COCH_2COCH_3) = 9$, $pK(CH_3COCH_2CO_2Et) = 10$, since the charge of the anion can now be divided between two oxygen atoms. Thus the anion of acetylacetone can be written as

$$\text{CH}_3 \cdot \text{C}\!\!=\!\!\text{CH}\!\!=\!\!\text{C} \cdot \text{CH}_3.$$
$$\overset{\|}{\underset{\text{O}^{\frac{1}{2}-}}{}} \qquad \overset{\|}{\underset{\text{O}^{\frac{1}{2}-}}{}}$$

It is arguable how far the increase in acidity in going from acetone to acetylacetone can be attributed to the spread of the charge and how far to resonance stabilization in the bond system. A similar problem was encountered in discussing the inorganic oxyacids, where it was concluded that there was no compelling evidence for resonance stabilization. Valency considerations make it certain that the anion of acetylacetone (for example) must have a mesomeric structure, and this might be the reason why acetylacetone is stronger than acetone by a factor of 10^{11}, compared with 10^5 for a pair such as ClOH and ClO(OH) (cf. Table 12). However, it could also be argued that the two oxygen atoms in chlorous acid are much closer together than in acetylacetone, thus increasing the repulsion between the negative charges and rendering the anion less stable. Once more it seems difficult to decide between the alternative explanations.

Groups other than carbonyl can act in the same way, notably the nitro group, where

$$\diagdown\!\!\text{CH} \cdot \text{NO}_2 \atop \diagup$$

[35] R. P. Bell, *Trans. Faraday Soc.*, **39**, 253 (1943).

ionizes to give

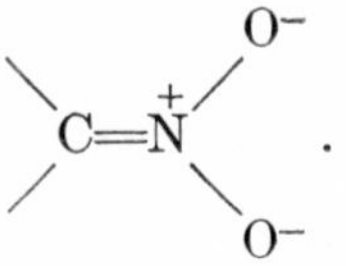

$$\diagdown \!\!\!\!\diagup C \!\!=\!\! \overset{+}{N} \diagdown^{\displaystyle O^-}_{\displaystyle O^-} \;.$$

Thus $pK(CH_3NO_2) = 10$.　More than one group can be active in the same molecule, for example, $pK(CH_2NO_2 \cdot CO \cdot CH_3) = 5$, there now being three oxygen atoms to share the negative charge.　The same groups can also enhance the acidity of

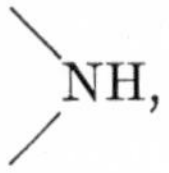

$$\diagdown \!\!\!\!\diagup NH,$$

so that $pK(NH_2NO_2) = 6.5$ (cf. $pK(NH_3) = 35$), while the amides and the urethanes are both more acidic than the amines.　Many more examples are given in Table 17 (chapter X) in connection with rates of ionization, which have often been studied more extensively than the corresponding equilibria.

It is of interest to inquire how far the effect of substituents upon acid strength is paralleled by their effect on other equilibria of the type $RX \rightleftharpoons R^- + X^+$, where X is an atom other than hydrogen. It was pointed out long ago[36] that the dissociation constants of the mercuric salts of some carboxylic acids are closely similar to those of the acids themselves, but only four acids were studied.　Somewhat more extensive information was obtained by Bell and Gelles,[37] who measured equilibrium constants for reactions of the type

$$RH + I_2 \rightleftharpoons RI + I^- + H^+$$

where RH is an ester, a ketone, or a nitroparaffin.　If we define

$$K_H = [R^-][H^+]/[RH], \qquad K_I = [R^-][I^+]/[RI],$$
$$K_{I_2} = [I^+][I^-]/[I_2],$$

then the observed equilibrium constants can be expressed as

$$K = [RI][I^-][H^+]/[RH][I_2] = K_H K_{I_2}/K_I,$$

whence

$$K_I = K_H K_{I_2}/K.$$

[36] H. Ley and H. Kissel, *Ber.*, **32**, 1361 (1899).
[37] R. P. Bell and E. Gelles, *Proc. Roy. Soc.*, A, **210**, 310 (1952).

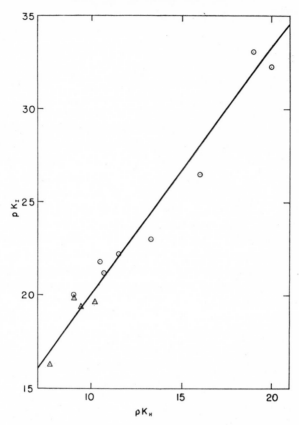

pK_I

pK_H

FIG. 8.—Equilibrium constants for the dissociation
of protons and of iodine cations.

It has been estimated that $K_{I_2} = 10^{-12}$,[38] whence K_I can be calculated. Figure 8 shows a plot of pK_I against pK_H for the thirteen
substances studied; there is clearly a good correlation over a range of
many powers of ten. This is probably because the main effect of
substituents in this series is to stabilize the anion R^- to a varying degree rather than to affect the strength of the bonds C—H or C—I, and
it is unlikely that similar regularities would hold good for a wider variation of structure.

There have been many attempts to relate the dissociation constants
of metallic complexes with the basic strengths of the ligands (i.e., the

[38] R. P. Bell and E. Gelles, *J. Chem. Soc.*, 2734 (1951). The value of K_{I_2}
is not important for the present argument, since it remains constant throughout.

acid strengths of the corresponding acids).[39] The expressions proposed are normally of the form $\log K_c = a \, pK + b$, where K_c relates to the complex, and a and b are constants characteristic of the central atom. This type of relation has been found to hold in a number of cases, but only for a series of closely related ligands, for example, for salicylaldehydes,[40] for acetylacetones,[41] and for oxines.[42] Only small variations in the structure of the ligand are permissible. Thus the complexing power of amines with silver ions bears no relation to their basic strength unless the comparison is restricted to amines of closely similar structure.[43] Moreover, the validity of such relationships depends markedly on the nature of the central atom, and it has been suggested[44] that they are likely to hold only when the ligand is attached essentially by σ-binding, as is the case for attachment to a proton. Apart from these valency considerations there is no doubt that steric effects are important in the attachment of several groups to a central atom of varying size, so that the laws governing the attachment of bases to metal ions will be more complicated than those for the normal acid-base function involving the proton.

[39] E.g., J. Bjerrum, *Chem. Rev.*, **46**, 381 (1950); A. E. Martell and M. Calvin, *The Chemistry of the Metallic Chelates* (New York, 1953), p. 76; G. Schwarzenbach, G. Anderegg, W. Schneider, and H. Senn, *Helv. Chim Acta*, **38**, 1147 (1955); H. M. Irving and H. D. Rossotti, *Acta Chem. Scand.*, **10**, 72 (1956).

[40] M. Calvin and R. W. Wilson, *J. Am. Chem. Soc.*, **76**, 2003 (1945).

[41] L. G. van Uitert, W. C. Fernelius, and B. E. Douglas, *J. Am. Chem. Soc.*, **75**, 457 (1953); L. G. van Uitert and W. C. Fernelius, *ibid.*, 3682 (1953).

[42] H. M. Irving and H. S. Rossotti, *J. Chem. Soc.*, 2904, 2910 (1954).

[43] W. C. Vosburgh and S. A. Cogswell, *J. Am. Chem. Soc.*, **65**, 2412 (1943); G. A. Carlson, J. P. McReynolds, and F. H. Verhoek, *ibid.*, **67**, 1334 (1945); R. J. Bruehlmann and F. H. Verhoek, *ibid.*, **70**, 1401 (1948); W. J. Peard and R. T. Pflaum, *ibid.*, **80**, 1593 (1958).

[44] J. G. Jones, J. B. Poole, J. C. Tomkinson, and R. J. P. Williams, *J. Chem. Soc.*, 2001 (1958).

CHAPTER VIII

The Rates of Acid-Base Reactions

IT is common experience that most reactions between acids and bases take place extremely rapidly, but it has nevertheless proved possible to obtain a large amount of information about the velocity constants of this type of reaction. Until recently most of this information derived from observations of catalysis by acids and bases, in which the formation of the primary product of the acid-base reaction between the catalyst and the substrate is detected by means of its further reaction (rearrangement, decomposition, or reaction with some other species). This kind of observation is limited to fairly slow reactions, and also to those in which the loss or gain of a proton is accompanied by a considerable structural change. In the last ten years a number of other methods have been devised for the direct observation of acid-base reactions not involving any subsequent chemical change; these are mostly the so-called *relaxation methods*, which are especially adapted for the study of fast reactions. In this chapter we shall deal only with these more direct methods, leaving acid-base catalysis for the succeeding chapter. This order of treatment is logical rather than historical.

There are a few acid-base reactions which are slow enough to be studied by conventional means, of which the best known is the neutralization of the nitroparaffins by hydroxyl ions, where the change of conductivity can be followed.[1] The same method can be used for studying the neutralization of nitroparaffins by solutions of ammonia and amines where it is found that the observed velocity cannot be attributed entirely to the hydroxyl ions present in the solutions but must also involve direct reactions with the amine molecules, e.g.,

---

[1] A. Hantzsch and A. Veit, *Ber.*, **32**, 615 (1899); W. F. K. Wynne-Jones, *J. Chem. Phys.*, **2**, 381 (1934); S. H. Maron and V. K. LaMer, *J. Am. Chem. Soc.*, **60**, 2588 (1938); R. P. Bell and A. D. Norris, *J. Chem. Soc.*, 118 (1941); R. P. Bell and J. C. Clunie, *Proc. Roy. Soc.*, A. **212**, 16 (1952). In the last paper the temperature change produced in the reaction is used to follow reactions with half-times of a few seconds.

$CH_3NO_2 + RNH_2 \rightarrow CH_2NO_2^- + RNH_3^+$.[2] As discussed in Chapter II, there is no doubt that these reactions consist of the direct ionization of the nitroparaffin molecule and do not involve the intermediate formation of the *aci*-isomer, as was originally believed.

Similar behavior is found with some other nitrocompounds provided that the reaction is slowed down by reducing the temperature. Thus, p,p',p''-trinitrotriphenylmethane reacts at a measurable rate with ethoxide ions in alcohol at $-60°C$, the neutralization being readily followed by the color of the anion produced.[3] If a weak acid is added to a solution of the anion, it is reconverted to the hydrocarbon at a measurable rate, and the observed kinetics again show that most of the observed velocity is due to reaction with undissociated acid molecules rather than with hydrogen ions. Similar reactions have been studied by Caldin and his collaborators over a wide temperature range.[4]

The above examples are exceptional, and it is found in general that an acid-base reaction which proceeds to an appreciable extent takes place too rapidly for measurement, even by the use of flow methods adapted to reaction times of a millisecond or less. A reaction between a very weak acid and a very weak base will proceed to a very small extent, and the velocity constant for the forward reaction may be low (since the activation energy must be at least equal to the endothermicity). However, the time taken to attain equilibrium will still be very short; for example, if the forward and reverse reactions both follow first-order kinetics, then the observed velocity constant for the attainment of equilibrium in either direction will be equal to the sum of the forward and reverse velocity constants.

This rapid attainment of equilibrium is generally characteristic of oxyacids. It has been reported[5] that the anion of p-nitrophenol reacts at a measurable rate with hydrogen ions at a low temperature, but later work[6] shows that the reaction times involved are certainly less than a millisecond. The slow reactions quoted above all involve the transfer of a proton to and from a carbon atom, and there is much evidence from catalyzed reactions (cf. Chapter IX) that reactions of this class are always slow. It is possible that acid-base reactions in-

[2] R. G. Pearson, *J. Am. Chem. Soc.*, **70**, 204 (1948).

[3] G. N. Lewis and G. T. Seaborg, *J. Am. Chem. Soc.*, **61**, 1894 (1939). These authors gave a more complex explanation of the observed phenomena, which seems very unlikely; cf. M. Kilpatrick, *ibid.*, **62**, 1094 (1940).

[4] E. F. Caldin and J. C. Trickett, *Trans. Faraday Soc.*, **49**, 772 (1953); E. F. Caldin and G. Long, *Proc. Roy. Soc.*, A, **228**, 263 (1955).

[5] G. E. K. Branch and J. Jaxon-Deelman, *J. Am. Chem. Soc.*, **49**, 1765 (1927).

[6] R. P. Bell and R. G. Pearson, *J. Chem. Soc.*, 3443 (1953).

volving nitrogen atoms occupy an intermediate position, though there is little direct evidence on this point. The anion of ethylenedinitramine reacts with ammonia according to the equation

$$
\begin{array}{c}
CH_2 \cdot NNO_2^- \\
| \\
CH_2 \cdot NHNO_2
\end{array}
+ NH_3 \rightarrow
\begin{array}{c}
CH_2 \cdot NNO_2^- \\
| \\
CH_2 \cdot NNO_2^-
\end{array}
+ NH_4^+
$$

at a rate which is just measurable by flow techniques.[7] The velocity constant at room temperature is about 10^5 l./mole sec., compared with 7×10^{-3} l./mole sec. for the corresponding reaction of nitroethane. Measurable reaction rates at low temperatures have been reported for the formation and neutralization of the anion of trinitroaniline, but it is not quite certain whether the observed color changes were caused by proton-transfer reactions.[8] In all of these examples the reaction involves an electronic rearrangement, and the charge in the anion resides on an oxygen atom. For this reason the acids concerned may be described as *pseudo acids*, though we have already seen (Chapter II) that there are difficulties in the precise definition of this term, which has been used in a variety of ways by different authors.

There is one reported example of an apparently slow reaction involving a simple acid-base system, namely, the change of conductivity with time which is observed when amines are dissolved in alcohols.[9] The interpretation of these results is not fully understood, but in the light of later work on rates of isotopic exchange in similar systems (cf. p. 121) it seems likely that slow acid-base reactions are actually involved.

The much faster reactions involved in most simple acid-base systems have been recently studied by a variety of *relaxation methods*, especially by Eigen.[10] In these methods the position of chemical equilibrium is perturbed by a rapid change in some external parameter (electric field, pressure, or temperature), and the rate at which the system changes to its new equilibrium state is studied either by direct observation or by its interaction with the perturbing agent. Such systems are usually characterized by a *relaxation time* τ, which is the time needed for the system to traverse a fraction $1/e$ of its path to the new equilibrium. For chemical systems τ is equal to the reciprocal

---

[7] Bell and Pearson, *loc. cit.* (6).

[8] Caldin and Long, *loc. cit.* (4).

[9] A. G. Ogston, *J. Chem. Soc.*, 1023 (1936); J. R. Schaefgen, M. S. Newman, and F. H. Verhoek, *J. Am. Chem. Soc.*, **66**, 1847 (1944).

[10] For a general account see M. Eigen, *Disc. Faraday Soc.*, **17**, 194 (1954).

of a first-order velocity constant and is of the same order of magnitude as the half-time of the reaction.

The principles of relaxation methods can be illustrated by the application of the *electric impulse* method to acid-base systems. The degree of dissociation of a weak electrolyte is increased to a calculable extent by the application of a strong electric field; this phenomenon is known as the dissociation field effect, or the second Wien effect. If the field is changed suddenly, the degree of dissociation will not change immediately to its new value, and Figure 9 shows how the degree of

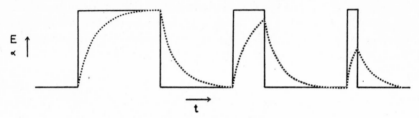

FIG. 9—Change of degree of dissociation for square-wave impulses of different durations.

dissociation α will change during a square-wave electric impulse of varying duration. Since the conductivity depends upon the degree of dissociation, the high-field conductivity of the system will vary with the duration of the impulse, and this variation can be used to determine the rate of dissociation. In practice it is often convenient to use a sine-wave impulse instead of a square one, and the conductivity is measured by comparison with a strong electrolyte so as to eliminate the part of the Wien effect which is due to interionic attraction. In order to obtain an appreciable change in the degree of dissociation, fields of the order of 10^5 volt/cm. must be used, with an impulse time of 10^{-5} to 10^{-7} sec., which is of the order of the relaxation time. The observed relaxation time may involve both the velocity constants of the reversible dissociation reaction, but since their ratio is given by the equilibrium constant of the reaction the separate constants can be obtained.

This method has been applied to measuring the rates of the reactions $CH_3CO_2H \rightleftharpoons H^+ + CH_3CO_2^-$ and $NH_3 + H_2O \rightleftharpoons NH_4^+ + OH^-$,[11] and also to the self-dissociation of water.[12] In the latter case the velocity constant for the reaction $H^+ + OH^- \rightarrow H_2O$ was found to be $1.3 \pm 0.2 \times 10^{11}$ l./mole sec. This is one of the highest velocity

[11] M. Eigen and J. Schön, *Z. Elektrochem.*, **59**, 483 (1955).
[12] M. Eigen and L. de Maeyer, *Z. Elektrochem.*, **59**, 986 (1955).

constants ever measured for a reaction in solution and corresponds closely with the theoretical expression for the rate of encounter of two ions of opposite charge.[13]   It is also interesting to note that measurements of the high-field conductivity of very pure ice have led to values for the equilibrium and velocity constants for the same process in ice.[14] In this case the ions are removed so fast at high field strengths that the conductivity is determined by the rate at which fresh ions are formed by dissociation.

Similar principles apply when a *high-frequency alternating field* is applied to a solution of a weak electrolyte.   This is illustrated in Figure 10, where the upper curve represents the variation of the field strength with time, and the lower three curves the corresponding vari-

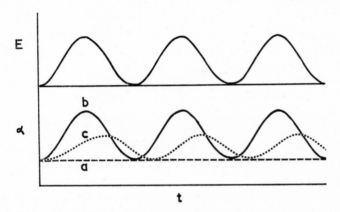

Fɪɢ. 10.—Variation of degree of dissociation in an alternating field.

ation of the degree of dissociation α for different reaction velocities. Curve (a) represents a low velocity, so that α remains throughout at the value corresponding to zero field, whereas for curve (b) the velocity is so high that α follows the instantaneous field strength and varies in phase with it.   The case of interest here is when the half-time of the reaction is of the same order of magnitude as the periodic time of the field; we then obtain a curve such as (c), which has a smaller amplitude than (b) and is now out of phase with the applied field. As first pointed out by Pearson,[15] the conductivity of the solution should vary with frequency in this region, but the effect is very small

[13] L. Onsager, *J. Chem. Phys.*, **2,** 599 (1934); P. Debye, *Trans. Electrochem. Soc.*, **82,** 265 (1942).

[14] M. Eigen and L. de Maeyer, *Z. Elektrochem.*, **60,** 1037 (1956).

[15] R. G. Pearson, *Disc. Faraday Soc.*, **17,** 187 (1954).

(because of the low fields employed) and would be difficult to detect experimentally. A more promising approach is to measure the dielectric loss, which arises from the phase difference between α and the applied field; this makes the process partially irreversible and leads to the dissipation of electrical energy as heat. This principle has recently been used to measure rate constants for the reaction $H_3BO_3 \rightleftharpoons H_2BO_3^- + H^+$ and should be applicable to a variety of systems.[16]

Exactly the same principles apply to the study of *ultrasonic absorption* in electrolyte solutions, except that the quantity displacing the equilibrium is the oscillating pressure of the sound wave rather than the electric field. The effect of pressure on the equilibrium constant is given by

$$\partial \ln K/\partial p = \Delta\bar{v}/RT$$

and since almost all reactions involve some volume change the effects observed are not confined to ionic reactions. In principle it would be equally informative to measure the dispersion of sound (variation of velocity with frequency), the heat produced, or the attenuation of the sound wave as a function of frequency; in practice the last is the most convenient. Not many measurements have been made on acid-base systems, but the reaction $H^+ + SO_4^{2-} \rightleftharpoons HSO_4^-$ has been studied.[17] It is interesting that the reaction $H^+ + SO_4^{2-}$ ($k = 4 \times 10^{10}$ l./mole sec.) is much faster than reactions of the type $M^{2+} + SO_4^{2-}$, where M is a metal, which have velocity constants in the range 10^4 to 10^6. This can be explained by supposing that the association of the sulfate ion with a metal cation requires the removal of one or more water molecules from the hydration shell of the latter, while in the formation of HSO_4^- from SO_4^{2-} the proton can be derived from one of the water molecules originally in contact with the anion, the charge being handed on by the same mechanism which is responsible for the abnormal mobility of the hydrogen ion in water.

There are several other methods for getting information about rapid acid-base reactions which, although strictly not relaxation methods, are closely allied to them. One of the most promising of these uses *polarography*, and will now be briefly described.[18] Under ordinary conditions the limiting current observed at a dropping or rotating cathode (corresponding to the flat part of the polarographic curve)

[16] W. R. Gilkerson, *J. Chem. Phys.*, **27**, 914 (1957).

[17] M. Eigen, G. Kurtze, and K. Tamm, *Z. Elektrochem.*, **57**, 103 (1953).

[18] For a general account of reaction kinetics in polarography, see P. Delahay, *New Instrumental Methods in Electrochemistry* (New York, 1954), ch. v.

is controlled by the rate at which the reducible species can diffuse to the electrode and is therefore determined by the concentration of this species. However, if a small quantity of a reducible species is in chemical equilibrium with a second species which is not reducible, then under suitable conditions the observed current will be controlled by the rate of the chemical process producing the reducible species. This was first shown for aqueous solutions of formaldehyde,[19] in which the equilibrium $CH_2O + H_2O \rightleftharpoons CH_2(OH)_2$ is far over to the right. Of the two species CH_2O and $CH_2(OH)_2$ only the former is reducible, so that under suitable conditions of drop rate, concentration, and so forth the observed current is a direct measure of the rate of the process $CH_2(OH)_2 \rightarrow CH_2O + H_2O$. It is difficult to get an exact mathematical solution for the kinetic problem involved, but an approximate absolute value for the velocity constant can easily be obtained and fairly accurate relative values for a series of similar reactions. In acid-base systems it is usually found that only one member of an acid-base pair is reducible at the cathode; for example, undissociated pyruvic acid, CH_3COCO_2H, is reducible, while the anion $CH_3COCO_2^-$ is not. In this system it is thus possible to get information about the rate of the reaction $CH_3COCO_2^- + H^+ \rightarrow CH_3COCO_2H$, for which k_2 is about 10^9 l./mole sec.[20] Similar measurements have been made with phenylglyoxylic acid and its derivatives.[21] In this system the reaction of the anion with hydrogen ions has a velocity constant of about 10^{11} l./mole sec., while its reactions with other acidic species such as H_2O and H_3BO_3 are considerably slower.

This procedure is limited to the rather small class of reducible acids and bases, but the scope of the polarographic method can be greatly extended by using a somewhat different principle. The cathodic reduction of azobenzene takes place according to the scheme $C_6H_5 \cdot N = N \cdot C_6H_5 + 2H^+ + 2\epsilon \rightarrow C_6H_5 \cdot NH \cdot NH \cdot C_6H_5$, the hydrogen ions being commonly supplied by a buffer system $A \rightleftharpoons B + H^+$. Under suitable conditions the rate of reduction, and hence the polarographic current, is determined by the rate at which hydrogen ions are supplied by the reaction $A \rightarrow B + H^+$, and since the equilibrium constant is known the velocity constant of the reverse reaction $B + H^+ \rightarrow A$ can also be determined. In principle this method is applicable to any nonreducible buffer system A—B (though in prac-

[19] R. Brdicka, *Coll. trav. chim. tchécoslov*, **12**, 213 (1947).

[20] (a) P. Rüetschi and G. Trümpler, *Helv. Chim. Acta*, **35**, 1957 (1952); (b) P. Delahay and T. J. Adams, *J. Am. Chem. Soc.*, **74**, 1437 (1952).

[21] K. Wiesner, M. S. Wheatley, and J. M. Los, *J. Am. Chem. Soc.*, **76**, 4858 (1954); M. S. Wheatley, *Experientia*, **12**, 339 (1956).

tice there are quantitative limitations), but so far it has been applied only to formic and acetic acids.[22]   For acetic acid the velocity constants are in fair agreement with those obtained by the electric impulse method, though no exact comparison can be made since the polarographic measurements were carried out in 50 percent alcohol. The method could presumably be extended to reducible substances other than azobenzene.

Interesting kinetic information has been obtained by Weller from studies of *fluorescence*,[23] particularly of β-naphthol. This compound is a weak acid ($pK = 10$), but on absorbing ultraviolet radiation it is converted into an excited form which is a much stronger acid ($pK = 3$). Both the excited naphthol molecule and the anion formed from it can lose energy as fluorescent radiation, so that the kinetic scheme is

(i) $ROH + h\nu \rightarrow ROH^*$

(ii) $ROH^* + B \rightleftharpoons RO^{-*} + A$

(iii) $ROH^* \rightarrow ROH + h\nu'$ (ultraviolet fluorescence)

(iv) $RO^{-*} \rightarrow RO^- + h\nu''$ (blue fluorescence)

where A—B represents any acid-base pair present in the solution. In practice the reverse of reaction (ii) is negligible, so that the intensities of the two types of fluorescence depend upon the competition between processes (ii) and (iii), and the velocity constant for (ii) can be evaluated in terms of the mean lifetime of the excited molecule, which is known from other experiments.   The base in reaction (ii) may be a water molecule, or it may be the anion of a weak acid when the experiment is carried out in a buffer solution.

Information about the rates of fast acid-base reactions has recently been obtained from studies of *nuclear magnetic resonance*, and in particular *proton magnetic resonance*.   In the latter the proton can adopt two orientations in a magnetic field, and the transitions between these two levels are observed by the absorption of radiation in the radio-frequency range.   The exact frequency of absorption, and also the fine structure of the absorption line, depend upon the environment of the proton, and although the differences involved are very small (usually a few parts per million) the resolving power in this range of frequencies is ample for detecting and measuring them.   We have already seen in Chapter III how such observations can be used for

[22] (a) P. Delahay and W. Vielstich, *J. Am. Chem. Soc.*, **77**, 4955 (1955); (b) P. Rüetschi, *Z. physik. Chem.* (Frankfurt), **5**, 323 (1956).

[23] A. Weller, *Z. Elektrochem.*, **56**, 662 (1952); **58**, 849 (1954); **60**, 1144 (1956); **61**, 956 (1957); *Z. physik. Chem.* (Frankfurt), **3**, 238 (1955).

studying equilibrium phenomena such as the configuration of the hydronium ion or the degree of dissociation of strong acids. If a solution contains two sets of protons in different environments, the observed spectrum depends upon the frequency with which the two sets can interchange. If this interchange is slow compared with the frequency used for making measurements, two distinct peaks will be observed in the spectrum, but if it is fast there will be only a single peak at an intermediate frequency. At some intermediate frequency there will be a change from one type of spectrum to the other, and in this frequency range the mean lifetime of the proton in one of its situations is of the same order of magnitude as $1/\nu$, where ν is the observing frequency. Similarly, the splitting of the lines into a number of components (which is due to the interactions between the observed nucleus and other magnetic nuclei) is lost if the mean lifetime is much smaller than $1/\nu$ and will be restored if either the lifetime or the frequency is increased. In principle, therefore, the velocity of the interchange process can be determined by observing the changes in the spectrum of a given solution when the frequency is progressively varied, or (which is usually more convenient) when the frequency is held constant and the reaction velocity progressively varied by changing some property of the solution such as the concentration or the pH.

Most of the kinetic information so far obtained by this method is qualitative or semiquantitative in nature. This is partly due to experimental limitations, but it is also difficult to give a quantitative theoretical treatment of the relation between the observed pattern and the velocity constants involved. Earlier treatments of this problem[24] were complicated and not always consistent, but a recent paper by McConnell[25] gives a much simpler derivation which should be useful in interpreting future observations.

Some of the earliest applications to acid-base kinetics are due to Ogg.[26] In very pure liquid ammonia the proton-resonance line shows a triplet structure, due to interaction with the nucleus N^{14}, but if very small amounts of the ions NH_2^- or NH_4^+ are introduced (the latter by adding a trace of water) the structure disappears. This is undoubtedly due to the exchange reactions $NH_3 + NH_2^- \rightleftharpoons NH_2^- + NH_3$ and NH_3

[24] H. S. Gutowsky, D. W. McCall, and C. P. Schlichter, *J. Chem. Phys.*, **21**, 279 (1953); H. S. Gutowsky and A. Saika, *ibid.*, **21**, 1698 (1953); H. S. Gutowsky and C. H. Holm, *ibid.*, **25**, 1228 (1956); H. M. McConnell and S. B. Berger, *ibid.*, **27**, 230 (1957); E. Grunwald, A. Loewenstein, and S. Meiboom, *ibid.*, **27**, 630 (1957).

[25] H. M. McConnell, *J. Chem. Phys.*, **28**, 430 (1958).

[26] R. A. Ogg, *J. Chem. Phys.*, **22**, 560 (1954); *Disc. Faraday Soc.*, **17**, 215 (1954).

$+NH_4^+ \rightleftharpoons NH_4^+ + NH_3$, but only a very rough estimate of the velocity constants could be obtained, partly because the very low ionic concentrations were not well defined. Similarly, an acid aqueous solution of an ammonium salt gave a triplet due to $N^{14}H_4^+$ and a singlet due to H_2O, but in a neutral solution these were merged into a single peak by the occurrence of exchange reactions involving NH_3 or OH^-. Similar results were obtained by observing the nuclear resonance of nitrogen rather than that of the proton.

Somewhat more quantitative results were obtained by Arnold[27] for proton magnetic resonance in ethyl alcohol. He concluded that in "pure" alcohol the lifetime of the hydroxyl proton was about 1 sec. but that this was reduced to about 0.01 sec. in either 10^{-5} M acid or 10^{-4} M alkali. This suggests velocity constants in the range 10^6 to 10^7 for exchange reactions such as $EtOH + EtOH_2^+ \rightleftharpoons EtOH_2^+ + EtOH$ and $EtOH + EtO^- \rightleftharpoons EtO^- + EtOH$.

The most extensive measurements in this field have been made by Loewenstein, Meiboom, and their collaborators on aqueous solutions of amines[28] and of hydrogen peroxide.[29] The results for methylamine are well suited to illustrate the kind of information which can be obtained. All the solutions used contained the methylamine essentially in the form of the cation $CH_3\overset{+}{N}H_3$. When the solution is sufficiently acid, the proton exchange is not fast enough to affect the spectrum, which consists of three distinct components, (1) a quadruplet from CH_3, the splitting being due to the protons of the $\overset{+}{N}H_3$ group, (2) a triplet from $\overset{+}{N}H_3$, the splitting being due to the N^{14} nucleus, and (3) a sharp single line from H_2O.[30] If the pH of the solution is increased, proton exchange becomes important, and the spectrum changes in a number of ways. With increasing pH the CH_3 quadruplet first broadens and then coalesces into a singlet which finally sharpens; similarly, the $\overset{+}{N}H_3$ triplet first broadens and then disappears, while the H_2O singlet first broadens and then sharpens again, simultaneously shifting slightly in the direction of the $\overset{+}{N}H_3$ frequency. Since the

[27] J. T. Arnold, *Phys. Rev.*, **102**, 136 (1956).

[28] Grunwald, Loewenstein, and Meiboom, *loc. cit.*; A. Loewenstein and S. Meiboom, *J. Chem. Phys.*, **27**, 1067 (1957).

[29] M. Anbar, A. Loewenstein, and S. Meiboom *J. Am. Chem. Soc.*, **80**, 2630 (1958).

[30] It is not immediately obvious why the CH_3 quadruplet is not further split by the N^{14} nucleus, or the $\overset{+}{N}H_3$ triplet by the CH_3 protons, but a quantitative theoretical treatment shows that these further splittings should not be detectable.

hydrogens of the CH_3 group are certainly not exchanging rapidly under these experimental conditions, all these effects must be due to protolytic exchange on the $\overset{+}{N}H_3$ group, also involving the H_2O protons. The sharp singlet which at high pH replaces both the $\overset{+}{N}H_3$ triplet and the H_2O singlet actually represents an average for both kinds of protons, the exchange between them being now too fast for two lines to be distinguishable. Information about the rate processes involved is best obtained from the broadening which takes place at intermediate acidities in all three components of the spectrum. Thus the broadening of either the CH_3 quadruplet or the $\overset{+}{N}H_3$ triplet gives a measure of the mean life of the $\overset{+}{N}H_3$ protons. Similarly the broadening of the H_2O singlet measures how long a proton remains on oxygen before it is transferred to nitrogen. By studying the way in which the three kinds of broadening depend upon the pH and upon the concentration of the methylammonium ions, Grunwald, Loewenstein, and Meiboom were able to discriminate between various exchange mechanisms and to obtain approximate velocity constants for some of them. The mechanisms considered (after excluding some improbable ones) were as follows:

(1) $CH_3\overset{+}{N}H_3 + H_2O \rightarrow CH_3NH_2 + H_3O^+$

(2) $CH_3\overset{+}{N}H_3 + OH^- \rightarrow CH_3NH_2 + H_2O$

(3a) $CH_3\overset{+}{N}H_3 + CH_3NH_2 \rightarrow CH_3NH_2 + CH_3\overset{+}{N}H_3$

(3b) $CH_3\overset{+}{N}H_3 + O{-}H + CH_3NH_2 \rightarrow CH_3NH_2 + H{-}O + CH_3\overset{+}{N}H_3.$
    $\qquad\qquad\qquad |$ $\qquad\qquad\qquad\qquad\qquad\qquad\qquad\quad |$
    $\qquad\qquad\qquad I$ $\qquad\qquad\qquad\qquad\qquad\qquad\qquad\quad H$

Reaction (1) was not detected for methylamine or dimethylamine (though it was for trimethylamine) and must therefore have had a velocity constant less than about 4×10^{-3} l. mole^{-1} sec.$^{-1}$; this is consistent with evidence from rates of isotopic exchange. Reaction (2) was not detectable for any of the amines studied, but it would not be significant at the acidities concerned even if its velocity constant were as high as 10^{10} to 10^{11} l. mole^{-1} sec.$^{-1}$; this is the magnitude suggested by the measurements of Eigen and Schön (*loc. cit.* [11]) for the reaction $NH_4^+ + OH^-$, using the electrical impulse method, and is also the predicted maximum rate for the encounter of two ions of opposite sign.[31]

---

[31] Onsager, also Debye, *loc. cit.* (13).

The observed exchange rate could therefore be attributed entirely to reactions (3a) and (3b), both of which show the same dependence on pH and concentration. At least part of the exchange must also involve a water molecule, since the H_2O singlet broadens at the same time as the other components of the spectrum, and a quantitative treatment shows that (3a) and (3b) are of roughly equal importance, each having a velocity constant of about 3×10^8. For dimethylamine and trimethylamine the reactions involving a water molecule are in-

TABLE 15.—VELOCITIES OF SIMPLE ACID-BASE REACTIONS

$$A(+ H_2O) \underset{k_2}{\overset{k_1}{\rightleftharpoons}} B + H_3O^+ \qquad k_1 \text{ in sec.}^{-1}, k_2 \text{ in l. mole}^{-1} \text{ sec.}^{-1}$$

Acid	Method	Reference†	$\log k_1$	$\log k_2$
H_2O	Electric impulse	12	-4.6	11.1
HSO_4^-	Ultrasonic	17	9.0	10.6
$MeCO_2H$	Electric impulse	11	5.9	10.7
$MeCO_2H$	Polarography	22a	5.5‡	10.9‡
$MeCO_2H$	Polarography	22b	5.3‡	10.6‡
HCO_2H	Polarography	22a	4.7‡	9.0‡
$MeCOCO_2H$	Polarography	20a	6.1	8.7
$MeCOCO_2H$	Polarography	20b	6.5	9.1
$C_6H_5COCO_2H$	Polarography	21	10.2	11.6
H_3BO_3	Dielectric loss	16	1.0	10.1
$C_{10}H_8OH^*$	Fluorescence	23	7.6	10.7
Me_3NH^+	Proton magnetic resonance	28	1.1	10.9

† References are to footnotes in this chapter.
‡ Denotes values in 50 percent alcohol.

creasingly important, the analogue of (3a) being undetectable for trimethylamine. Measurements of proton magnetic resonance obviously offer a valuable method for detecting the participation of a solvent molecule in proton-transfer reactions, which may be more usual than is commonly supposed.

Table 15 collects some of the results for fast acid-base reactions obtained by several of the above methods. In the two cases where comparisons can be made, there is fair agreement between different authors and different methods, and it is interesting to note that most of the velocity constants for reactions of the type $H^+ + X^-$ fall in the range 10^{10} to 10^{11} l. mole^{-1} sec.$^{-1}$; i.e., they must take place at nearly every encounter between the ions.

The methods so far described in this chapter are applicable to reactions which take place much more rapidly than those studied by chemical means. Slower acid-base reactions have been extensively studied by measuring the rate of *hydrogen isotope exchange.* This sometimes supplements information obtained from acid-base catalysis and can also be used for studying the slow rate of ionization of simple molecules where no suitable chemical reaction can be found. Since the masses of the hydrogen isotopes differ by a large factor, the reaction velocity can be considerably affected by the replacement of one isotope by another (cf. Chapter XI), and this must be taken into account in interpreting the results.

Only a few examples of this method will be given here. In order to carry out the required isotopic analyses it is usually necessary to separate one of the substances from the reaction mixture by physical or chemical means; this is commonly a laborious procedure, and much of the information obtained is of a qualitative or semiqualitative nature. Thus Reyerson[32] found that acetylene does not exchange with deuterium oxide under neutral conditions but does so in fairly concentrated alkali; the introduction of deuterium into the gaseous acetylene was observed by spectroscopic examination. In this example the slow reaction $C_2H_2 + OD^- \rightarrow C_2H^- + HDO$ is followed by the rapid one $C_2H^- + D_2O \rightarrow C_2HD + HDO$, so that it is the velocity of the former process which is measured. The equilibrium $C_2H_2 + OH^- \rightleftharpoons C_2H^- + H_2O$ (or the analogous one involving deuterium) is so far over to the left that no appreciable ionization of the acetylene can be detected. Moreover, even if a means of detection could be found, the approach to equilibrium would be a very rapid one, since it involves the sum of the velocity constants for the forward and reverse reactions. The use of isotopic exchange has the advantage that it involves only the slow forward reaction, thus giving a slow observable process.

There are many other examples of the use of isotope exchange for studying the rate of ionization of active CH groups, usually in the presence of hydroxyl ions. Thus Bonhoeffer[33] has reported rough measurements for a number of ketones, carboxylic acids, esters, nitriles, and so forth, and Hine and his collaborators[34] have recently made a thorough study of compounds of the type CHXYZ, where X, Y, and Z are halogens. In this last work the deuterium compound CDXYZ was dissolved in an aqueous solution, and the extent of conversion to

[32] L. H. Reyerson, *J. Am. Chem. Soc.,* **57,** 779 (1935).

[33] K. F. Bonhoeffer, *Trans. Faraday Soc.,* **34,** 252 (1938).

[34] J. Hine, N. W. Burske, M. Hine, and P. B. Langford, *J. Am. Chem. Soc.,* **79,** 1406 (1957), and earlier papers.

CHXYZ determined from time to time by extracting with octane and examining the infrared spectrum. Information about details of reaction mechanisms can often be obtained by comparing the rate of isotopic exchange with that of other processes, such as chemical reaction or the racemization of optically active compounds. This approach has been used particularly by Ingold and his school.[35]

The above examples all refer to the ionization of carbon acids, and much less is known about other types of acids and bases. As might be expected, protons attached to oxygen exchange with hydroxylic solvents too fast for measurement by ordinary analytical means; on the other hand, some measurable exchange rates have been observed with the cations of ammonia and the amines. In the earliest observations[36] solutions of ND_4NO_3 in 54 percent aqueous nitric acid were precipitated after a short time by adding acetone and the isotopic composition of the precipitate measured. At 0°C the exchange had half-times in the range of 1 to 10 minutes, and half-times up to 10 hours were observed in later work[37] in which the rate of exchange of alkylammonium salts with butanol in chloroform solution was studied by a similar method. The most thorough study of this kind has been carried out by Swain,[38] who measured the rate of exchange of deuterium or tritium between alkylammonium ions and methanol or ethanol, both species being dissolved in the nonexchanging solvent dimethylformamide. The rate of exchange was found to be proportional to the concentrations of amine cation and of alcohol, and inversely proportional to the hydrogen ion concentration, showing that a proton must have been lost in the transition state. This cannot be due to a pre-equilibrium $NR_3H^+ \rightleftharpoons NR_3 + H^+$, since this would itself cause isotopic exchange, and it must be assumed that the proton is lost from an alcohol molecule. It is doubtful, however, whether the free ions MeO^- or EtO^- can be present in kinetically significant concentrations, and the mechanism proposed by Swain is

$$S + MeOH + NR_3H^+ \rightleftharpoons SH^+ + MeO\text{-----}H\text{-----}NR_3 \quad (fast)$$

$$MeO\text{-----}H\text{-----}NR_3 \rightarrow MeOH + NR_3 \quad (slow)$$

where S is the solvent and the slow reaction of the hydrogen-bonded

[35] See C. K. Ingold, *Structure and Mechanism in Organic Chemistry* (Ithaca, N. Y., 1953), pp. 569–575.

[36] A. L. Brodskii and L. V. Sulima, *Doklady Akad. Nauk S.S.S.R.*, **74**, 513 (1950).

[37] L. Kaplan and K. E. Wilzbach, *J. Am. Chem. Soc.*, **76**, 2593 (1954).

[38] C. G. Swain and M. M. Labes, *J. Am. Chem. Soc.*, **79**, 1084 (1957); C. G. Swain, J. T. McKnight, and V. P. Kreiter, *ibid.*, **79**, 1088 (1957).

intermediate brings about exchange of hydrogen between the amine and the alcohol.

Simpler behavior is found in the exchange of phosphine with deuterium oxide,[39] which is catalyzed both by hydrogen ions and by hydroxyl ions. Phosphine has very feeble acidic and basic properties in aqueous solution, and there is little doubt that the velocities of the two exchange processes are determined by those of the reactions $PH_3 + D_3O^+ \rightarrow PH_3D^+ + D_2O$ and $PH_3 + OD^- \rightarrow PH_2^- + HDO$, PH_2D being formed when either of these reactions is reversed in a solvent consisting mainly of D_2O. As we have seen in Chapter VII, by making reasonable assumptions about the velocities of these reverse processes it is possible to use the observed rates of isotopic exchange to estimate the appropriate equilibrium constants, leading to $pK(PH_4^+) = -12$, $pK(PH_3) = 27$.

In general, measurements of isotopic exchange rates have not added greatly to our knowledge of the velocities of acid-base reactions, though they have often served to confirm or extend our understanding of reaction mechanisms. The most useful field for obtaining new information is probably that of very weak acids and bases, since by using the radioactive isotope tritium it is possible to measure extremely small exchanges, thus giving information about very low reaction velocities.

[39] R. E. Weston and J. Bigeleisen, *J. Am. Chem. Soc.*, **76**, 3074 (1955).

CHAPTER IX

Acid-Base Catalysis

THE study of catalysis by acids and bases constitutes the most fruitful method of obtaining information about the rates of acid-base reactions. Its use depends upon the fact that the gain or loss of a proton by a molecule (the substrate) will often lead to further reaction, especially when it is accompanied by an electronic rearrangement; the reaction thus brought about may consist of a rearrangement or decomposition of the substrate, or it may involve another reagent present in solution. The function of the catalyst is thus to donate or to remove a proton, thereby bringing the substrate into a more reactive state.

The early study of catalysis by acids and bases was concerned chiefly with the use of catalyzed reactions for investigating general problems of physical chemistry. For example, the first correct formulation of the kinetic laws of a first-order reaction was made by Wilhelmy in 1850 in connection with his measurements of the catalytic inversion of cane sugar by acids.[1] Catalytic reactions also played an important part in the foundation of the classical theory of electrolytic dissociation toward the end of the nineteenth century, and kinetic measurements (notably on the hydrolysis of esters) were used widely for investigating the state of electrolyte solutions.

The classical theory of acid-base catalysis assumed that hydrogen and hydroxyl ions are the only effective catalysts, that the reaction velocity is proportional to the concentration of the catalyzing ion, and that the degrees of dissociation of the catalyzing ions were given directly by their electrolytic conductivities. These assumptions gave a good general description of the facts, but a number of discrepancies arose when they were applied quantitatively. The next phase in the study of acid-base catalysis, especially associated with the name of J. N. Brönsted, dealt mainly with the clearing up of these discrepancies, partly by the application of modern views on electrolyte solu-

[1] L. F. Wilhelmy, *Pogg. Ann.*, **81**, 413, 499 (1850).

tions and partly by the deduction from experiment of new laws governing catalytic phenomena. The most important of the latter were the concept of general acid-base catalysis and the establishment of relations between catalytic power and acid-base strength. In this way the systematics of acid-base catalysis were largely established in the decade 1920–1930, and little has been added later to the fundamental aspects of this subject. This part of the story is well known[2] and will not be repeated here, though comment is needed on some particular points.

The subject of *salt effects* arises in all kinetic work involving electrolytes, and it was a thorough investigation of these effects which served to clarify many of the early misunderstandings about acid-base catalysis. Since the catalyst is commonly ionic, the same problems often arise even when no other electrolyte has been added to the system. Salt effects are commonly classified as *primary* and *secondary*. Secondary salt effects are not essentially kinetic in nature but arise from the effect of ionic environment on ionic equilibria. In acid-base catalysis these are commonly the dissociation equilibria of weak acids or weak bases which are acting as catalysts; a change in the ionic environment affects the concentration of hydrogen or hydroxyl ions in the solution and hence the velocity of a reaction catalyzed by these ions. This type of effect can be investigated by thermodynamic measurements on the catalyst solution, without any addition of reactant, and at sufficiently low ionic concentrations it can be accounted for by the theory of interionic attraction.[3]

Primary salt effects arise in the actual kinetic step of the reaction and appear in their simplest form when all the electrolytes present in the solution are completely dissociated, so that there are no equilibria which can be displaced. If we are considering the effect of environment upon the velocity v of a reaction between two species X and Y, the fundamental equation is

$$v = k[\text{X}][\text{Y}]f_\text{X}f_\text{Y}/f_\ddagger, \qquad (34)$$

where k is independent of environment and the symbol $\ddagger$ refers to the transition state of the reaction. This expression was originally advanced by Brönsted[4] on not very clear theoretical grounds but would now be regarded as a consequence of the transition-state theory of reaction velocities. Equation (34) leads to useful predictions when both X and Y bear charges, since the charge on the transition state will then differ from either, and both theory and experiment show that in

[2] See, for example, R. P. Bell, *Acid-Base Catalysis* (Oxford, 1941).

[3] See Bell, *op. cit.* (2), ch. ii.

[4] J. N. Brönsted, *Z. physikal. Chem.*, **102**, 169 (1922).

dilute solutions the activity coefficients of ions depend primarily upon their charges. However, in most instances of acid-base catalysis the substrate is uncharged; thus for hydrogen ion catalysis of a substrate S Equation (34) becomes

$$v = k[S][H^+]f_S f_{H^+}/f_{\ddagger}, \tag{35}$$

where the transition state now has a single positive charge. In this equation f_S is accessible experimentally, but there is no way of measuring the ratio $f_{H^+}/f_{\ddagger}$ except by the kinetic experiments themselves, and the interionic theory only makes the prediction that it should differ little from unity in dilute solution.

For many purposes this uncertainty does not matter, since the primary salt effect can often be neglected in dilute solutions or eliminated by extrapolation to zero ionic strength. Moreover, in the particular case of catalysis by solutions of strong acids the activity factor in (35) has exactly the same form as that occurring in the definition of the acidity function (Chapter VI, Equation 25), and this provides a means of correlating kinetic behavior. Salt effects sometimes occur, however, which are much greater than would be expected and which are highly specific to the nature of the ion added.[5] This is particularly the case for reactions in which the transition state has a negative charge (for example, in reactions involving hydroxyl ions and an uncharged substrate), where the addition of metallic cations often has a large and specific effect. The modern tendency is to explain individual behavior in electrolyte solutions in terms of incomplete dissociation, even in systems formerly regarded as completely dissociated, and this approach has been successful in interpreting thermodynamic behavior as well as conductivities and optical properties.[6] Some of the abnormal kinetic salt effects can be explained in a similar way. For example, the decomposition of diacetone alcohol, catalyzed by hydroxyl ions, is considerably retarded by the addition of calcium, barium, or thallous ions,[7] and the same is true for the reaction of hydroxyl ions with nitroethane.[8] There is a considerable amount of evidence that species $CaOH^+$, $BaOH^+$, and $TlOH$ are not completely dissociated, and estimates of their degrees of dissociation have been obtained from measurements of solubility, e.m.f., conductivity, and (for $TlOH$) ultraviolet absorption. Within the rather large uncertainties of these estimates the same degrees of dissociation are consistent with the above

[5] M. Kilpatrick, *Ann. Rev. Phys. Chem.*, **2**, 269 (1951).

[6] For a recent discussion see *Disc. Faraday Soc.*, **24**, sec. II (1957).

[7] R. P. Bell and J. E. Prue, *J. Chem. Soc.*, 362 (1949).

[8] R. P. Bell and M. H. Panckhurst, *J. Chem. Soc.*, 2836 (1956).

kinetic results if it is assumed that only the unassociated hydroxyl ions are reactive. Similar conclusions were reached in a study of the effect of cations on the reaction between hydroxyl ions and ethoxycarbonyl-trimethylammonium iodide,[9] though here the reaction is between two oppositely charged ions and shows a large negative primary salt effect even with cations such as K^+ and Rb^+ which do not associate with OH^-. The association of the ions Ca^{2+}, Ba^{2+}, and Tl^+ was shown by the abnormally large retarding effect produced by their salts. The divalent metallic cations also associate with many carboxylate anions, and similar retarding effects are observed in the decomposition of nitramide, catalyzed by these anions.[10]

In all these reactions it appears that no reactivity can be attributed to the associated species, such as $TlOH$, $CaOH^+$, and $R \cdot COOCa^+$, Another way of expressing the same fact is to say that the cations Tl^+, Ca^{2+}, and so forth do not associate with the transition state of the reaction. There is no reason why this should always be so, and it is interesting to note that in the alkaline hydrolysis of ethyl acetate there is no retarding effect of these cations.[11] This can be interpreted by saying that the species $TlOH$ and $CaOH^+$ have the same reactivity as free hydroxyl ions, or, alternatively, that the ions Tl^+ and Ca^{2+} associate with the transition state to the same extent as with hydroxyl ions. The different behavior of different reactions can be rationalized to some extent by considering the charge distribution in the transition states, and there are certainly also reactions in which added cations can associate more strongly with the transition state than with the initial state, thus causing an acceleration rather than a retardation. A notable example is the catalytic effect of various cations, for example Cu^{2+}, in the bromination of ethyl acetoacetate and 2-carbethoxycyclo-pentanone.[12] These reactions are kinetically of zero order with respect to bromine, and the rate-determining step is believed to be the loss of a proton to a basic species, the anion formed being then brominated rapidly. In the absence of other basic catalysts the water molecule acts as the proton acceptor. The accelerating effect of metallic cations can formally be attributed to the formation of a complex with the initial keto ester, this complex having a higher reactivity than the uncomplexed ester, and this was in fact the explanation put forward by Pedersen. No complex formation can, however, be detected with the keto forms of these esters, and it seems more satisfactory (and is

[9] R. P. Bell and G. M. Waind, *J. Chem. Soc.*, 1979 (1950).
[10] R. P. Bell and G. M. Waind, *J. Chem. Soc.*, 2357 (1951).
[11] Bell and Waind, *loc. cit.* (9).
[12] K. J. Pedersen, *Acta Chem. Scand.*, **2**, 252, 385 (1948).

kinetically equivalent) to attribute the accelerating effect to the participation of the cation in stabilizing the transition state. For example, in the bromination of ethyl acetoacetate the transition state will resemble the anion which is eventually formed, and this will certainly be stabilized by cupric ions in the forms of the complex.

$$CH_3C{=\!=}CH{=\!=}C \cdot OEt$$

$$\underset{Cu}{\overset{\tfrac{1}{2}+O\diagdown\qquad\diagup O^{\tfrac{1}{2}+}}{}}$$

The same type of effect occurs in reactions which are not normally regarded as acid-base catalyzed, notably some decarboxylations. Thus the decarboxylation of the anion of acetonedicarboxylic acid is catalyzed by the ions Mg^{2+}, Be^{2+}, Zn^{2+}, Cd^{2+}, Ca^{2+}, Pb^{2+}, Co^{2+}, Ni^{2+}, Al^{3+}, and La^{3+}, the effectiveness of the ion running parallel with its power of forming a complex with the malonate ion.[13] This is understandable if the mechanism is formulated as

$$
\begin{array}{ccc}
CH_2 & CH_2 & CH_2 \\
\diagup\diagdown & \diagup\diagdown & \diagup\diagdown \\
O{=}C\quad C\quad C{=}O & \rightarrow & O{=}C\quad C{=}CH_2 \quad + CO_2. \\
| \quad\; || \quad\; | & & | \qquad\quad | \\
{-}O \quad O \quad O^- & & {-}O \qquad O^-
\end{array}
$$

The anion on the right (derived from the enol of acetoacetic acid, which undergoes further decarboxylation) is structurally similar to the malonate ion, and if the transition state resembles the final state the parallelism mentioned is to be expected. Similar behavior is shown by other decarboxylation reactions[14] and by the hydrolysis of the esters and amides of α-amino acids.[15]

All these catalytic effects of metallic ions could be formally described as "salt effects." Alternatively, they may be referred to as "acid catalysis" (in the sense of Lewis and his school) since they involve the acceptance of electron pairs by the metallic cations. Neither of these descriptions is very helpful, in view of the highly specific way in which the effects depend upon the nature of the metallic ion and of the reaction. This specificity is partly due to the valency behavior of the transition elements, but it also involves the geometry of the mole-

[13] J. E. Prue, *J. Chem. Soc.*, 2331 (1952).

[14] H. A. Krebs, *Biochem. J.*, **36**, 303 (1942); A. Kornberg, S. Ochoa, and A. H. Mehler, *J. Biol. Chem.*, **174**, 159 (1948); F. J. Speck, *ibid.*, **178**, 315 (1948); R. Steinberger and F. H. Westheimer, *J. Am. Chem. Soc.*, **73**, 429 (1951); K. J. Pedersen, *Acta Chem. Scand.*, **6**, 285 (1952).

[15] H. Kroll, *J. Am. Chem. Soc.*, **74**, 2036 (1952); L. Meriwether and F. H. Westheimer, *ibid.*, **78**, 5119 (1956).

cule and the co-ordination number and stereochemistry of the catalyst. In particular, all the substrates showing marked metal ion catalysis have at least two points of attachment disposed so as to favor chelation with the catalyst ion.

It does not appear that purely electrostatic interactions can lead to highly specific salt effects in aqueous solution; for example, the ion $Co(NH_3)_6^{3+}$ is without catalytic action in the decarboxylation of acetone dicarboxylic acid in spite of its high charge. The position is otherwise in nonaqueous solvents of lower dielectric constant, where electrostatic interactions are much greater. We have already seen in Chapter IV the importance of ion-pair formation for acid-base equilibria in nonaqueous solvents, and recent work by Winstein and his collaborators[16] has shown that they also play an important part in the solvolysis reactions of many organic compounds, leading to large and specific salt effects. Somewhat similar behavior has been observed by Eastham[17] in the base-catalyzed mutarotation of tetramethyl- and tetraacetyl-glucose in pyridine and nitromethane. The catalytic effect of uncharged bases alone is very low, but it is greatly enhanced by the addition of a wide variety of salts. For example, 0.02M $LiClO_4$ increases the catalytic effect of pyridine by a factor of ten, though the magnitude of the effect varies widely from one salt to another. In the absence of salt the mechanism of the reaction (which involves the intermediate formation of the aldehydic form of glucose) would be written schematically as

$$H \diagdown \quad \diagup OH + B \quad \rightarrow \quad H \diagdown C{=}O + BH^+$$

so that the transition state will involve a considerable separation of positive and negative charge. Eastham considers that an ion pair M^+X^- can stabilize the transition state electrostatically by a configuration such as

$$H \diagdown C \diagup O{\cdots}HB^+$$

[16] A. H. Fainberg and S. Winstein, *J. Am. Chem. Soc.*, **78**, 328, 2763, 2767, 2777, 2780, 2784 (1956).

[17] A. M. Eastham, E. L. Blackall, and G. A. Latremouille, *J. Am. Chem. Soc.*, **77**, 2182 (1955); E. L. Blackall and A. M. Eastham, *ibid.*, **77**, 2184 (1955).

where the effectiveness of an ion pair will obviously depend upon its individual geometry and charge distribution. Eastham has termed these effects "electrolyte catalysis," and they are likely to occur fairly frequently in solvents of low dielectric constant.

It will be seen that there are many phenomena which are not adequately described in terms of the original concept of salt effects, though in aqueous solutions there is still a wide area in which primary salt effects can be neglected and secondary effects satisfactorily dealt with by the interionic theory. This is commonly true in solutions of ionic strength less than 0.1 not containing multiply charged ions, though an exception must be made for the ions Tl^+ and Ag^+.

The second modification which Brönsted introduced into the classical theory was the idea of *general acid-base catalysis*, and this is now generally accepted essentially in its original form. It was closely bound up with the definition of acids and bases, discussed in Chapter II. As soon as it was realized that the hydrogen and hydroxyl ions in water were not unique but were members of the general class of proton donors and proton acceptors respectively, it became natural to expect that they would not have a monopoly of catalytic power. This was soon found to be the case for a number of reactions, notably the iodination of acetone,[18] the decomposition of nitramide,[19] and the mutarotation of glucose.[20] The experimental evidence for general acid-base catalysis in aqueous solution rests essentially on the form of the observed rate laws in solutions containing weak acids and bases; for example, if a reaction exhibits general catalysis both by acids and bases, its velocity in an acetate buffer solution will be given by an expression of the form

$$v = v_0 + k_H[H_3O^+] + k_{OH}[OH^-] + k_{HOAc}[HOAc] + k_{OAc}[OAc^-] \quad (36)$$

where the so-called "spontaneous" rate v_0 is really due to catalysis by water molecules. This kind of behavior is found not only in catalyzed reactions but in any other experimental study of the rates of acid-base reactions. Thus several of the investigations of fast processes described in the last chapter revealed terms in the rate equation which did not involve either hydrogen ion or hydroxyl ions. In principle all the constants in Equation (36) can be determined experimentally by making measurements in buffer solutions of varying ratios and con-

[18] H. M. Dawson and F. Powis, *J. Chem. Soc.*, 2135 (1913), and later papers.
[19] J. N. Brönsted and K. J. Pedersen, *Z. physikal. Chem.*, **108**, 185 (1923).
[20] T. M. Lowry and G. F. Smith, *J. Chem. Soc.*, 2539 (1927); J. N. Brönsted and E. A. Guggenheim, *J. Am. Chem. Soc.*, **49**, 2554 (1927).

centrations, but of course this will be difficult in practice if some of the terms contribute little to the observed velocity, and under these conditions the small uncertainties due to salt effects may make it impossible to decide whether some of these terms are present at all. These difficulties become especially great in solvents of lower dielectric constant, such as the alcohols, where both primary and secondary salt effects are much greater than in water and our knowledge of acid-base equilibria is less complete.

The position is simpler in principle in nondissociating solvents such as the hydrocarbons, where the solvent itself has no catalytic power and there are no analogues of the hydrogen and hydroxyl ion. For example, in a solution of acetic acid in benzene the only species which can be catalytically active is the acetic acid molecule, and simpler rate laws might be expected. In practice, however, there are frequently complications due to association in this type of solvent, and it will be shown later that the actual kinetic processes may also be more complex.

Early workers on acid-base catalysis had no clear ideas about the *mechanism* of catalysis, which was regarded as some kind of "influence." These early views envisaged reactions which could take place in the absence of a catalyst but were facilitated by its presence; however, evidence gradually accumulated to show that most of the reactions subject to acid-base catalysis cannot take place at all in the complete absence of catalysts, apparently spontaneous reactions being usually due to catalysis by solvent molecules or by some adventitious acidic or basic impurity. This indicates that the catalyst takes part in some fundamental way in the reaction mechanism, and the present view is that acid-base catalysis always involves *an acid-base reaction between catalyst and substrate.*

Before discussing the kinetic consequences of this, it is interesting to note that there are some acid-catalyzed reactions which can take place readily in the absence of catalyst, and for which the older view of facilitation by the catalyst is probably still appropriate. For example, trioxan and paraldehyde (the cyclic trimers of formaldehyde and acetaldehyde) depolymerize to give the aldehyde by homogeneous, first-order gas reactions at moderate temperatures.[21] Their depolymerization is also catalyzed by acids under a wide variety of conditions, namely, by gaseous acids in a heterogeneous gas reaction,[22] on the

[21] C. C. Coffin, *Canad. J. Res.*, **7**, 75 (1932); R. P. Bell and R. le G. Burnett, *Trans. Faraday Soc.*, **34**, 420 (1938).

[22] R. P. Bell and R. le G. Burnett, *Trans. Faraday Soc.*, **33**, 355 (1937).

surface of a sulfonic acid resin,[23] and in both aqueous[24] and non-aqueous[25] solution. It is likely that the uncatalyzed reaction takes place by a simultaneous electron shift in three bonds, e.g.,

since any stepwise mechanism would involve a highly unstable intermediate, for example, the di-radical $\dot{O} \cdot CH_2 \cdot \dot{O} \cdot CH_2$ or the dipolar species $\overset{-}{O} \cdot CH_2 \cdot \overset{+}{O} : CH_2$. An acid catalyst will certainly donate a proton to one or more of the oxygen atoms, and it may be that the presence of a positive charge lowers the activation energy needed for the electron shift. The same kind of explanation can be given for the effect of hydrogen ions in the decarboxylation reactions discussed earlier in this chapter. An alternative explanation is that the addition of a proton makes it easier for the reaction to proceed in stages, e.g.,

where the intermediate does not now involve any separation of charge.

We return now to the *kinetic analysis* of acid-base catalysis. This has already been discussed by several authors, with examples,[26] and in this chapter special attention will be given to some of the less usual cases which can arise.

It is customary to classify these reaction mechanisms according to the number of proton transfers involved. Of course, in any truly

[23] A. W. Schnizer, G. J. Fisher, and A. F. Maclean, *J. Am. Chem. Soc.*, **75**, 4347 (1953).

[24] A. Skrabal, W. Stockmair, and H. Schreiner, *Z. physikal. Chem.*, **169**, 177 (1934); J. F. Walker and A. F. Chadwick, *Ind. Eng. Chem.*, **39**, 974 (1947); M. Paul, *J. Am. Chem. Soc.*, **72**, 3813 (1950); **74**, 141 (1952); R. P. Bell and A. H. Brown, *J. Chem. Soc.*, 774 (1954); R. P. Bell, K. N. Bascombe, and J. C. McCoubrey, *ibid.*, 1286 (1956).

[25] R. P. Bell, O. M. Lidwell, and M. W. Vaughan-Jackson, *ibid.*, 1792 (1936); R. P. Bell and R. le G. Burnett, *Trans. Faraday Soc.*, **35**, 474 (1939); R. P. Bell and B. G. Skinner, *J. Chem. Soc.*, 2955 (1952).

[26] K. J. Pedersen, *J. Phys. Chem.*, **38**, 581 (1934); *Trans. Faraday Soc.*, **34**, 237 (1938); A. Skrabal, *Z. Elektrochem.*, **46**, 146 (1940); Bell, *loc. cit.* (2), ch. vi; *Advances in Catalysis*, **4**, 151 (1952).

catalytic reaction the catalyst must be finally regenerated, so that every initial proton transfer must be reversed; however, from the kinetic point of view we are not interested in fast reactions which occur after the rate-determining step, and the number of kinetically significant proton transfers is usually either one or two.

We shall treat first *base-catalyzed reactions involving a single proton transfer*, which probably constitute the most important class of reactions, and initially only aqueous solutions will be considered. For a substrate SH the sequence of reactions is

$$\text{(a)} \quad \text{SH} + \sum_i \text{B}_i \underset{k_{-1}}{\overset{k_1}{\rightleftharpoons}} \text{S}^- + \sum_i \text{A}_i$$

$$\text{(b)} \quad \text{S}^- \overset{k_2}{\rightarrow} \text{X}$$

(37)

where reaction (b), giving the products X, does not involve an acid-base reaction, though it may involve some other reagents present in the solution.[27] For the sake of simplicity we shall suppose that reaction (b) is irreversible, or is made effectively so by removing the product X as quickly as it is formed. If it is assumed that the concentrations of the acid-base pairs A_i—B_i are held constant during a given reaction then the first stage of the reaction can be characterized by the two first-order velocity constants k_1 and k_{-1}, the values of which will depend on the concentrations of acids and bases present in the system. k_1 can be expressed in the form $k_1 = \sum \pi_i [\text{B}_i]$, where the π_i are characteristic velocity constants for proton transfers to the different bases, and k_{-1} is related to k_1 through K_{SH}, the conventional acid strength of the substrate. If we consider the hypothetical equilibrium between SH and S$^-$, we have

$$k_1/k_{-1} = [\text{S}^-]_e/[\text{SH}]_e = K_{\text{SH}}/[\text{H}^+]_i = K_{\text{SH}}[\text{OH}^-]/K_w. \quad (38)^{28}$$

Similarly, the second stage of the reaction is characterized by a first-order velocity constant k_2, which may well depend upon the concentration of other reactants. For example, in halogenation reactions showing acid-base catalysis it will involve the concentration of halogenating species in the solution.

The general solution for the kinetic scheme (37) is

[27] These reagents may be acids or bases, but it is implied that their reaction in (37b) shall not involve the transfer of a proton. For example, the reaction may consist of solvolysis by a water molecule, which could not be brought about by any other acidic or basic species.

[28] It should be noted that (38) does not require that the equilibrium between SH and S$^-$ should be actually established under experimental conditions.

$$1 - \frac{[X]}{a} = \frac{\rho_2}{\rho_2 - \rho_1} e^{-\rho_1 t} - \frac{\rho_1}{\rho_2 - \rho_1} e^{-\rho_2 t} \tag{39}$$

where a is the initial concentration of substrate, $[X]$ the concentration of product after time t, and ρ_1 and ρ_2 the roots of the equation $\rho^2 - (k_1 + k_{-1} + k_2)\rho + k_1 k_2 = 0$. This does not represent a reaction of any simple order. Further, the reaction velocity is not a simple function of the base concentrations (including $[OH^-]$) and the effects of different catalysts are not additive. In practice, however, simpler behavior is usually found, corresponding to special cases for the relative values of k_1, k_{-1}, and k_2. These will now be treated separately.

(a) $k_1 \ll k_{-1}$. This corresponds to the commonest case in which SH is a very weak acid and the hydroxyl ion concentration is not great enough to convert an appreciable proportion of it into S^-, even if equilibrium is reached. Equation (39) reduces to a single exponential term, corresponding to a first-order reaction with velocity constant k. Since $[S^-]$ is now small throughout, the same result can be obtained by the usual steady state approximation. The observed first-order velocity constant k is given by

$$\frac{1}{k} = \frac{1}{k_1} + \frac{k_{-1}}{k_1 k_2} = \frac{1}{\sum \pi_i [B_i]} + \frac{\sum \pi_i' [A_i]}{k_2 \sum \pi_i [B_i]}$$

$$= \frac{1}{\sum \pi_i [B_i]} + \frac{K_w}{k_2 K_{SH} [OH^-]} \, . \tag{40}$$

Equation (40) corresponds qualitatively to general base catalysis, but the reaction velocity is not a linear function of catalyst concentrations, and the effect of different catalysts is not additive.

(b) $k_1 \ll k_{-1}$ and $k_2 \gg k_{-1}$. Equation (40) becomes

$$k = k_1 = \sum \pi_i [B_i]. \tag{41}$$

This corresponds to general base catalysis, with the reaction velocity a linear function of the catalyst concentrations; the observed velocity is determined directly by the proton transfers from the substrate to the bases.

(c) $k_1 \ll k_{-1}$ and $k_2 \ll k_{-1}$. Equation (40) becomes

$$k = k_1 k_2 / k_{-1} = k_2 K_{SH} [OH^-] / K_w, \tag{42}$$

corresponding to specific catalysis by hydroxyl ions. The first stage of the reaction is now effectively at equilibrium, and the reaction rate depends only on $[OH^-]$, although the proton transfers taking place involve all the bases in solution.

If we now drop the restriction $k_1 \ll k_{-1}$, there are still two cases giving simple expressions. The assumption $k_1 \sim k_{-1}$ means that the substrate is a strong enough acid and the hydroxyl ion concentration high enough so that an appreciable proportion of SH would be converted into S^- if equilibrium were reached.

(d) $k_1 \sim k_{-1}$ and $k_2 \gg k_{-1}$. [S^-] still remains small, since it is removed by the rapid second stage of the reaction, and we arrive at the same result as (41), $k = \sum \pi_i [B_i]$.

(e) $k_1 \sim k_{-1}$ and $k_2 \gg k_{-1}$. The first stage of the reaction is effectively in equilibrium throughout, and an appreciable proportion of substrate is actually present as S^-. Equation (39) gives approximately $\rho_1 = k_1 k_2 / (k_{-1} + k_1)$, $\rho_2 = k_{-1} + k_1$, and since $\rho_2 \gg \rho_1$ the second term of (39) is negligible except for very small values of t. This again represents first-order kinetics, with a velocity constant

$$ k = \frac{k_1 k_2}{k_1 + k_{-1}} = \frac{k_2 K_{SH}[OH^-]}{K_w + K_{SH}[OH^-]} . \tag{43} $$

Equation (43) corresponds qualitatively to specific catalysis by hydroxyl ions, but the velocity is not proportional to [OH^-]; in fact, it should reach a limiting value at high concentrations of alkali corresponding to complete conversion of SH into S^-.[29]

The great majority of acid-base-catalyzed reactions show either general catalysis with a linear dependence on catalyst concentrations (cases (b) and (d) above and their analogues for acid catalysis) or else specific catalysis by hydrogen or hydroxyl ions, with approximate proportionality to [H^+] or [OH^-] (case (c) above and its analogue). There are no experimental data which show the full complications of Equation (39), but there are examples to illustrate the behavior represented by (40) and by (43), which we shall now consider.

The *decomposition of the diazoacetate ion* according to the equation $N_2 : CHCO_2^- + H_2O \rightarrow N_2 + CH_2OHCO_2^-$ is extremely sensitive to catalysis by hydrogen ions and also by other acidic species, but there are a number of "anomalies" in its quantitative behavior.[30] In the first place, when the only acidic or basic species present are those derived from the solvent (i.e., in solutions of strong acids or bases) the plot of reaction velocity against hydrogen ion concentration is far from linear, curving strongly toward the concentration axis. (Because of the ex-

---

[29] The conversion of SH into S^- will of course remove OH^- from the solution, and our initial supposition that the acid-base concentrations do not change during a reaction will be satisfied only if the concentration of catalyst is considerably greater than that of substrate.

[30] C. V. King and E. D. Bolinger, *J. Am. Chem. Soc.*, **58**, 1533 (1936).

treme sensitivity of the reaction toward hydrogen ions the concentration range which could be conveniently studied was $[H^+] = 10^{-13} - 10^{-10}$, i.e., in alkaline solution throughout.) In the second place, although measurements in buffer solutions reveal qualitatively general acid catalysis by the species C_6H_5OH, NH_4^+, piperidinium ion, and $H_2PO_4^-$, the observed velocity constants cannot be represented by the usual type of expression $k = k_0 + k_H[H^+] + k_A[A]$. If k is plotted against $[A]$ at constant $[H^+]$ (i.e., constant buffer ratio $[A]/[B]$), curves concave to the concentration axis are obtained instead of the usual straight lines, and the catalytic effect of an acid A appears to depend on the concentration of the corresponding base B: thus a plot of k against $[A]$ at constant $[B]$ does give a straight line, whose slope depends upon the value of $[B]$.

This behavior was left unexplained by the authors, but it can be accounted for by the reaction scheme

$$N_2 \colon CHCO_2^- + \sum A_i \underset{k_{-1}}{\overset{k_1}{\rightleftharpoons}} N \equiv \overset{+}{N} \cdot CH_2CO_2^- + \sum B_i$$

$$N \equiv \overset{+}{N} \cdot CH_2CO_2^- + H_2O \overset{k_2}{\rightarrow} N_2 + CH_2OHCO_2H$$

in which $k_1 \ll k_{-1} \sim k_2$. This is the exact analogue of case (b) above for basic catalysis, and if the solution contains only one acid-base pair A—B in addition to the solvent we obtain for the observed velocity constant

$$\frac{1}{k} = \frac{1}{k_0 + k_H[H^+] + k_A[A]} + \frac{K}{k_2[H^+]} \tag{44}$$

where K is the equilibrium constant

$$[H^+][N \equiv \overset{+}{N} \cdot CH_2CO^-]/[N_2 \colon CHCO_2^-].$$

Remembering that $[H^+] = K_A[A]/[B]$, where K_A is the acidity constant of A, it will be seen that (44) predicts qualitatively all the kinetic features mentioned above.[31] In fact, all the velocity constants of King and Bolinger (about 100 in all) can be represented quantitatively by the following choice of constants (all in l.min^{-1} mole^{-1}):

$k_0 = 3.0 \times 10^{-3}$ $k_H = 7 \times 10^6$ $K/k_2 = 2.03 \times 10^{-9}$

$k(C_6H_5OH) = 4.0$ $k(NH_4^+) = 1.2$ k (piperidinium) $= 0.014$.

[31] The linear relation between k and $[A]$ at constant $[B]$ follows only if $k_0 \ll k_H[H^+] + k_A[A]$, which is so for the buffer solutions used.

This involves using only one constant (K/k_2) in addition to those required in any conventional example of general acid catalysis, and it seems probable that the above analysis is essentially correct. In particular, (44) predicts that the rate will go to zero in strongly alkaline solution rather than to the "spontaneous" rate k_0. This agrees with the observation that diazoacetates are fairly stable in concentrated alkalies in spite of the fact that k_0 corresponds to a half-time of a few hours.

A similar type of kinetics is shown by the base-catalyzed *aldol condensation of acetaldehyde*, for which the mechanism is

(a) $\quad CH_3CHO + \sum B_i \underset{k_{-1}}{\overset{k_1}{\rightleftharpoons}} CH_2CHO^- + \sum A_i$

(b) $\quad CH_3CHO + CH_2CHO^- \overset{k_2}{\rightarrow} \underset{\underset{O^-}{|}}{CH_3CH} \cdot CH_2CHO \qquad\qquad (45)$

(c) $\quad \underset{\underset{O^-}{|}}{CH_3CH} \cdot CH_2CHO + \sum A_i \rightleftharpoons CH_3CHOHCH_2CHO + \sum B_i$

where the third step is much faster than the other two. This differs from the reaction scheme (37) in that step (b) now involves a second molecule of substrate, its rate being given by $k_2[S^-][SH]$. Assuming as before that $k_1 \ll k_{-1} \sim k_2[SH]$, we find for the velocity in a simple buffer solution,

$$-\frac{2}{d[SH]/dt} = \frac{1}{[SH](k_0 + k_{OH}[OH^-] + k_B[B])}$$

$$+ \frac{K_w}{[SH]^2 k_2 K_{SH}[OH^-]} \qquad\qquad (46)$$

where the factor 2 on the left arises from the fact that reaction 45(b) consumes two molecules of acetaldehyde. The form of (46) suggests that the course of a single reaction will not be expressible by a simple kinetic order, and since further the later stages of the reaction show chemical complications the most useful information can be obtained from initial rates, which can be measured fairly accurately by a dilatometric method.

Although Equation (46) has not been confirmed in full, kinetic studies[32] reveal the following points which are consistent with it.

(1) In sodium hydroxide solutions the apparent order with respect to aldehyde is two at low aldehyde concentrations, falling somewhat with increasing concentration.

(2) At constant aldehyde concentration the rate is not quite linear in the hydroxyl ion concentration but falls off more rapidly at low concentrations and becomes zero in slightly acid solution.

(3) Measurements in buffer solutions give evidence for general base catalysis by the species CO_3^{2-} and $H_2BO_3^-$.

Further support comes from a study of deuterium exchange. If the condensation takes place in deuterium oxide, it is clear that every reversal of reaction 45(a) will lead to the introduction of deuterium into acetaldehyde, and hence ultimately into the aldol. At high aldehyde concentrations $k_2[SH] \gg k_{-1}$ (so that 45(a) will rarely be reversed) but with decreasing aldehyde concentration, the extent of deuteration should increase. Bonhoeffer and Walters[33] showed that in 10M acetaldehyde no detectable amount of deuterium is attached to the carbon of the aldol produced, and more recent work[34] shows that in the range 0.05M to 1.4M the extent to which the unchanged aldehyde is deuterated increases with decreasing concentration and is quantitatively consistent with the above reaction scheme.

The correspondence between isotope exchange and kinetic behavior extends to the analogous aldol condensation of acetone.[35] This is well established as a second-order reaction catalyzed specifically by hydroxyl ions, corresponding to $k_2[SH] \ll k_{-1}$ at all values of $[SH]$ studied. This should lead to facile isotope interchange, and in fact it was found[36] that a molar solution of acetone in alkaline D_2O takes up deuterium about 1,000 times as quickly as it undergoes condensation.

The kinetic schemes so far discussed all involve a proton transfer followed by a chemical reaction. Recently, Zollinger[37] has shown that under suitable conditions the azo-coupling reaction can be regarded as

[32] R. P. Bell, *J. Chem. Soc.*, 1637 (1937); A. Broche, *Colloque National de Cinétique* (Strasbourg, 1953); A. Broche and R. Gibert, *Bull. Soc. chim. France*, 131 (1955); R. P. Bell and P. T. McTigue, unpublished measurements.

[33] K. F. Bonhoeffer and W. D. Walters, *Z. physikal. Chem.*, **181**, 441 (1938).

[34] R. P. Bell and M. J. Smith, *J. Chem. Soc.*, 1691 (1958).

[35] It is more convenient here to study the reverse reaction, the depolymerization of diacetone alcohol, but the known equilibrium constant can be used to deduce the velocity of the forward reaction.

[36] Bonhoeffer and Walters, *loc. cit.* (33).

[37] H. Zollinger, *Helv. Chim. Acta*, **38**, 1597, 1617, 1623 (1955).

a two-stage process in which a reversible coupling reaction *precedes* a proton transfer of comparable velocity, i.e.,

$$ArN_2^+ + R\text{---}H \underset{k_{-1}}{\overset{k_1}{\rightleftharpoons}} H\text{---}\overset{+}{R}\text{---}N{=}N\text{---}Ar$$

$$H\text{---}\overset{+}{R}\text{---}N{=}N\text{---}Ar + B \overset{k_2}{\rightarrow} R\text{---}N{=}N\text{---}Ar + A \tag{47}$$

where k_1 and k_2 are second-order velocity constants, and $k_1 \ll k_{-1} \sim k_2[B]$. The scheme (48) gives for the observed second-order constant k,

$$\frac{1}{k} = \frac{1}{k_1} + \frac{k_{-1}}{k_1 k_2 [B]} . \tag{48}$$

Zollinger found that the reaction between 4-chlorodiazobenzene and 2-naphthol-6,8-disulfonic acid showed general base catalysis by pyridine and its homologues, with a nonlinear dependence of reaction velocity upon catalyst concentration which agreed quantitatively with (48), k_1 having the same value throughout but k_2/k_{-1} varying from one catalyst to another. This interpretation is strongly supported by the effect of replacing hydrogen by deuterium in the substance R—H. At low base concentrations (or with water as the only catalyst) a large isotope effect is observed—$k_H/k_D = 6.6$—but with increasing concentration of pyridine the effect decreases considerably. This is in accord with (47) and (48), since only the second stage of (47) should show any considerable kinetic isotope effect (cf. Chapter XI). Finally, the analogous reaction between 2-methoxydiazobenzene and naphthalene-2,4-disulfonic acid shows no detectable catalysis by bases nor any effect of replacing hydrogen by deuterium at the coupling position; both observations are consistent with $k_2[B] \gg k_{-1}$ in the reaction scheme. This last example is probably more typical of aromatic electrophilic substitution in general, since investigations of nitration, bromination, and sulfonation[38] show at most a small hydrogen isotope effect, though the conditions under which these reactions take place did not make it possible to establish the absence of base catalysis.

Returning to the more usual type of catalyzed reaction (Equation

[38] L. Melander, *Nature*, **163**, 599 (1949); *Acta Chem. Scand.*, **3**, 95 (1949); *Arkiv Kemi*, **2**, 211 (1950); **6**, 219 (1953); W. M. Lauer and W. E. Noland, *J. Am. Chem. Soc.*, **75**, 3689 (1953); T. G. Bonner, F. Bowyer, and G. Williams, *J. Chem. Soc.*, 2650 (1953). There is, however, a considerable deuterium isotope effect in the iodination of phenol; cf. E. Grovenstein, *J. Am. Chem. Soc.*, **79**, 2972 (1957).

37), the only reaction which has been reported to conform quantitatively to Equation (43), or its analogue for acid catalysis, is the alkaline hydrolysis of $C_6H_5NHCOCF_3$,[39] which has $pK = 11.9$, so that there is conversion of an appreciable fraction of the substrate into its conjugate base. The predicted behavior is also shown qualitatively by the hydrolysis of formamide in concentrated alkali,[40] and the hydrolysis of a number of amides in concentrated acid.[41] The plot of reaction velocity against $[H^+]$ or $[OH^-]$ is linear in dilute solution and falls off with increasing concentration, as predicted by (43), but instead of leveling off to a constant value it passes through a maximum in the range $4M$ to $6M$. These concentrations are so high that the simple equilibrium expressions used in the above derivations will certainly break down, and it becomes necessary to invoke acidity functions or some equivalent treatment.

We must now consider the kinetic analysis of catalyzed reactions involving *two proton transfers*. These comprise the so-called *prototropic isomerizations*, notably keto-enol tautomerism. The simplest mechanisms for catalysis by acids and bases are as follows:

Acid catalysis

$$\backslash CH \cdot C{:}O + A \rightleftharpoons \backslash CH \cdot C{:}OH^+ + B \rightleftharpoons \backslash C{:}C \cdot OH + A \quad (49)$$

Base catalysis

$$\backslash CH \cdot C{:}O + B \rightleftharpoons \backslash C{:}C \cdot O^- + A \rightleftharpoons \backslash C{:}C \cdot OH + B \quad (50)$$

and similar schemes can be written for analogous transformations such as lactam-lactim, nitroso-*iso*nitroso, nitro-*aci*nitro, and three-carbon tautomerism

$$\backslash CH \cdot C{:}C \rightleftharpoons \backslash C{:}C \cdot CH.$$

[39] S. S. Biechler and R. W. Taft, *J. Am. Chem. Soc.*, **79**, 4927 (1957).

[40] R. P. Bell and C. G. Miller, unpublished measurements.

[41] A. Benrath, *Z. anorg. Chem.*, **151**, 53 (1926); H. von Euler and A. Ölander, *Z. physikal. Chem.*, **131**, 107 (1928); T. W. J. Taylor, *J. Chem. Soc.*, 2741 (1930); O. Reitz, *Z. Elektrochem.*, **44**, 693 (1938); B. S. Rabinovitch and C. A. Winkler, *Canad. J. Res.*, **B20**, 73 (1942); J. T. Edward, H. P. Hutchison, and S. C. R. Meacock, *J. Chem. Soc.*, 2520 (1955); J. T. Edward and S. C. R. Meacock, *ibid.*, 2000 (1957); D. Rosenthal and T. I. Taylor, *J. Am. Chem. Soc.*, **79**, 2684 (1957).

For simplicity we shall write the two isomers schematically as HS and SH, and if the over-all reaction is made irreversible by removing the product as quickly as it is formed the kinetic scheme for acid catalysis becomes

$$\text{HS} + \sum \text{A}_i \underset{k_{-1}}{\overset{k_1}{\rightleftharpoons}} \text{HSH}^+ + \sum \text{B}_i \overset{k_2}{\to} \text{SH} + \sum \text{A}_i. \tag{51}$$

Provided that the acid-base composition of the solution remains constant during a reaction, the kinetics can again be described by three first-order constants k_1, k_{-1}, and k_2, all of which will now depend upon the concentrations of the acids and bases present. A kinetic analysis can be carried out just as for reactions involving a single proton transfer, with the following results:

(a) $k_1 \sim k_{-1} \sim k_2$. Complicated kinetics result (cf. Equation 38); there is no experimental evidence for this case.

(b) $k_1 \ll k_{-1} \ll k_2$. The rate is now determined by the first step in (51), and only the first proton transfer is kinetically significant. Hence we have

$$k = k_1 = \sum \pi_i [\text{A}_i] \tag{52}$$

i.e., general acid catalysis.

(c) $k_1 \ll k_{-1} \gg k_2$. The first step of (51) is now effectively at equilibrium, and the rate is given by

$$v = [\text{HSH}^+] \sum \pi_i' [\text{B}_i] = [\text{HS}] \sum \pi_i' [\text{B}_i][\text{HSH}^+]/[\text{HS}].$$

The observed first-order constant is therefore

$$\begin{aligned} k &= \sum \pi_i' [\text{B}_i][\text{HSH}^+]/[\text{HS}] \\ &= \sum \pi_i' [\text{B}_i][\text{H}^+]/K_{\text{HSH}} = \sum \pi_i' [\text{A}_i]K_i/K_{\text{HSH}} \end{aligned} \tag{53}$$

where K_i and K_{HSH} are the acid strengths of A_i and HSH^+. This result is experimentally indistinguishable from (52), so that general acid catalysis is again observed although the rate-determining step is actually the transfer of a proton from basic catalysts to the ion HSH^+. This is in contrast to reactions involving a single proton transfer, where the same kinetic scheme led to specific catalysis by hydrogen ions. The identical form of (52) and (53) is of course due to the fact that in both cases the transition state is composed of one molecule of HS and one molecule of A_i. This does not mean, however, that the two mechanisms are identical, since the structures of the two transition states are different. For example, if a keto-enol change is catalyzed by an acid HX, the transition states for cases (b) and (c) are

$$\backslash \underset{/}{CH \cdot \overset{/}{C} \colon} O \cdots \overset{+}{H} \cdots \overset{-}{X}$$

(b)

$$\overset{-}{X} \cdots \overset{+}{H} \cdots \backslash \overset{/}{C} \colon\colon \overset{/}{C} \colon OH$$

(c)

(d) $k_1 \ll k_{-1} \sim k_2$. The concentration of HSH$^+$ is still small throughout, so that the steady state treatment can be applied, giving

$$
\frac{1}{k} = \frac{1}{k_1} + \frac{k_{-1}}{k_1 k_2} = \frac{1}{\sum \pi_i [A_i]} + \frac{\sum \pi_i'' [B_i]}{\sum \pi_i [A_i] \sum \pi_i' [B_i]}
$$
$$
= \frac{1}{\sum \pi_i [A_i]} + \frac{1}{K_{HSH} \sum K_i \pi_i' [A_i]}
$$

(54)

where $k_1 = \sum \pi_i [A_i]$, $k_2 = \sum \pi_i [B_i]$, $k_{-1} = \sum \pi_i'' [B_i]$. If only a single acid-base pair is effective, Equation (54) reduces to

$$
k = \pi \pi' [A] / (\pi' + \pi'')
$$

(55)

which represents general acid catalysis with linear dependence of velocity upon concentration. If catalysis involves more than one acid-base pair, including those derived from the solvent, then the reaction will show the qualitative characteristics of general acid catalysis but in general will not follow the usual quantitative laws. In particular, the velocity will not be a linear function of catalyst concentration, and the effect of several catalysts present simultaneously will not be additive. A simple result is, however, still obtained if we can write

$$
\pi_1' / \pi_1'' = \pi_2' / \pi_2'' = \cdots = \pi_i' / \pi_i'' = \cdots = \beta
$$

(56)

when (53) becomes

$$
k = \frac{\beta}{1 + \beta} \sum \pi_i [A_i].
$$

(57)

Although there is no reason why (56) should be generally valid, it is likely to hold approximately for catalysts of similar structure, and this may be why the more complex behavior represented by (54) has not been observed in prototropic reactions.

(e) $k_1 \sim k_{-1} \ll k_2$. If equilibrium were attained in the first stage of the reaction, a considerable proportion of HS would be converted to HSH$^+$; however, since $k_2 \gg k_{-1}$ the concentration of HSH$^+$ remains very small and the steady state treatment can again be applied, giving results identical with (d).

(f) $k_1 \sim k_{-1} \gg k_2$. The solution will now contain an appreciable proportion of HSH⁺, and it is necessary to distinguish between the rate of disappearance of HS and the rate of appearance of SH. In keto-enol transformations any analytical method will normally include HSH⁺ with HS, so that the latter is the appropriate choice. Proceeding as for (43), we find

$$k = \frac{k_1 k_2}{k_1 + k_{-1}} = \frac{\sum \pi_i [A_i] \sum \pi_i' [B_i]}{\sum \pi_i [A_i] + \sum \pi_i'' [B_i]} = \frac{\sum \pi_i' K_i [A_i]}{[H^+] + K_{HSH}} . \quad (58)$$

This predicts general acid catalysis, but also an inverse dependence on hydrogen ion concentration. In practice the latter is likely to be important only at high acidities, and under these conditions general catalysis by acids other than the hydrogen ion will be difficult to detect; moreover, the simple equilibrium expressions used in the above derivation will break down. The situation is thus similar to that just discussed for the hydrolysis of amides.

The kinetics of prototropic isomerization have rarely been directly investigated, and it is usual to employ some other process, for example racemization, isotope exchange, or halogenation, as a measure of the rate of enolization. In acid catalysis according to scheme (49) the hydrogen atom attached to carbon is not removed until the second step of the reaction is accomplished, so that the rate of racemization or isotope exchange will be equal to the rate of formation of enol and independent of its reversion to the keto form or to the cation

$$\diagdown CH \cdot C \overset{\diagup}{\colon} OH^{+}.^{42}$$

Similarly, the cation will be even less reactive than the keto form toward halogens or other electrophilic reagents; hence, provided that the reaction between halogen and enol is fast enough, the rate of halogenation will also be equal to the rate of enol formation and independent of the concentration or nature of the halogenating agent, as is usually found. However, at sufficiently low halogen concentrations and high acidities the reaction

$$\diagdown C \overset{\diagup}{\colon} C \cdot OH + H^{+} \rightarrow \diagdown CH \cdot C \overset{\diagup}{\colon} OH^{+}$$

will begin to compete with the halogenation reaction

---

[42] Expressions (51) to (58) all apply to the rate of *formation* of enol, any reverse reaction being neglected.

$$\overset{\diagdown}{\underset{\diagup}{C}}:\overset{\diagup}{C}\cdot OH + X_2 \rightarrow \overset{\diagdown}{\underset{\diagup}{C}}X\cdot\overset{\diagup}{C}:O + H^+ + X^-.$$

The rate of halogenation should then be less than the rate of enolization and should depend upon the halogen concentration. This has been observed in the iodination of acetophenone[43] and the bromination of acetone[44] in concentrated aqueous acids.

Equations analogous to (51) to (58) can easily be derived for *base-catalyzed prototropy*, but it must now be observed that the formation of the anion

$$\overset{\diagdown}{\underset{\diagup}{C}}:\overset{\diagup}{C}\cdot O^-$$

will lead to racemization and isotope exchange without involving the enol at all. Similarly, it should react with halogens even more rapidly than the enol itself. Observed rates of base-catalyzed racemization, isotope exchange, or halogenation are therefore rates of ionization rather than rates of enolization. As Hammett has expressed it, "There is no reason to suppose that the formation of an electrically neutral enol form represents anything more than an unimportant by-path into which a portion of the reacting substance may transiently stray."[45] These reactions can therefore be regarded as involving a single proton transfer, since all subsequent events are kinetically unimportant, and general base catalysis will be observed as in Equation (41).

In the base-catalyzed halogenation of a ketonic substance the enolate ion will be in rapid equilibrium with enol,[46] and both enol and enolate can react with halogen. The kinetic scheme is thus

(a) $\quad SH + \sum B_i \underset{k_{-1}}{\overset{k_1}{\rightleftharpoons}} S^- + \sum A_i \overset{\text{fast}}{\rightleftharpoons} HS + \sum B_i$

(b) $\qquad S^- + X_2 \underset{k_3}{\rightarrow} SX + X^-$ $\qquad\qquad\qquad$ (59)

(c) $\qquad HS + X_2 \underset{k_4}{\rightarrow} SX + X^- + H^+.$

Under ordinary conditions the relative or absolute rates of (b) and (c)

[43] L. Zucker and L. P. Hammett, *J. Am. Chem. Soc.*, **61**, 2779 (1939).

[44] R. P. Bell and G. Archer, *J. Chem. Soc.*, in press, 1959.

[45] L. P. Hammett, *Physical Organic Chemistry* (New York, 1940) p. 231.

[46] This assumption is not obviously correct, since the halogenation reactions are themselves very fast, but the experimental results quoted below confirm its validity.

are kinetically unimportant, since both are much faster than (a), but by studying the bromination of ethyl malonate at very low bromine concentrations[47] it has been possible to obtain approximate values for k_3 and k_4. The same values will apply at higher bromine concentrations, and it can be concluded that at $pH > 3$ most of the bromination takes place through the anion, while below pH 3 bromination of the enol becomes more important.[48] Similar conclusions were reached for the iodination of ethyl malonate,[49] the method used in this case being to combine equilibrium measurements with a kinetic study of the reverse reaction. The application of this method to the iodination of 2-ethoxycarbonylcyclohexanone[50] showed that for this reaction halogenation takes place to an equal extent through the enol and the enolate ion at about pH 5. It seems likely that in general both routes can contribute significantly under different conditions, though the rate-determining step in base catalysis is always the formation of the anion.

The kinetic analyses given so far in this chapter have been developed for aqueous solutions, in which the catalysts are in equilibrium with the species H_2O, H_3O^+, and OH^- and there is no association of ions to give ion pairs. The results would also apply to any analogous amphiprotic solvent, such as an alcohol, though there is little systematic experimental work on catalysis in such solvents. However the situation is different if we go to an *aprotic solvent*, i.e., one which does not take any part in acid-base equilibria. This can be illustrated by considering catalysis by a single uncharged acid dissolved in such a solvent, for example, a solution of trichloroacetic acid in benzene.

If the reaction involves only a single proton transfer, the kinetic scheme is as before

$$S + A \underset{k_{-1}}{\overset{k_1}{\rightleftharpoons}} SH^+ + B^-, \qquad SH^+ \overset{k_2}{\rightarrow} X \tag{60}$$

assuming that the solution is sufficiently dilute for ion pairing to be neglected. If $k_{-1} \ll k_2$, the rate will be determined by k_1 and will be equal to $\pi_A[A]$; π_A is characteristic of A, and the behavior is typical of general acid catalysis. If $k_{-1} \gg k_2$, the first stage is at equilibrium, but the concentrations of A and B^- are no longer related to the concentration of any "hydrogen ion," and there is no analogue of the

[47] R. P. Bell and M. Spiro, *J. Chem. Soc.*, 429 (1953).

[48] This reaction and the others mentioned in this paragraph show no detectable catalysis by acids, so that even in solutions of strong acids the observed reaction is due to basic catalysis by water molecules.

[49] R. P. Bell and P. Engel, *J. Chem. Soc.*, 247 (1957).

[50] R. P. Bell and D. C. Vogelsong, *J. Chem. Soc.*, 243 (1958).

specific hydrogen ion catalysis encountered in water. If none of the base B^- has been added to the system, we have $[SH^+] = [B^-] \propto [S]^{\frac{1}{2}}[A]^{\frac{1}{2}}$, so that the reaction would not follow any simple kinetic order.

In most aprotic solvents it is more realistic to regard the ions as being present in the form of ion pairs (cf. p. 54), so that the reaction scheme for a single proton transfer becomes $S + A \rightleftharpoons SH^+ \cdot B^- \rightarrow X$. If the first step is rate-determining, we find general acid catalysis with simple kinetics, as before. When the second step is rate-determining, we still have simple kinetics, since the reaction velocity is $k_2 K [S][A]$, where K is the equilibrium constant for the first stage. However, the value of k_2 may well now depend upon the nature of B, even if no proton transfer is involved in the second stage.

Similar considerations apply to reactions involving two proton transfers in aprotic solvents. If the first step is rate-determining, the problem reduces to a single proton transfer. When the second step is rate-determining, the assumption of free ions leads to the same prediction as in aqueous solution, since the composition of the transition state is still equivalent to one molecule of substrate plus one molecule of acid, and this remains true even if the ions HSH^+ and B^- are associated in a pair. However, the ion pair initially formed in the first proton transfer may well have a configuration which is unfavorable for the second proton transfer, which involves the removal of a proton from a different atom. This raises the possibility that the second proton transfer may involve another basic species. This could be a second molecule of substrate, giving (for a keto-enol transformation) a transition state such as

$$\overset{\diagdown}{\underset{\diagup}{}}CH \cdot \overset{\diagup}{C} : \overset{+}{O}H$$

$$\overset{\diagdown}{\underset{\diagup}{}}CH \cdot C : O \qquad B^-$$

or a second ion pair, with the transition state

$$\overset{\diagdown}{\underset{\diagup}{}}CH \cdot \overset{\diagup}{C} : \overset{+}{O}H$$

$$B^- \qquad \qquad B^-$$

$$\underset{+}{HO} : C \cdot CH \diagdown$$

Either of these possibilities would of course lead to kinetic orders higher than the first in substrate or catalyst.

The above considerations suggest that the kinetics of catalysis in aprotic solvents may be more complex than in aqueous solution, in spite of the apparent chemical simplicity of the system. This general conclusion is borne out by the existing experimental material,[51] which is only incompletely understood. In particular the reaction velocity is rarely directly proportional to the catalyst concentration, the apparent order being sometimes greater and sometimes less than unity. This may be related to the kinetic predictions made in the last paragraph, but an additional complication arises in that the catalysts mainly used in these investigations were carboxylic acids, which are associated to a varying extent in aprotic solvents.

Returning to the general problem of prototropic reactions, the discussion so far has assumed that the two proton transfers take place consecutively, as in Equations (49) to (51). There is another possibility, the so-called *concerted mechanism*, in which the transition state contains *two* catalyst molecules, one acid and one base.[52] This can be written schematically as

$$B_1 + HS + A_2 \rightleftharpoons A_1 + SH + B_2 \tag{61}$$

or more specifically

$$B_1 + HX \cdot Y{:}Z + A_2 \rightleftharpoons A_1 + X{:}Y \cdot ZH + B_2 \tag{62}$$

where A_1—B_1 and A_2—B_2 may be either the same or different acid-base pairs. The concerted mechanism makes no distinction between acid and base catalysis, and the mechanism so far considered (which will be distinguished by the name *consecutive mechanism*) postulates two separate routes:

$$
\begin{aligned}
&\text{(a)} \quad HS + A \rightleftharpoons HSH^+ + B \rightleftharpoons SH + A \\
&\text{(b)} \quad HS + B \rightleftharpoons S^- + A \rightleftharpoons SH + B.
\end{aligned}
\tag{63}
$$

---

[51] For a summary see Bell, *loc. cit.* (2), pp. 103–107.

[52] Other names have been given to this mechanism, notably *ternary*, *synchronous*, and *"push-pull."* The first indicates the number of species in the transition state and has been widely used. However, Ingold (*Structure and Mechanism in Organic Chemistry* [Ithaca, N. Y., 1953], p. 551) has used the description *bimolecular* for the same mechanisms, referring to the number of catalyst molecules involved, so that confusion can easily arise. The second and third might imply either that the acid and the base arrive simultaneously to the substrate molecule or that the two proton transfers take place simultaneously, neither of which need be the case. We have therefore preferred *concerted* as least likely to cause misunderstanding.

On the other hand, Equations (61) and (62) do not imply a ternary collision, since just the same kinetic result is achieved if the substrate first associates with the acid and is subsequently attacked by the base, or vice versa. The real distinction between (61) and (63) is that in the latter the intermediate stage involves the separation of two entities rather than an association, and the transition state contains only one catalytic species.

If the formation of ion pairs can be neglected, as is usually the case in aqueous solution, there appears to be a ready means of distinguishing between the consecutive and concerted mechanisms. Provided that the concentration of intermediates is low, scheme (61) leads to an observed velocity constant of the form

$$k = \sum_i \sum_j k_{ij}[A_i][B_j] \tag{64}$$

where k_{ij} is a constant characteristic of each acid-base combination. The number of constants can often be reduced if we make the reasonable assumption that the relative effectiveness of any two acids is independent of the base with which they are coupled, and similarly for any two bases. This leads to

$$k = \left\{ \sum_i k_i'[A_i] \right\} \left\{ \sum_j k_j''[B_j] \right\} \tag{65}$$

which when expanded still consists of a sum of terms each involving the product of two concentrations. On the other hand, we have seen that under the same conditions scheme (63) leads to the rate equation

$$k = \sum k_i[A_i] + \sum k_j[B_j] \tag{66}$$

independent of the relative rates of the two successive steps.

Although (66) differs radically in form from (64) and (65), it is not easy to distinguish the two possibilities experimentally in aqueous solution. This is because of the presence of a large and constant concentration of water molecules, which can act either as acid or as base so that any term in (64) involving $k[X][H_2O]$ is indistinguishable from the corresponding term $k[X]$ in (66). A real distinction becomes possible in the case of terms involving two solute species; for example, in an acetate buffer solution the concerted mechanism would predict a term in $[HOAc][OAc^-]$. The only reaction where such a product term has been established in aqueous solution is the iodination of acetone, as first reported by Dawson and Spivey.[53] Their data cer-

---

[53] H. M. Dawson and E. Spivey, *J. Chem. Soc.*, 2180 (1930). These authors

tainly require such a term, but it might be objected that they refer to solutions containing high and variable concentrations of electrolyte ($> 0.75\text{M}$) in which complications might arise from salt effects. However, more recent work[54] at a constant ionic strength of 0.2 confirms the necessity for a product term somewhat larger than that found by Dawson and Spivey. The rate expression obtained by Bell and Jones is

$$10^6 v = 5 \times 10^{-4}[\text{H}_2\text{O}] + 1600[\text{H}^+] + 1.5 \times 10^7[\text{OH}^-] \\ + 5.0[\text{HOAc}] + 15[\text{OAc}^-] + 20[\text{HOAc}][\text{OAc}^-] \tag{67}$$

where v is the rate of disappearance of halogen in moles per liter per minute, referred to a ketone concentration of one mole per liter, and the last term contributes up to 20 percent of the observed velocity. Less extensive measurements with trimethylacetate and glycollate buffers indicated the presence of product terms of similar magnitude.

It is reasonable to attribute these product terms to a concerted process, but this of course leaves open the question of whether the remaining terms in (67) represent concerted processes involving a molecule of water. An apparently strong argument against the concerted interpretation has been put forward by Pedersen.[55] This interpretation would allot the terms in equation (67) according to the following scheme:

Velocity	5×10^{-4}	1,600	1.5×10^7	5	15	20
Acid	H_2O	H_3O^+	H_2O	HOAc	H_2O	HOAc
Base	H_2O	H_2O	OH^-	H_2O	OAc^-	OAc

This means that when the acid is H_2O changing the base from H_2O to OAc^- increases the velocity by a factor of 3×10^4, but when the acid is HOAc the same change of base produces only a fourfold increase. Similarly, a change of the acid from H_2O to HOAc increases the velocity by 10^4 when the base is H_2O, but only by 30 percent when the base is OAc^-. These large discrepancies seem quite unreasonable, and on this basis Pedersen rejected the general application of the concerted mechanism.

This argument has been widely quoted, but it has been shown to be invalid by Swain[56] who pointed out that the interpretation of several

attributed the product term to catalysis by a complex $\text{HOAc} \cdot \text{OAc}^-$. There is no evidence for the existence of such a complex, and the assumption is kinetically equivalent to the concerted mechanism.

[54] R. P. Bell and P. Jones, *J. Chem. Soc.*, 88 (1953).
[55] K. J. Pedersen, *J. Phys. Chem.*, **38**, 590 (1934).
[56] C. G. Swain, *J. Am. Chem. Soc.*, **72**, 4578 (1950).

of the terms in (67) is not unambiguous. For example, the term $15[OAc^-]$ might conceal either $k[OAc^-][H_2O]$ or $k[HOAc][OH^-]$, which are kinetically indistinguishable; the observed term will in general be a sum of the two. The scheme given above must therefore be replaced by the following:

Velocity	5×10^{-4}	1,600	1.5×10^7	5	15	20
Acid	H_2O	H_3O^+ H_3O^+	H_2O	HOAc H_3O^+	H_2O HOAc	HOAc
Base	H_2O	OH^- H_2O	OH^-	H_2O OH^-	OAc^- OH^-	OAc^-

Swain showed that on this basis the discrepancies pointed out by Pedersen no longer arose and that the experimental coefficients could in fact be represented approximately by an expression having the form of (65). If we use the numerical values of (67) rather than the original ones of Dawson and Spivey, such an expression is[57]

$$10^6 v = 10^{-5}\{[H_2O] + 10^2[HOAc] + 1.7 \times 10^6[H^+]\}\{[H_2O]$$
$$+ 1.4 \times 10^4[OAc^-] + 3 \times 10^{10}[OH^-]\}$$
$$= 7 \times 10^{-4}[H_2O] + 1000[H^+] + 1.7 \times 10^7[OH^-]$$
$$+ 5.2[HOAc] + 7.7[OAc^-] + 14[HOAc][OAc^-] \quad (68)$$

using values for the ionic product of water and the dissociation constant of acetic acid appropriate to an ionic strength of 0.2. The coefficients in (68) agree with those in (67) within a factor of two, and no better agreement could be expected in view of the simplifying assumption made in obtaining (65) from (64). Further, Swain showed that the application of the same treatment to the mutarotation of glucose predicted no observable product term in $[HOAc][OAc^-]$, in agreement with experiment, and the same is true for the depolymerization of dihydroxyacetone,[58] which proceeds by a similar mechanism. On these grounds Swain concluded that the concerted mechanism was of major importance in the iodination of acetone and the mutarotation of glucose, and probably for other reactions showing catalysis by both acids and bases in aqueous solution.

However, it now seems certain that this is not so. In the first place, the agreement between (67) and (68) is deceptive. The factor $10^2[HOAc]$ in the first line of (68) contributes very little to the coefficients of $[HOAc]$ and $[OAc^-]$ in the second line but enters directly

---

[57] The numerical values differ somewhat from those in the original paper of Bell and Jones, which contains a misprint and some arithmetical errors; however, the conclusions remain unchanged.

[58] R. P. Bell and E. C. Baughan, *J. Chem. Soc.*, 1947 (1937).

into the coefficient of [HOAc][OAc⁻]. This factor can therefore be adjusted within wide limits to fit the observed value of the product term. In fact, any coefficient between zero and about 1,000 could be accommodated by the concerted scheme. The approximate agreement found with the observed value of 20 is thus illusory.

In the second place, there is other experimental evidence which speaks strongly against the concerted mechanism. The hydration of acetaldehyde, $CH_3CHO + H_2O \rightarrow CH_3CH(OH)_2$, takes place at a measurable rate and is catalyzed by acids and bases, its mechanism resembling that of the mutarotation of glucose.[59] At low catalyst concentrations the observed velocity expression has the usual form (66), but if the coefficients are interpreted in terms of the concerted mechanism a considerable product term in [HOAc][OAc⁻] is predicted for higher concentrations. Moreover, in this case the prediction can be made within fairly narrow limits, since all the coefficients in (65) are closely defined by the results at low catalyst concentrations. However, measurements at higher concentrations using a thermal method for studying fast reactions[60] revealed no detectable product term even when it ought to have contributed 70 percent of the total reaction velocity. The concerted mechanism can thus be excluded for this reaction.

Finally, some general arguments have been advanced by Bell and Jones (*loc. cit.* [54]) on the consequences of the concerted mechanism for any reaction which shows general catalysis both by acids and by bases in aqueous solution. These arguments are too long to reproduce here, but they lead to the following conclusion for a typical buffer solution composed of an acid HX and its anion X: *either* the product term k [HX][X⁻] must contribute a large part of the observed velocity in dilute buffer solutions *or* the relation $\alpha + \beta = 1$ must hold for the exponents of the Brönsted relations.[61] Neither of these results is found in practice, and we must conclude that the concerted mechanism has no general application to those reactions which are known to exhibit general acid-base catalysis in aqueous solution, although it prob-

[59] R. P. Bell and W. C. E. Higginson, *Proc. Roy. Soc.*, A, **197**, 141 (1949); R. P. Bell and B. de B. Darwent, *Trans. Faraday Soc.*, **46**, 34 (1950); R. P. Bell and M. H. Rand, *Bull. Soc. chim. France*, 115 (1955); R. P. Bell, M. H. Rand, and K. M. A. Wynne-Jones, *Trans. Faraday Soc.*, **52**, 1093 (1956).

[60] R. P. Bell and J. C. Clunie, *Nature*, **167**, 363 (1951); *Proc. Roy. Soc.*, A, **212**, 33 (1952).

[61] These are the exponents in the equations $k_A = G_A K_A^{\alpha}$ and $k_B = G_B(1/K_A)^{\beta}$ which relate catalytic power to acid-base strength and will be dealt with in the next chapter.

ably accounts for the small term in [HOAc][OAc$^-$] observed in the prototropy of acetone.

The best-known cases of prototropic change involve oxygen atoms, which can easily assume either a positive or a negative charge, giving —OH$^+$ or —O$^-$. Conditions are therefore favorable for the consecutive mechanisms, which involve the formation of the free ions HSH$^+$ or S$^-$. The formation of S$^-$ is less likely when the oxygen atom is replaced by a nitrogen atom, and clear evidence for a concerted mechanism has been found for a system of this kind, namely, the interconversion of isomeric methyleneazomethines, RR′CH·N:CR″R‴ ⇌ RR′C:N·CHR″R‴. This evidence does not depend upon the form of the kinetic equations but on a comparison of rates of racemization, deuterium uptake, and isomerization. In the examples chosen the two isomers are of comparable stability, so that their rate of interconversion can be directly measured. In an alcoholic solution of sodium ethoxide all these three rates are initially the same,[62] showing that no free intermediate anion is formed, as would be demanded by the consecutive mechanism for basic catalysis. This reaction constitutes the only one for which the concerted mechanism has been established in a hydroxylic solvent.

In solvents of low dielectric constant the formation of free ions becomes less likely, so that a concerted mechanism may be favored even for reactions which do not follow it in water or similar solvents. In fact, the concerted mechanism was first put forward by Lowry[63] on the basis of observations on the mutarotation of tetramethylglucose in media of low dielectric constant. This reaction was very slow in dry pyridine (possessing no acid properties) or in dry cresol (possessing hardly any basic properties), but was rapid in a mixture of the two solvents or in either solvent when moist, suggesting that both an acid and a base must take part in the reaction.[64] It is difficult to attach any quantitative significance to this result, in view of the drastic changes of medium involved, but the same point is made more strongly by the measurements of Swain and Brown[65] on the same reaction in

[62] C. K. Ingold and C. L. Wilson, *J. Chem. Soc.*, 1493 (1933); 93 (1934); S. K. Hsü, C. K. Ingold, and C. L. Wilson, *ibid.*, 1774 (1935); E. de Salas and C. L. Wilson, *ibid.*, 319 (1938); S. K. Hsü, C. K. Ingold, C. G. Raisin, E. de Salas, and C. L. Wilson, *J. chim. phys.*, **45**, 232 (1948); R. Perez Ossorio and E. D. Hughes, *J. Chem. Soc.*, 426 (1952). For a summary see Ingold, *op. cit.* (52), p. 572.

[63] T. M. Lowry, *J. Chem. Soc.*, 2554 (1927).

[64] E. M. Richards and T. M. Lowry, *J. Chem. Soc.*, 1385 (1925); T. M. Lowry and I. J. Faulkner, *ibid.*, 2883 (1925).

[65] C. G. Swain and J. F. Brown, *J. Am. Chem. Soc.*, **74**, 2534, 2538 (1952).

dilute benzene solutions of amines and phenols. They found that the reaction was kinetically of the third order, the velocity being proportional to the product of the concentrations of phenol, amine, and tetramethylglucose, as expected from Equation (64). It is also of great interest that 2-hydroxypyridine is a powerful specific catalyst for the mutarotation: at a concentration of 0.001 M it is 7,000 times as effective as a mixture of 0.001 M pyridine and 0.001 M phenol, though it is only one ten-thousandth as strong a base as pyridine and one one-hundredth as strong an acid as phenol. Since, further, the velocity is proportional to the first power of the concentration of 2-hydroxypyridine, it is clear that the operation of the concerted mechanism is facilitated by the presence of an acidic and a basic group in the same catalyst molecule. Similarly, carboxylic acids are much more effective catalysts than phenols of comparable strength, probably because the carboxyl group can act simultaneously as an acid and as a base,[66] i.e.,

This kind of catalysis has been termed *polyfunctional*, and may be responsible for the action of enzymes.

However, it must not be concluded that acid-base catalysis in solvents of low dielectric constant necessarily involves a concerted process. Such a process cannot operate when catalysis is effected by a single acid or base present in an aprotic solvent, and there are many examples of this,[67] including typical prototropic reactions such as the halogenation of acetone,[68] the racemization and inversion of optically active ketones,[69] and the mutarotation of nitrocamphor.[70] Moreover, in the isomerization of mesityl oxide oxalic ester in chlorobenzene,[71] which depends kinetically on the interconversion of two isomeric enols, the velocity in a solution containing both an amine and an acid is no

---

[66] See also work by Eastham and his collaborators (*loc. cit.* [17]) on the mutarotation of tetramethylglucose in nitromethane.

[67] For references see Bell, *op. cit.* (2), pp. 103–107.

[68] R. P. Bell and A. D. S. Tantram, *J. Chem. Soc.*, 370 (1948).

[69] R. P. Bell and E. F. Caldin, *J. Chem. Soc.*, 382 (1938); R. P. Bell, O. M. Lidwell, and J. Wright, *ibid.*, 1861 (1938).

[70] R. P. Bell and J. A. Sherred, *J. Chem. Soc.*, 1202 (1940).

[71] R. P. Bell and S. M. Rybicka, *J. Chem. Soc.*, 24 (1947).

greater than the sum of the velocities for the two catalysts separately, in contrast to the behavior found by Swain for the mutarotation reaction.

The status of the concerted mechanism has been discussed at some length because unduly dogmatic statements have been made from time to time both for and against its validity.   As will have been seen, there is good evidence that it operates in some reactions, especially in non-aqueous solvents, but it appears to be of minor importance for most reactions in water.   This conclusion has recently been confirmed by Swain and his collaborators[72] on the basis of the hydrogen isotope effects found in a number of reactions.

[72] C. G. Swain, A. J. DiMilo, and J. P. Cordner, *J. Am. Chem. Soc.*, **80**, 5983 (1958).

CHAPTER X

Rates, Equilibria, and Structures in Acid-Base Reactions

THIS chapter will be concerned mainly with the relation between the equilibrium constants of acid-base reactions and their forward and reverse rates. Relations between equilibrium constants and structure have already been considered in Chapter VI, so that the present discussion also implies relations between rates and structure. Moreover, there are many cases in which rates are easier to measure (though more difficult to interpret) than equilibria and can be compared directly with structures. We shall first consider the general basis and experimental evidence for this type of relation, followed by its molecular interpretation, with special reference to exceptional cases.

The so-called *Brönsted relation* was proposed by Brönsted and Pedersen[1] in 1924 on the basis of their experimental work on the decomposition of nitramide. It relates the effectiveness of a catalyst to its acid-base strength, having the form

$$k_A = G_A K^\alpha, \qquad k_B = G_B (1/K)^\beta \tag{69}$$

where k_A and k_B are the catalytic constants for acid and base catalysis and K the conventional strength of the acid A, or of the acid corresponding to the base B. G_A and α are constants for a series of similar catalysts but depend on the nature of the reaction and also on the solvent and the temperature. Analogous statements hold for G_B and β. The exponents α and β are always positive and less than unity.

We have seen in the last chapter that many catalyzed reactions are determined kinetically by a single acid-base reaction between the catalyst and the substrate, and when this is so k_A or k_B in Equation (69) is just the second-order velocity constant for this reaction. The interpretation is not quite so simple when the reaction involves two consecutive proton transfers, of which the first is effectively at equilibrium. Thus for acid catalysis we may have

[1] J. N. Brönsted and K. J. Pedersen, *Z. physikal. Chem.*, **108**, 185 (1924).

$$\text{HS} + \sum \text{A}_i \rightleftharpoons \text{HSH}^+ + \sum \text{B}_i \text{ (equilibrium)}$$

$$\text{HSH}^+ + \sum \text{B}_i \underset{k_2}{\rightarrow} \text{SH} + \sum \text{A}_i$$

where $k_2 = \sum \pi_i[\text{B}_i]$. The observed reaction velocity is then given by

$$v = [\text{HSH}^+] \sum \pi_i[\text{B}_i] = [\text{HS}] \sum \pi_i[\text{A}_i]K_i' \qquad (70)$$

where K_i is the equilibrium constant $[\text{B}_i][\text{HSH}^+]/[\text{A}_i][\text{HS}]$, related to the conventional strength K_i of the acid A_i by $K_i' = K_i/K_{\text{HSH}}$. The observed catalytic constant thus becomes

$$k_\text{A}^i = \pi_i K_i/K_{\text{HSH}}. \qquad (71)$$

Now the second stage of the reaction is equivalent to a one-stage basic catalysis of the substrate HSH^+, for which we can write the usual type of Brönsted relation

$$\pi_i = G(1/K_i)^\beta \qquad (72)$$

giving on substitution in (71)

$$k_\text{A}^i = \frac{G}{K_{\text{HSH}}} K_i^{1-\beta}. \qquad (73)$$

Since $\beta < 1$, this is equivalent to (69), and it is thus understandable that the same type of relation applies to prototropic reactions whether or not there is a pre-equilibrium with the catalyst.

Although the Brönsted relation was devised for catalyzed reactions, we should also expect it to hold for the velocities of acid-base reactions determined by the methods described in Chapter VIII. This is probably the case, but there are very few investigations which provide data for a series of similar acids or bases. Table 16 hows the results obtained by Lewis and Seaborg[2] for the neutralization of the anion of *p-p'-p''*-trinitrotriphenylmethane by a number of weak acids in alcohol solution at −60°C. It does not appear that any considerable part of the reaction velocity is due to hydrogen ions. This point was not really tested by Lewis and Seaborg but was established by Caldin and Long for a similar reaction with trinitrotoluene.[3] On the other hand, the solvent alcohol reacts at an appreciable rate with the anion, and the constants for the other acids have been corrected by subtracting this rate. Acid strengths in alcohol at −60° are not available, and Table 16 contains for comparison their pK values in water at 25°C;

[2] G. N. Lewis and G. T. Seaborg, *J. Am. Chem. Soc.*, **61**, 1894 (1939).

[3] E. F. Caldin and G. Long, *Proc. Roy. Soc.*, A, **228**, 263 (1955).

these are likely to be a rough measure of their strengths in any solvent. There is a clear parallelism between the last two columns of the table, corresponding to a Brönsted relation with an exponent of about 0.4. The individual deviations are probably little greater than the experimental uncertainty, especially for the weaker acids, where the velocities are only slightly greater than those in the pure solvent.

Values have also been reported for the rate of reaction of hydrogen ions with the anions of eight substituted phenylglyoxylic acids,[4] using the polarographic method previously described (p. 114). In this case

TABLE 16.—NEUTRALIZATION OF ANION OF p, p', p''-TRINITROTRIPHENYL-METHANE BY ACIDS AT $-60°C$

Velocity constant k in l. mole^{-1} sec.$^{-1}$

Acid	pK in water	k (corrected)
Monochloroacetic	2.80	30
Furoic	3.15	10
α-Naphthoic	3.70	5.2
Lactic	3.85	3.1
Benzoic	4.15	5.0
Acetic	4.75	2.9
p-Nitrophenol	7.10	0.9
2,4-Dichlorophenol	7.55	0.8
Hydrocyanic	9.15	0.05
Boric	9.20	0.01
β-Naphthol	9.60	0.03
Phenol	9.85	0.01

there appears to be no relation between the rate and the dissociation constant of the acid. However, the dissociation constants involved vary by a factor of less than three. Moreover, the velocity constants are so high ($\sim 10^{11}$ l./mole sec.) that they are probably determined by the encounter rate of the ions rather than by factors of a more chemical nature.

As already mentioned, most of the experimental evidence for the Brönsted relation comes from studies of catalysis; in fact, provided that a series of closely similar acids or bases is studied, this type of relation has been found to hold with fair accuracy in all reactions investigated. (We shall return later to the interesting question of what constitutes "closely similar" in this context.) The earlier evidence on this point has been summarized[5] and will not be repeated

[4] M. S. Wheatley, *Experientia*, **12**, 339 (1956).
[5] R. P. Bell, *Acid-Base Catalysis* (Oxford, 1941), ch. v and pp. 107–111.

here.   One later investigation is of interest in view of the large number of catalysts investigated.   The reaction

$$CH_3CH(OH)_2 \rightarrow CH_3CHO + H_2O$$

goes almost to completion in 92.5 percent aqueous acetone and can be conveniently studied by a dilatometric method.[6]   It is catalyzed both by acids and by bases, the former being particularly studied.   The catalysts used included 45 carboxylic acids and phenols with strengths in water ranging over ten powers of ten.   The observed catalytic constants follow a Brönsted relation with an exponent of 0.54, the maximum logarithmic deviation being 0.3 and the mean deviation 0.1. Catalysts of other types showed larger deviations and will be discussed later in this chapter.

The simple expressions in (69) are often modified by including a *statistical correction*, which is best explained by means of an example. Suppose that we have as catalyst a carboxylic acid $CH_3(CH_2)_nCO_2H$ whose catalytic effect is given correctly by Equation (69), and that we wish to compare it with a dicarboxylic acid $CO_2H(CH_2)_nCO_2H$, where n is so great that the effect of the carboxyl groups upon one another is negligible.   The tendency of the carboxyl groups to lose a proton will be essentially the same in the two acids, but the first dissociation constant of the dibasic acid (K') will be twice as great as that of the monobasic acid (K), since the ion $CO_2H(CH_2)_nCO_2^-$ can be formed by losing a proton from either end of the chain (see Chapter VII, p. 98).   Similarly, the catalytic constant of the dibasic acid (k_A') will be twice that of the monobasic acid (k_A), since in the former case the substrate can approach either end of the catalyst molecule. This is not, however, what is predicted by Equation (69) as it stands, which gives

$$k_A'/k_A = (K'/K)^\alpha = 2^\alpha.$$

The correct result is obtained if we reckon both the dissociation constant and the catalytic power *per carboxyl group*, giving

$$\tfrac{1}{2}k_A' = G_A(\tfrac{1}{2}K')^\alpha = G_A K^\alpha = k_A.$$

A similar problem arises if we compare the two acids $CO_2H(CH_2)_nCO_2^-$ (I) and $CO_2H(CH_2)_nCO_2CH_3$ (II), where n is again large.   In this case the tendency to lose a proton from the carboxyl group (and hence the catalytic power) will be the same for the two acids.   On the other hand, the dissociation constant of (I) will be only half that of (II),

[6] R. P. Bell and W. C. E. Higginson, *Proc. Roy. Soc.*, A, **197**, 141 (1949).

since the conjugate base $CO_2^-(CH_2)_nCO_2^-$ has two equivalent groups to which a proton can be added, whereas $CO_2^-(CH_2)_nCO_2CH_3$ has only one such point. Here again the straightforward use of Equation (69) leads to an incorrect prediction, and in order to obtain the correct result it is necessary to multiply the observed dissociation constant of (I) by two before inserting it in the equation.

These arguments can easily be generalized. Thus if we have an acid-base pair A—B in which A has p dissociable protons bound equally firmly and B has q equivalent points at which a proton can be attached, then the catalytic power of A is related to its observed dissociation constant by the equation

$$k_A/p = G_A(qK/p)^\alpha. \tag{74}$$

A similar treatment for base catalysis by B gives

$$k_B/q = G_B(p/qK)^\beta. \tag{75}$$

Analogous but more complicated equations can be developed[7] for the case in which the various protons or points of attachment are not all equivalent.

Although the idea of a statistical correction is undoubtedly correct in principle, it is of very limited application in practice. Almost the only clear-cut experimental evidence in support of it is the catalysis of the nitramide decomposition by the anions of polycarboxylic acids,[8] where the omission of the correction would considerably worsen the agreement with experiment. There are no other extensive investigations of polycarboxylic acids, and it is doubtful whether (74) and (75) can be justifiably applied to most other classes of catalysts. For example, for the pair $H_2PO_4^-$—HPO_4^{2-} we have formally $p = 2$, $q = 3$, but the two protons and the three equivalent oxygen atoms are now so close together that they can hardly be regarded as independent. A more extreme case is the ion NH_4^+ ($p = 4$) where the hydrogen atoms are so close together that the chance of proton transfer on collision is probably less than four times the chance for an analogous ion containing only one hydrogen atom. In any case the concept of an "analogous ion" is a somewhat nebulous one, since in a system of this kind it is impossible to substitute some of the hydrogens by other

---

[7] F. H. Westheimer, *J. Org. Chem.*, **2**, 431 (1938).

[8] Brönsted and Pedersen, *loc. cit.* (1). This paper also contains the first suggestion of the statistical correction, though in an incomplete form. The correct treatment was first given by J. N. Brönsted, *Chem. Rev.*, **5**, 322 (1928). The application to the decomposition of nitramide is illustrated by Bell, *op. cit.* (5), table XV, p. 86.

groups without radically affecting the nature of the remaining hydrogens. For this reason some authors have preferred to introduce the factor p only when the protons are attached to p different atoms, i.e., $p = 1$ for NH_4^+, but $p = 2$ for hydrogen peroxide H—O—O—H, or the hydrazinium ion $H_3\overset{+}{N}\cdot\overset{+}{N}H_3$.

Similar problems arise in comparing the reactivity of different substrates. For example, when reactions (involving the methyl group) of the ketones CH_3COCH_3 and $C_6H_5COCH_3$ are compared, it is clearly correct to take into account the number of methyl groups. On the other hand, it is doubtful whether there is much quantitative significance in attaching statistical factors of 3, 2, and 1 to a series such as $C_6H_5COCH_3$, $C_6H_5COCH_2X$, and $C_6H_5COCHX_2$, where X may be, for example, an alkyl group or a halogen atom.

Fortunately, it is often immaterial whether or not these statistical corrections are taken into account. This is obviously so when we are considering a series of substances having the same values of p and q (e.g., a series of monocarboxylic acids). Moreover, since the effect on the predicted rate of applying the statistical correction rarely exceeds a factor of two, it can safely be neglected when considering much larger effects, amounting perhaps to several powers of ten. In view of the ambiguities mentioned above we shall frequently omit the statistical correction in the remainder of this chapter.

So far we have considered only the effect of varying the catalyst in a given reaction, but since the processes concerned are acid-base reactions between catalyst and substrate the distinction between these two reactants is somewhat artificial. We might expect also to find a *relation between the reaction velocity and the acid-base strength of the substrate* when the catalyst remains the same and a series of similar substrates is investigated. The effect upon the velocity of substituents in the substrate usually parallels the effect which they would be expected to have upon its acid-base strength, but it is rarely possible to make a quantitative test, since the substrates concerned are usually such weak acids or bases that their strengths are not directly measurable. There is, however, a good deal of information for compounds containing the group

$$\diagdown \!\!\!\!\underset{\diagup}{C}H\cdot CO\!\!-\!\!,$$

which are frequently sufficiently strong acids for the direct measurement of pK. Their halogenation is catalyzed by bases, and the rate of the "spontaneous" reaction represents that of the process

$$\text{CH·CO}- + H_2O \rightarrow \ \text{C:C(O}^-)- + H_3O^+.$$

Table 17 contains rate and equilibrium data for a number of these compounds, together with some others in which the activating group

TABLE 17.—RATE AND EQUILIBRIUM DATA FOR
CARBON ACIDS AT 25°C IN WATER

$$HB \underset{k_2}{\overset{k_1}{\rightleftharpoons}} H^+ + B^-, \ K_a = k_1/k_2$$

No.	Compound	K_a*	k_1, sec.$^{-1}$	k_2 l./mole/sec.
1	CH_3NO_2	6.1×10^{-11}	4.3×10^{-8}	6.8×10^2
2	$C_2H_5NO_2$	2.5×10^{-9}	3.7×10^{-8}	1.5×10
3	$CH_3CHClNO_2$	$<10^{-7}$	5.7×10^{-7}	—
4	$C_2H_5O_2CCH_2NO_2$	1.5×10^{-6}	6.3×10^{-3}	4.2×10^3
5	$CH_3COCH_2NO_2$	8.0×10^{-6}	3.7×10^{-2}	3.8×10^3
6	$CH_2(NO_2)_2$	2.7×10^{-4}	(8.3×10^{-1})†	3.2×10^3
7	CH_2BrNO_2	$\cdots$	1.3×10^{-3}	—
8	$CH(NO_2)_3$	Strong	—	—
9	CH_3COCH_3	10^{-20}	4.7×10^{-10}	5×10^{10}
10	CH_3COCH_2Cl	3×10^{-17}	5.5×10^{-8}	1.7×10^9
11	$CH_3COCHCl_2$	10^{-15}	7.3×10^{-7}	7×10^8
12	$CH_3COCH_2CO_2C_2H_5$	2.1×10^{-11}	1.2×10^{-3}	5.8×10^7
13	$CH_3COCHC_2H_5CO_2C_2H_5$	2×10^{-13}	7.5×10^{-6}	3.8×10^7
14	$CH_3COCHBrCO_2C_2H_5$	$\cdots$	6.0×10^{-3}	—
15	$CH_3COCH_2COCH_3$	1.0×10^{-9}	1.7×10^{-2}	1.7×10^7
16	$CH_3COCHCH_3COCH_3$	1.0×10^{-11}	8×10^{-5}	8×10^6
17	$CH_3COCHBrCOCH_3$	1×10^{-7}	2.3×10^{-2}	2.3×10^5
18	$CH_3COCH_2COC_6H_5$	4×10^{-10}	1.1×10^{-2}	2.7×10^7
19	$CH_3COCHBrCOC_6H_5$	$\cdots$	5.5×10^{-3}	—
20	$CH_3COCH_2COCF_3$	2×10^{-5}	1.5×10^{-2}	7.5×10^2
21	$C_6H_5COCH_2COCF_3$	1.5×10^{-7}	8.3×10^{-3}	5.5×10^4
22	$C_6H_5COCH_2NC_5H_5^+$	3.1×10^{-11}	—	—
23	S (ring) $\ COCH_2COCF_3$	8.0×10^{-7}	1.0×10^{-2}	1.2×10^4
24	$O=$ (ring) $H \ CO_2C_2H_5$	3×10^{-11}	2.3×10^{-3}	8×10^7
25	$O=$ (ring) $H \ CO_2C_2H_5$	1.1×10^{-11}	9.7×10^{-6}	3×10^6
26	$O=$ (ring) $COCH_3$	8.1×10^{-11}	—	—
27	$O=$ (ring) $COCH_3$	1.5×10^{-8}	—	—
28	$CH_2(CHO)_2$	1×10^{-5}	—	—

TABLE 17.—(*Continued*)

No.	Compound	K^*	k_1, sec.$^{-1}$	k_2, l./mole/sec.
29	CH_3COCH_2CHO	1.2×10^{-6}	—	—
30	$CH(COCH_3)_3$	1.4×10^{-6}	—	—
31	$CH_3COCHCH_3SO_2C_2H_5$	$\cdots$	1.8×10^{-4}	—
32	$CH_3COCH_2CO_2CH_3$	1×10^{-10}	$(3.3 \times 10^{-2})\ddagger$	3×10^8
33	$CH_3SO_2CH_3$	(10^{-23})	$(3 \times 10^{-12})\S$	—
34	$CH_3SO_2CH_2SO_2CH_3$	1×10^{-14}	—	—
35	$CH(SO_2CH_3)_3$	Strong	—	—
36	$CH_3SO_2CH(COCH_3)_2$	2×10^{-5}	—	—
37	CH_3CN	(10^{-25})	7×10^{-14}	—
38	$CH_2(CN)_2$	6.5×10^{-12}	1.5×10^{-2}	2.3×10^9
39	$C_2H_5O_2CCH_2CN$	$<10^{-9}$	1.2×10^{-3}	—
40	$CH(CN)_3$	Strong	—	—
41	$CH_3CO_2C_2H_5$	$(10^{-24.5})$	—	—
42	$CH_2(CO_2C_2H_5)_2$	5×10^{-14}	2.5×10^{-5}	5×10^8
43	$CHBr(CO_2C_2H_5)_2$	$\cdots$	3.0×10^{-4}	—
44	$CHC_2H_5(CO_2C_2H_5)_2$	10^{-15}	3×10^{-7}	3×10^8
45	CH_3CO_2H	(10^{-24})	3×10^{-13}	—
46	$CH_2(CO_2H)_2$	$\cdots$	$(2.8 \times 10^{-3})\dagger$	—
47	CH_3COCH_2COOH	$\cdots$	1.2×10^{-1}	—
48	CH_3CONH_2	(10^{-25})	$(3 \times 10^{-14})\S$	—

Source: The compilation by R. G. Pearson and R. L. Dillon, *J. Am. Chem. Soc.*, 75, 2439 (1953), where references are given.

* This is the gross acid constant uncorrected for enol content.

† Estimated from data at 0° taking E_a as 18 kcal.

‡ Estimated from compounds 16 and 31.

§ Estimated from rate of deuterium exchange catalyzed by hydroxide ion assuming same ratio for $k(H_2O)/k(OH)$ as for acetone.

is —CN or —NO₂ rather than —CO—. For some of the compounds the rate of ionization has been determined by measuring hydrogen isotope exchange rather than halogenation.

Figure 11 shows a plot of log k_1 against pK for the seventeen ketonic substances in Table 17 whose acid strengths are approximately known. There is clearly an approximate parallelism between the two quantities, but the individual deviations for some substances are certainly larger than the experimental uncertainties. Since $K = k_1/k_2$, a similar plot would be obtained for log k_2 against pK. The slope of the line in Figure 11 is less than unity throughout, but it shows definite signs of curvature. The range of acid strengths covered (about 10^{15}) is of course much greater than can be investigated for a series of similar catalysts.

We shall now consider the experimental evidence for *deviations from the Brönsted relation,* i.e., how "similar" do a series of substances have to be in order that relations like (69) shall be approximately obeyed? It is relevant here to consider not only variations in catalyst for a given reaction (which have usually been carried out on a somewhat conservative basis), but also variations of substrate and the use of

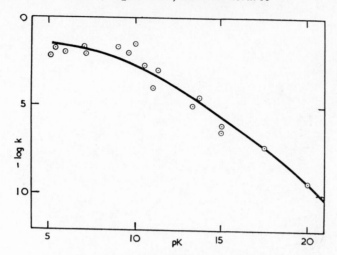

Fig. 11.—Rate and equilibrium constants for the
ionization of ketonic substances.

noncatalytic methods for studying acid-base reactions. It is instructive to compare the rates of the forward and the reverse reactions of the type

$$\text{HX}(+\text{H}_2\text{O}) \underset{k_2}{\overset{k_1}{\rightleftharpoons}} \text{H}_3\text{O}^+ + \text{X}^-$$

for four acids with pK in the range 9 to 10, and these are given in Table 18. The values for the first two were obtained from their rates of bromination catalyzed by the solvent, the third from measurements of proton magnetic resonance, and the fourth from measurements of dielectric loss. Although these four acids have approximately the same strength, the rates of their proton-transfer reactions vary by some eight powers of ten. Many examples of such deviations can be

TABLE 18.—RATES OF DISSOCIATION OF WEAK ACIDS

$$\text{Acid} (+\text{H}_2\text{O}) \underset{k_2}{\overset{k_1}{\rightleftharpoons}} \text{Base} + \text{H}_3\text{O}^+.$$

Acid	pK	$\log k_1$	$\log k_2$
Nitromethane	10.2	−7.4	2.8
Benzoylacetone	9.6	−2.1	7.5
Trimethylammonium ion	9.8	+1.1	10.9
Boric acid	9.1	+1.0	10.1

found; for example, the data for the compounds in Table 17 containing nitro and cyano groups do not fall on the line drawn in Figure 10 for the substituted ketones.

In work on catalyzed reactions the catalysts studied have nearly always belonged to a few restricted classes of compounds. Thus in acid catalysis there is little information outside the carboxylic acids and the phenols. The substances in Table 18 which give slow reactions are pseudo acids (in the sense that their ionization involves a marked electronic rearrangement) and it might be expected that this class of substance would be an ineffective acid catalyst. Similarly, since the reverse reactions in Table 18 are also slow for pseudo acids, the anions derived from them should be abnormally ineffective in basic catalysis. These predictions were made by Brönsted and Pedersen[9] in their first paper on the Brönsted relation, and they did in fact show that in the decomposition of nitramide the anions of nitrourethane and nitramide were respectively 6 and 130 times less effective than carboxylate anions of equal basic strength. Similar behavior has been found recently[10] for acid catalysis in the reaction

$$CH_3CH(OH)_2 \rightarrow CH_3CHO + H_2O.$$

A large number of carboxylic acids and phenols obeyed the Brönsted relation, but seven pseudo acids were much less effective catalysts, as shown in Table 19. The table also shows that a second class of acids showed large positive deviations, which will be discussed later in this chapter. It is likely that similar positive and negative deviations would be observed in many other reactions if a sufficiently wide range of catalysts was investigated.

We now turn to the *molecular interpretation of the Brönsted relation* and of deviations from it. Consider the general acid-base reaction

$$A_1 + B_2 \underset{\pi_{2,1}}{\overset{\pi_{1,2}}{\rightleftharpoons}} B_1 + A_2 \tag{76}$$

where K_1 and K_2 are the conventional strengths of A_1—B_1 and A_2—B_2, and the equilibrium constant of (76) is $K = K_1/K_2$. Suppose first that A_2—B_2 is kept constant and that we make a small variation in A_1—B_1, for example, by chemical substitution. If this variation in-

---

[9] Brönsted and Pedersen, *loc. cit.* (1). This paper, although the first to put forward the Brönsted relation, contains a remarkably complete discussion of the limitations of this type of relation and of the structural information which might be obtained by the study of such deviations.

[10] Bell and Higginson, *loc. cit.* (6); R. P. Bell and R. G. Pearson, *J. Chem. Soc.*, 3443 (1953).

TABLE 19.—DEVIATIONS FROM THE BRÖNSTED RELATION IN THE
REACTION $CH_3CH(OH)_2 \rightarrow CH_3CHO + H_2O$

Negative deviations		Positive deviations	
Catalyst	Logarithmic deviation	Catalyst	Logarithmic deviation
Benzoylacetone enol	-1.4	Benzophenone oxime	$+1.2$
1,3-Diketo-5-dimethyl-		Acetophenone oxime	$+1.4$
cyclohexane enol		Diethyl ketoxime	$+2.1$
(dimedone)	-1.1	Chloral hydrate	$+0.7$
Nitromethane	-1.4	Water	$+1.6$
l-Nitropropane	-1.5		
Nitroethane	-1.7		
2-Nitropropane	-1.9		
Ethylenedinitramine	-1.2		

creases the acid strength of A_1 (and hence decreases the basic strength
of B_1), it is reasonable to suppose that $\pi_{1,2}$ will increase and $\pi_{2,1}$ will
decrease. However, since A_2—B_2 remains the same, we must have

$$\{\partial \log (\pi_{1,2}/\pi_{2,1})\}_2 = (\partial \log K)_2 = \alpha \log K_1$$

which is satisfied by writing

$$(\partial \log \pi_{1,2})_2 = \alpha_1 \, d \log K_1,$$
$$(\partial \log \pi_{2,1})_2 = -(1 - \alpha_1)d \log K_1, \tag{77}$$

where α_1 is positive and less than unity. Exactly analogous arguments
apply to the case in which A_1—B_1 is held constant and A_2—B_2 varies,
and the general expressions covering variations of both pairs are

$$d \log \pi_{1,2} = \alpha_1 d \log K_1 - (1 - \alpha_2)d \log K_2,$$
$$d \log \pi_{2,1} = \alpha_2 d \log K_2 - (1 - \alpha_1)d \log K_1, \tag{78}$$

with both α_1 and α_2 positive and less than unity, but not necessarily
equal. If α_1 and α_2 can be assumed constant over a certain range of
velocities and equilibrium constants, then (78) can be integrated,
giving

$$\pi_{1,2} = GK_1^{\alpha_1}(1/K_2)^{1-\alpha_2}, \qquad \pi_{2,1} = GK_2^{\alpha_2}(1/K_1)^{1-\alpha_1}, \tag{79}$$

equivalent to the usual form of relation (69). In this formulation the
requirement that the variations should be among series of similar
molecules is concealed in the assumption, implicit in (77), that the
velocity is a unique function of the acid strength.

Since the original formulation of the Brönsted relation a number of analogous *linear free energy relationships* have been found to hold between the rates or equilibrium constants, and the Brönsted relation could now be regarded as a special case of the *Hammett equation*, according to which the effect of a substituent on the reactivity of a compound can be represented by the product of two factors, one of which (σ) is characteristic of the substituent, and the other (ρ) is a measure of the sensitivity to substituent influences of the reaction being considered.[11] However, the Hammett relation was originally devised to deal only with benzene derivatives substituted in the meta or para positions,[12] and although the Brönsted relation applies only to the limited class of acid-base reactions it usually covers a wider range of compounds; for example, both aromatic and aliphatic compounds are commonly covered by the same relation. It is therefore worth while to seek a molecular interpretation applicable to this particular class of reaction.

An interpretation in terms of *molecular potential—energy curves* was advanced almost simultaneously by Horiuti and Polanyi[13] and by Bell,[14] the two treatments corresponding respectively to a covalent and an ionic formulation. The former is probably closer to reality, and will be followed here.

A proton transfer is a special case of the general class of reaction $XZ + Y \rightarrow X + ZY$. The course of such a reaction is commonly depicted by an energy diagram such as the full line in Figure 12, in which the distance between the lowest and the highest points represents the activation energy of the reaction. However, this picture needs a number of qualifications and amplifications. Three co-ordinates are necessary to specify the distances between X, Y, and Z, so that the complete energy diagram is a surface in four dimensions. If we make the assumption (reasonable, but not necessarily correct) that we need consider only configurations in which X, Y, and Z are in a straight line, then the number of co-ordinates can be reduced by one and the energies now lie on a three-dimensional surface. The most probable path of the system during reaction can be represented by a line on the

[11] For a recent review of the Hammett equation see H. H. Jaffé, *Chem Rev.*, **53**, 191 (1953). Further refinements have been introduced by R. W. Taft, *J. Am. Chem. Soc.*, **80**, 2436 (1958).

[12] More recently a similar treatment has been applied to a number of reactions in the aliphatic series; see R. W. Taft, *J. Am. Chem. Soc.*, **74**, 2729, 3120 (1952); **75**, 4231, 4538 (1953); R. W. Taft and M. M. Kreevoy, *ibid.*, **79**, 4011 (1957); S. S. Biechler and R. W. Taft, *ibid.*, **79**, 4927 (1957); W. A. Pavelich and R. W. Taft, *ibid.*, **79**, 4935 (1957).

[13] J. Horiuti and M. Polanyi, *Acta Physicochim. U.R.S.S.*, **2**, 505 (1935).

[14] R. P. Bell, *Proc. Roy. Soc.*, A, **154**, 414 (1936).

surface which follows the lowest possible energy contours between the the initial and the final state, so that a two-dimensional diagram like Figure 12 represents a section (though not a plane section) of the energy surface.

In general all three distances XZ, ZY, and XY will change during the important stages of the reaction, so that the abscissa in Figure 12 (the so-called "reaction co-ordinate") is not related simply to the geometry of the system. However, in the particular case of proton transfers $(Z = H^+)$ the position is simpler. Since the proton has no

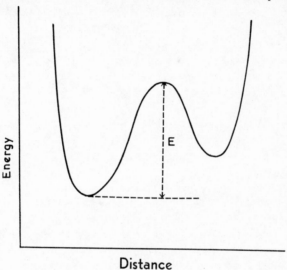

FIG. 12.—Energy diagram for a proton-transfer reaction.

attendant sheath of electrons, the repulsions between X and H and between Y and H can be neglected. The only important repulsion term is that between X and Y, and since these are always considerably heavier than H it is a good approximation to picture the reaction process as the movement of the proton between two centers X and Y which remain stationary at a fixed distance apart. The original four-dimensional problem is thus reduced to a two-dimensional one, and the reaction co-ordinate has a simple significance, namely, the distance of the proton from either X or Y.

The energy diagram can now be amplified and made more specific, as shown in Figure 13.[15] The two heavy curves represent the energies

[15] Zero-point energies have been omitted in this diagram and in Figures 14 and 15, as they do not affect the arguments of this chapter. A more detailed discussion of the energy diagram is given by Bell, *op. cit.* (5), pp. 154–167.

of the two separate systems XH + Y and X + YH as a function of the distances X − H and Y − H. The relative positions of the two curves are chosen so that the vertical distance between the two minima is equal to the energy change in the reaction. The energy of the transition state is given approximately by the point of intersection of the two curves. Its true position is a little lower, as indicated by the broken line, because of resonance between the two valency states, but there are theoretical reasons for believing that this resonance lowering is small in reactions involving a transfer of charge.[16] The point of

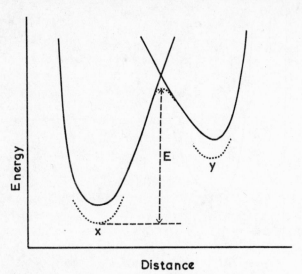

Fig. 13.—More detailed energy diagram for a proton-transfer reaction.

intersection is lowered if the two curves are moved closer together horizontally, but this does not necessarily imply a reduction in the energy of activation, since energy must be expended against forces of repulsion in bringing X and Y together. The minimum activation energy will be achieved by some compromise between these two factors, and the minima of the full curves in Figure 13 represent energies somewhat higher than those corresponding to infinite separation in the systems XH + Y and X + HY. The original energy levels are indicated in the figure by the broken curves x and y. If we take into account all these factors, the actual activation energy for reaction from left to right is that given by the vertical line E in the figure.

[16] R. A. Ogg and M. Polanyi, *Trans. Faraday Soc.*, **31**, 604, 1375 (1935); M. G. Evans and M. Polanyi, *ibid.*, **34**, 11 (1938).

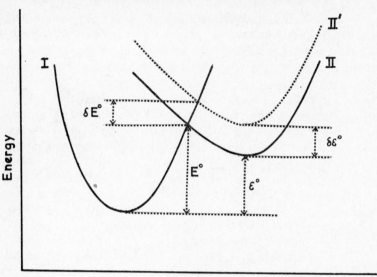

Distance

FIG. 14.—Molecular basis for the Brönsted relation.

It can be shown[17] that this kind of picture is consistent with the observed activation energies of catalyzed reactions, but, as is usual with this kind of calculation, no quantitative predictions are possible. It can, however, be used to obtain a reasonable basis for the Brönsted relation, as shown in Figure 14, in which the resonance energy lowering has been omitted for the sake of clarity; the energy needed to overcome repulsion has also been neglected, since this will be the same for any series of similar reactions. As a concrete example, curve I may be taken to represent SH + B, where SH is a substrate and B a basic catalyst, while curve II represents the reaction products S$^-$ + BH$^+$. The activation energy is then E^0, and the energy change in the reaction ϵ^0. Now suppose that the basic catalyst is modified slightly by the introduction of a substituent, producing a slightly weaker base. The simplest way in which this can be represented in the diagram is to replace curve II by II$'$, which has the same shape and position along the distance axis but is displaced vertically in the direction of higher energy. The consequent changes in E^0 and ϵ^0 are shown in the diagram as δE^0 and $\delta\epsilon^0$, and it is clear from the geometry of the figure that

$$\delta E^0 = \frac{s_1}{s_1 + s_2}\, \delta\epsilon^0 = \beta\delta\epsilon^0 \qquad (80)$$

[17] R. P. Bell and O. M. Lidwell, *Proc. Roy. Soc.*, A, **176**, 114 (1940).

where s_1 and s_2 are the slopes of the two curves at the point of inter-section, both reckoned as positive.

Equation (80) is clearly closely related to (77) and (78). In fact, for the present example the latter could be written as

$$(\delta G^{\ddagger})_{SH} = \beta \delta G_{BH} \tag{81}$$

where $G^{\ddagger}$ is the free energy of activation and G_{BH} the standard free energy of the acid-base pair BH^{+}—B relative to any standard acid-base system. The problem of relating (80) and (81) is the same as was considered in Chapter V in connection with molecular models and thermodynamic quantities. Energy diagrams such as Figures 13 and 14 take no account of thermal motions and are strictly appropriate only at absolute zero. At a finite temperature δG and δH will both differ from $\delta \epsilon^0$. Similarly, $\delta G^{\ddagger}$ and $\delta H^{\ddagger}$ will both differ from δE^0. Thus although at first sight Equation (80) might seem to imply a relation between observed activation energies and enthalpy changes, it could equally well be regarded as relating observed velocity constants (exp. $-G^{\ddagger}/RT$) to observed equilibrium constants (exp. $-G/RT$). We saw in Chapter V that there was some justification for regarding free energies rather than enthalpies as being closely related to molecu-lar models, and just the same arguments suggest that the relation be-tween reaction velocities and equilibrium constants may be simpler than that between observed activation energies and enthalpy changes.[18] There is a certain amount of experimental support for this view,[19] but there are few reactions in which accurate activation energies are avail-able for a range of catalysts, so that the comparison between rates and equilibrium constants at a given temperature is usually the only one possible in practice.

Figure 14 implies that a change in the strength of the catalyst or sub-strate can be represented by a vertical displacement of the energy curves, without any change of shape. It is likely that this assumption is too restrictive, even for a series of substances with very similar struc-tures, since any change in the energy of a bond is usually accompanied by a change in the shape of the whole energy curve, including the curvature at the minimum (i.e., the fundamental frequency). How-ever, as long as the shape is a unique and continuous function of the strength, it is easily shown that relations of the form of (78) will still

[18] M. G. Evans and M. Polanyi, *Trans. Faraday Soc.*, **32**, 1333 (1936).

[19] K. J. Pedersen, *J. Phys. Chem.*, **38**, 501 (1934); G. F. Smith, *J. Chem. Soc.*, 1744 (1934); G. F. Smith and M. Smith, *ibid.*, 1413 (1937); E. C. Baughan and R. P. Bell, *Proc. Roy. Soc.*, A, **158**, 464 (1937). For a summary see Bell, *op. cit.* (5), table XXIII, p. 176.

hold, and that they can be integrated over a range of acid strengths to give (79). While (80) and (81) imply the same value for α_1 and α_2 in (78) and (79), both being related to the slopes of the energy curves at their point of intersection, this equality is no longer predicted if the curves undergo changes in shape as well as in position.

The best evidence for this change in shape comes from the variation in the observed values of α and β. It is rarely possible in practice to study a very wide range of catalyst strengths, but the results in Figure 11 for a number of ketonic substrates suggest a large change of α over the whole range. The range of velocities is about 10^7, corresponding to 10 kcal/mole in activation energy, and a consideration of the energy curves involved[20] shows that their curvature over this range of energy is not sufficient to account for any considerable variations in α, so that changes of shape must also be involved. Similar evidence comes from a study of the effect of varying the basic catalyst in the halogenation of the same series of ketonic substances. For each of these the Brönsted relation is accurately obeyed for a series of carboxylate anion catalysts, but the value of β varies considerably along the series, as shown in Table 20. In this table the quantity R is the catalytic constant (in l./mole sec.) of the anion of a hypothetical acid of $pK = 4$, obtained by interpolating the results for carboxylate anions. In the computation of R a statistical correction was applied for the number of equivalent hydrogen atoms in the substrate, counting as independent atoms attached to the same carbon. Once more the variation of β along the series is much too large to explain without assuming changes in the shapes of the energy curves, but the smooth relation between R, β, and pK shows that the shape and the acid strength change in parallel when the substituents in the ketone are varied. This smooth relation is not, however, maintained if we move away from the closely similar substrates in Table 20; for example, the values for nitromethane (log $R = -4.80$, $\beta = 0.67$, $pK = 10.2$)[21] and ethyl nitroacetate (log $R = +0.41$, $\beta = 0.66$, $pK = 5.8$)[22] do not fit into the same series.

The shapes of the energy curves can also be made responsible for the large differences in rate which have already been noted for acid-base systems of widely differing structures, in particular the low rates observed for systems involving a large structural change on ionization (cf. Tables 18 and 19). For example, curves (a) and (b) in Figure 15 might represent respectively the loss of a proton by a nitroparaffin and

[20] Bell and Lidwell, *loc. cit.* (17).
[21] K. J. Pedersen, *Kgl. Danske Vid. Selsk. Math-fys. Medd.*, **12**, 1 (1932).
[22] R. P. Bell and T. Spencer, *Proc. Roy. Soc.*, A, **251**, 41 (1959).

TABLE 20.—VARIATIONS IN THE BRÖNSTED EXPONENT IN THE BASE-
CATALYZED HALOGENATION OF KETONIC SUBSTANCES

Substrate	$\log R$	β	pK_s	Reference
CH_3COCH_3	-8.56	0.88	20.0	(1)
$CH_3COCH_2CH_2COCH_3$	-7.85	0.89	18.7	(1)
CH_3COCH_2Cl	-5.29	0.82	16.5	(1)
CH_3COCH_2Br	-5.03	0.82	16.1	(1)
$CH_3COCHCl_2$	-3.78	0.82	14.9	(1)
$CH_2COCHCO_2C_2H_5$ $\underset{(CH_2)_3}{\big\vert \diagdown}$	-1.76	0.64	13.1	(2)
$CH_3COCH_2CO_2C_2H_5$	-1.06	0.59	10.5	(3)
$CH_2COCHCO_2C_2H_5$ $\underset{(CH_2)_4}{\big\vert \diagdown}$	-0.60	0.58	10.0	(4)
$CH_3COCH_2COC_6H_5$	-0.45	0.52	9.7	(3)
$CH_3COCH_2COCH_3$	-0.24	0.48	9.3	(3)
$CH_3COCHBrCOCH_3$	$+0.26$	0.42	8.3	(3)

1. R. P. Bell and O. M. Lidwell, *Proc. Roy. Soc.*, A, **176**, 88 (1940).
2. R. P. Bell, R. D. Smith, and L. A. Woodward, *ibid.*, **192**, 479 (1948).
3. R. P. Bell, E. Gelles, and E. Möller, *ibid.*, **198**, 310 (1949).
4. R. P. Bell and H. L. Goldsmith, *ibid.*, **210**, 322 (1952).

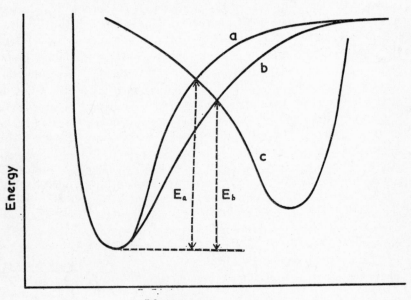

FIG. 15.—Energy curves for proton transfer with and
without structural change.

a phenol of equal strengths. If curve (c) corresponds to the system BH, where B is the base to which the proton is being lost, then it is clear from the diagram that the activation energy for the nitroparaffin, E_a, will be greater than that for the phenol, E_b, corresponding to the observed difference in rates. The same is of course true for the reverse process, corresponding to the addition of a proton to the anions of the nitroparaffin and the phenol.

In this and similar cases it is easy to see why the energy curve for the pseudo acid is initially the steeper of the two, although the two curves end up at the same level, corresponding to the equal strengths of the two acids. When a proton is lost by a nitroparaffin, the initial stage of the reaction is equivalent to the removal of a proton from the group

which is a very difficult process; hence the initial part of the energy curve is steep. As the distance between the proton and the anion increases, the negative charge shifts from the carbon to the oxygen of the nitro group with consequent stabilization of the anion, and the curve flattens off, as in Figure 15, curve (a).

The same kind of argument applies to any acid-base pair whose interconversion involves a considerable charge shift, and it is of interest to construct a simple electrostatic model of this situation. In this the anion consists of two conducting spheres of radii a and b connected by a conducting wire, as in Figure 16. It is convenient to assume that a and b are so far apart that the interaction between them can be neglected, though this assumption is not a necessary feature of the model. If the proton is close to sphere a, most of the negative charge will be resident on this sphere, but as it moves away the charge will pass gradually into sphere b, and when the proton is at an infinite distance the charge will be shared between the two spheres in proportion to their capacities (i.e., their radii). If r is the distance of the proton

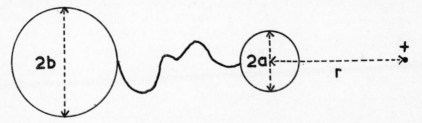

FIG. 16.—Electrostatic model for proton transfer with charge shift.

from the center of sphere a and ϕ the energy of the system corresponding to this distance, then simple electrostatics gives

$$\frac{\phi}{D} = \frac{\rho + K}{\rho^2(1 + K)} \tag{82}$$

where $\rho = r/a$, $K = b/a$, and D is the energy needed to remove the
proton from $r = a$ to $r = \infty$. Figure 17 shows how the energy varies
with the distance for various values of K. $K = 0$ corresponds to a
simple acid in which the charge remains on one atom, while high values

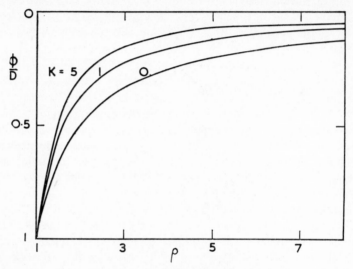

Fig. 17.—Variation of energy with distance for
the model in Figure 16.

of K represent acids in which the negative charge moves to a more elec-
tronegative atom (for example, from carbon to oxygen) as dissociation
progresses. The figure shows that high values of K correspond to
steep energy curves, and hence to slow proton-transfer reactions.

Table 19 shows that there are some acids, for example the oximes,
which are considerably *more* effective catalysts than carboxylic acids
or phenols of the same strength. This is probably because their anions
have the negative charge concentrated on a single oxygen atom, whereas in the anions of carboxylic acids it is divided equally between two
oxygen atoms. Thus the oximes might be said to have "less pseudo-
character" than the carboxylic acids. At first sight it is surprising
that the phenols fall in line with the carboxylic acids rather than with

the oximes, but it must be remembered that the phenols owe their relatively high acidity (as compared with the alcohols) to the partial transfer of the anionic charge to the benzene ring, as represented by resonance structures of the type

so that the process of dissociation is in fact accompanied by an appreciable spread of the charge away from the oxygen atom.

We shall now consider some of the more specific deviations from the Brönsted relation, beginning with *primary, secondary, and tertiary amines.* For the limited class of ring-substituted anilines there is an excellent relation between basic strength and catalytic power in the decomposition of nitramide in aqueous solution.[23] Similar relations hold for the same reaction in isoamyl alcohol[24] and in *m*-cresol,[25] still using the pK values in water as a measure of basic strength. The catalytic constants of N-methylaniline and N-dimethylaniline in *m*-cresol deviate considerably from the relation holding for the primary anilines, though these deviations disappear if the basic strengths are measured in *m*-cresol instead of in water. Similarly, in the nitramide decomposition in water, catalysis by dimethylamine and trimethylamine does not conform to the equation for primary amines.[26] The same point is illustrated by the rates at which the series NH_3, NH_2Me, $NHMe_2$, and NMe_3 react with nitroethane to form the anion; these bear no relation to the basic strengths of the substances concerned.[27]

The above rather fragmentary observations suggest that substitution on the nitrogen atom is too drastic a structural variation for the validity of the Brönsted relation. The same point is brought out very clearly by systematic work on catalysis by amines in the decomposition of nitramide.[28] If log k_b is plotted against pK, the results in aqueous solution give two parallel straight lines, one for primary amines and the other for tertiary amines; i.e., a tertiary amine is about twice as effective a catalyst as a primary amine of the same pK. The same effect appears even more markedly when the kinetic data refer to anisole

[23] J. N. Brönsted and H. C. Duus, *Z. physikal. Chem.*, **117**, 299.

[24] J. N. Brönsted, and J. E. Vance, *Z. physikal. Chem.*, **163A**, 240 (1933).

[25] J. N. Brönsted, A. L. Nicholson, and A. Delbanco, *ibid.*, **169A**, 379 (1934).

[26] H. L. Pfluger, *J. Am. Chem. Soc.*, **60**, 1513 (1938).

[27] R. G. Pearson, *J. Am. Chem. Soc.*, **70**, 204 (1948).

[28] R. P. Bell and A. F. Trotman-Dickenson, *J. Chem. Soc.*, 1288 (1949); R. P. Bell and G. L. Wilson, *Trans. Faraday Soc.*, **46**, 407 (1950).

solution.   In the plot of log k_b (anisole) against pK (water) there are now four parallel straight lines, represented by the equations

Primary aromatic amines	$\log k_b = -5.39 + 0.64\ pK$
Secondary aromatic amines	$\log k_b = -5.04 + 0.64\ pK$
Tertiary aromatic amines	$\log k_b = -4.42 + 0.64\ pK$
Tertiary heterocyclic amines	$\log k_b = -3.49 + 0.64\ pK,$

showing that there is a factor of nearly 100 between the catalytic power of a primary aromatic amine and a tertiary heterocyclic amine of the same pK.

Similar anomalies arise when we consider the pK values of primary, secondary, and tertiary amines in different solvents.   Thus on going from water to ethyl alcohol we find the following average changes of pK,[29]

	$pK(EtOH) - pK(H_2O)$
Primary amines	1.0 ± 0.2
Secondary amines	0.6 ± 0.2
Tertiary amines	-0.3 ± 0.3

again showing a clear separation into three classes.   Finally, there is the well-known anomaly in the effect of successive alkyl groups on the basic strengths of aliphatic amines in water; for example, we have $pK(NH_4^+) = 9.25$, $pK(MeNH_3^+) = 10.62$, $pK(Me_2NH_2^+) = 10.77$, and $pK(Me_3NH^+) = 9.80$, instead of the steady rise in basic strength which would be expected.

It seems certain that the main explanation of all these anomalies lies in the interaction of the cations with water, which will vary considerably in a series such as NH_4^+, $MeNH_3^+$, $Me_2NH_2^+$, and Me_3NH^+. This can be expressed either by saying that the degree of hydrogen bonding with the solvent depends upon the number of hydrogen atoms in the cation[30] or that the alkyl groups act by excluding water molecules from close interaction with the positive charge.[31]   In either case the effect of alkyl substitution is to decrease the stabilization of the cation by interaction with the solvent, thus acting in the opposite direction to the inductive effect.   This could well produce the observed order of basic strengths.   This view is supported by the observed entropy changes in the reaction

[29] Data from H. Goldschmidt and E. Mathiesen, *Z. physikal. Chem.*, 119, 439 (1926).
[30] A. F. Trotman-Dickenson, *J. Chem. Soc.*, 1293 (1949).
[31] A. G. Evans and S. D. Hamann, *Trans. Faraday Soc.*, 47, 34 (1951).

$$\diagdown\!\!-\!\text{NH}^+ + \text{H}_2\text{O} \rightarrow \diagdown\!\!-\!\text{N} + \text{H}_3\text{O}^+,$$

given in Table 6 (p. 64), which become more negative with increasing alkyl substitution, corresponding to decreasing orientation of water molecules round the cation.[32] Even more convincing is the fact that when the basic strengths of the alkylamines are investigated by indicator measurements in solvents with little or no power of hydrogen bonding we find the expected order

$$pK(\text{RNH}_3^+) > pK(\text{R}_2\text{NH}_2^+) > pK(\text{R}_3\text{NH}^+).^{[33]}$$

An alternative explanation of the observed order in aqueous solution has been advanced by H. C. Brown and his co-workers[34] in terms of steric strain between the alkyl groups in the cation, but this effect should be independent of the solvent and cannot explain the observations in nonaqueous media. Further arguments against this interpretation have recently been advanced by Hall,[35] and the solvation picture is to be preferred.

It is now clear why the relative strengths in water are not adequate to account for the catalytic effects of primary, secondary, and tertiary amines in nonaqueous solvents, since the effect of hydration will not operate in the latter case. The position is similar even when both rates and equilibria are studied in aqueous solution, since the transfer of the proton is incomplete in the transition state, and the interaction with the solvent will be less than it is in the final state, in which the proton has been completely transferred. This picture agrees with the observation that in the plots of log k_b against $pK(\text{H}_2\text{O})$ in the decomposition of nitramide the separation between primary and tertiary amines is much greater for k_b (anisole) than for $k_b(\text{H}_2\text{O})$.

Another type of deviation from the Brönsted relation is associated with the presence of *large groups* in the catalyst or the substrate.

[32] It should be mentioned that the values of Δc_p change in the opposite direction. This is at first sight unexpected, but a plausible explanation can be given in terms of a more detailed model. Cf. D. H. Everett, D. A. Landsman, and B. R. W. Pinsent, *Proc. Roy. Soc.*, A, **215**, 416 (1952).

[33] R. P. Bell and J. W. Bayles, *J. Chem. Soc.*, 1518 (1952); R. G. Pearson and D. C. Vogelsong, *J. Am. Chem. Soc.*, **80**, 1038 (1958); J. W. Bayles and A. Chetwyn, *J. Chem. Soc.*, 2328 (1958).

[34] H. C. Brown, H. Bartholomay, and M. D. Taylor, *J. Am. Chem. Soc.*, **66**, 435 (1944).

[35] H. K. Hall, *J. Am. Chem. Soc.*, **79**, 5441 (1957).

The ordinary type of steric hindrance has little effect on acid-base equilibria on account of the small size of the proton, but it may of course affect the rate of an acid-base reaction, since the two species A_1 and B_2 must be close together in the transition state, and this may be hindered by the presence of bulky groups in one or both reactants. There are few clear examples of this effect in reactions catalyzed by acids or bases, though it appears in the catalytic effect of substituted pyridines and their cations in the hydration of acetaldehyde,[36] where the presence of alkyl substituents in the 2- and 6-positions causes a lowering of the catalytic power. An effect in the opposite direction has been observed in the anion-catalyzed halogenation of various ketones and esters.[37] For most substrates and carboxylate anions the Brönsted relation is accurately obeyed, but if both the catalyst and the substrate contain a large group (alkyl, aryl, or bromine) near the seat of reaction the observed velocity is greater than anticipated by up to 300 percent. This means that the proximity of the two large groups in the transition state must lower its energy. This probably depends not so much on any direct attraction between the groups as on the necessity of making a cavity in the solvent, thereby doing away with some of the attractions between the water molecules. When the two groups are close together, they will cause the separation of fewer water molecules than when they are apart, and this factor will tend to stabilize the transition state. The order of magnitude of this effect is illustrated by the work of Butler on the solubilities of homologous series of molecules in water. He found that the addition of each CH_2 group caused on the average an increase of 160 cal/mole in the free energy of solution.[38] Since the effect may be increased by the direct attraction between the groups, it could easily account for the observed deviations from the Brönsted relation.

An interesting problem arises in connection with the *catalytic activity of the bicarbonate ion*, acting as a base. The conventional pK of carbonic acid is 6.35, which would correspond to a high catalytic activity for HCO_3^-. However, as shown in Chapter III (p. 29), only a small proportion of the dissolved carbon dioxide is present as H_2CO_3, and the true pK of this species is 3.89. It is this last figure which gives a true measure of the tendency of the species HCO_3^- to accept a proton,

[36] R. P. Bell, M. H. Rand, and K. M. A. Wynne-Jones, *Trans. Faraday Soc.*, **52**, 1093 (1956). See also S. Searles and G. J. Cvejanovich, *J. Am. Chem. Soc.*, **72**, 3200 (1950).

[37] R. P. Bell, E. Gelles, and E. Möller, *Proc. Roy. Soc.*, A, **198**, 308 (1949).

[38] J. A. V. Butler, *Trans. Faraday Soc.*, **33**, 229 (1937).

and hence of its activity as a basic catalyst. It was predicted by Brönsted and Pedersen in 1924 that the bicarbonate ion would be a relatively weak basic catalyst, and this has been confirmed by later studies on the velocity of the reaction $CO_2 + H_2O \rightarrow H_2CO_3$, which is catalyzed by basic anions. The effect of HCO_3^- is about 100 times smaller than would be expected on the basis of $pK = 6.35$ and is consistent with $pK = 3.89$.[39] A somewhat similar explanation may account for the low catalytic effect of the borate ion in the bromination of ethyl malonate.[40] The Raman spectra of borate solutions[41] show that in aqueous solution the borate ion exists, at least predominantly, as $B(OH)_4^-$ rather than as $B(OH)_2O^-$. Thus it can only act as a proton acceptor by the simultaneous loss of a water molecule and might well be an ineffective basic catalyst in spite of the high pK of boric acid (9.1). There are probably many instances in which the rates of acid-base reactions can give more information than equilibria about the state of dissolved species, but little work has been done along these lines.

Finally, we shall consider some special problems connected with the catalytic effect of *hydrogen fluoride and related species* in aqueous solution, which have recently been investigated in a number of reactions.[42] The acid HF has a pK of 3.18 ,so that the species HF and F^- should act as acid and basic catalysts respectively in suitable reactions. This was confirmed for six different reactions, and the catalytic constants observed were close to those for a carboxylic acid of similar pK, for example, monochloroacetic acid. Since no electronic rearrangement is involved in the ionization of HF, it might have been expected to resemble acids such as the oximes, which are much more powerful catalysts than are carboxylic acids of the same pK (cf. p. 174). However, this is not really a legitimate comparison, since the proton is attached to a different kind of atom in the two cases and we may expect considerable differences in the shapes of the energy curves involved. The H—F bond energy (134 kcal/mole) is much greater than that of H—O (110 kcal/mole), and the greater acidity of HF is due to the counterbalancing effect of the electron affinities (94 and 54 kcal/mole for fluorine and oxygen respectively). The effect of the electron

[39] F. J. W. Roughton and V. H. Booth, *Biochem. J.*, **32**, 2049 (1938); cf. A. R. Olson and P. V. Youle, *J. Am. Chem. Soc.*, **62**, 1027 (1940).

[40] R. P. Bell, D. H. Everett, and H. C. Longuet-Higgins, *Proc. Roy. Soc.*, A, **186**, 443 (1946).

[41] J. O. Edwards, G. C. Morrison, V. F. Ross, and J. W. Schulz, *J. Am. Chem. Soc.*, **77**, 266 (1955). See also p. 13.

[42] R. P. Bell and J. C. McCoubrey, *Proc. Roy. Soc.*, A, **234**, 192 (1956).

affinity will come into play gradually as the proton is removed from the fluorine or oxygen atom, and the corresponding energy curves will therefore be steeper for H—F than for H—O— if we are comparing two hypothetical acids of equal strength. This will lead to a higher activation energy and a lower velocity for the fluorine acid, as actually observed.

The solutions investigated also contained the ion HF_2^-, which can act either as an acid or as a base, i.e.,

$$HF_2^- + B \rightarrow A + 2F^-$$

$$HF_2^- + A \rightarrow B + 2HF.$$

As discussed in Chapter III (p. 33), these equilibria cannot be used to obtain a measure of acid-base strength comparable with conventional dissociation constants, and it is therefore interesting to discover whether HF_2^- can act catalytically as an acid or as a base. It was actually found that in the iodination of acetone and similar reactions HF_2^- is closely comparable with HF as an acid catalyst but that no basic catalysis by HF_2^- could be detected; certainly it is much less effective than F^- in this respect.

Although this behavior probably could not have been predicted, it is possible to give a reasonable interpretation. Thermodynamic investigations show that the process $HF + F^- \rightarrow HF_2^-$ is almost thermoneutral.[43] If the substrate is HS, the transition states for acid catalysis by HF and HF_2^- can be written as

(a) $HS + HF \rightarrow HS\text{----}\overset{\delta+}{H}\text{----}\overset{\delta-}{F}$

(b) $HS + HF_2^- \rightarrow HS\text{----}\overset{\delta+}{H} \begin{array}{c} F^{\delta-} \\ \diagup \\ \diagdown \\ F^{\delta-} \end{array}$

and it is reasonable to suppose that the activation energies of the two processes are not very different. Moreover, since both processes involve the association of two polyatomic species, they probably have similar entropy changes, and the similarity of reaction velocities is understandable.

We can regard the transition state (b) as being formed from HSH^+ and two fluoride ions, and in the halogenation of acetone this is almost

[43] H. H. Broene and T. de Vries, *J. Am. Chem. Soc.*, **69**, 1644 (1947).

certainly the rate-determining step, since acid catalysis in this type of reaction is believed to involve a pre-equilibrium with the catalyst (cf. p. 143). This suggests that in basic catalysis by fluoride ions part of the observed velocity might involve the co-operation of two fluoride ions, which remove a proton to form an HF_2^- ion, giving a contribution to the velocity proportional to $[F^-]^2$. Thus suppose that we have a fluoride solution in equilibrium with any acid-base pair A—B through the reactions.

$$A + F^- \underset{k_{-1}}{\overset{k_1}{\rightleftharpoons}} B + HF,$$

$$A + 2F^- \underset{k_{-2}}{\overset{k_2}{\rightleftharpoons}} B + HF_2^-.$$

At equilibrium at 25°C. we have $[HF_2^-]/[HF][F^-] = 3.9$ (*loc. cit.*, [43]), and hence

$$\frac{k_2}{k_{-2}} \bigg/ \frac{k_1}{k_{-1}} = \frac{[HF_2^-]}{[HF][F^-]} = 3.9,$$

$$k_2/k_1 = 3.9k_{-2}/k_{-1}.$$

This means that if the back reactions involving HF and HF_2^- have comparable velocities, the term in $[F^-]^2$ will make a considerable contribution to the forward velocity at reasonable fluoride concentrations. In view of the comparable catalytic power of HF and HF_2^- in the acid-catalyzed iodination of acetone it might therefore seem remarkable that no terms in $[F^-]^2$ have been detected in basic catalysis of this and similar reactions. However, if B in the above equations is an uncharged molecule, then A will have a single positive charge, as for example in the cation $CH_3C(:\overset{+}{O}H)CH_3$, which will favor the bringing together of two fluoride ions. In the base-catalyzed reactions of uncharged substrates the reaction involving two negatively charged ions will be less probable. A term in $[F^-]^2$ is more likely to occur with substrates such as $\overset{+}{N}R_3 \cdot CH_2COCH_3$, but so far no experimental evidence is available on this point.

It is less easy to see why HF_2^- is much less effective than F^- in basic catalysis, since the thermoneutrality of the reaction $HF + F^- \rightarrow HF_2^-$ would again lead to the prediction of similar activation energies for the two processes

$$SH + F^- \rightarrow \overset{\delta-}{S} \cdots \overset{+}{H} - \overset{\delta-}{F}$$

and

$$SH + HF_2^- \rightarrow \overset{\delta-}{S} \text{----} \overset{+}{H} \text{----} \overset{\delta-}{F} \text{----} \overset{+}{H} \text{----} \overset{\delta-}{F} .$$

It is possible that the difference depends upon entropy factors. The ion F^- is more strongly hydrated than most anions, and the loosening of water molecules in the transition state will produce an increase of entropy favorable to reaction. On the other hand, the negative charge in HF_2^- is less concentrated, and the orientation of water molecules will not change greatly in forming the transition state.

Basic catalysis by HF_2^- would imply a term proportional to $[HF]^2$ in acid catalysis, and in this case the charge on the substrate should not be important. The absence of such a term is therefore consistent with the low catalytic power of HF_2^- as a base.

CHAPTER XI

Isotope Effects in Acid-Base Reactions

SINCE all the processes so far considered involve the transfer of a proton from one species to another, it is to be anticipated that the substitution of hydrogen by deuterium or tritium will affect both the rates and the equilibrium constants of these processes. There are in fact two reasons why isotope effects involving hydrogen will usually be much greater than those for any other elements. In the first place, the mass ratios $m_H:m_D:m_T = 1:2:3$ differ greatly from unity, while the corresponding ratios for other common elements are nearly always between unity and 1.1. In the second place, the low mass of these nuclides in itself favors large isotope effects, since these are essentially quantum effects, depending upon deviations from classical mechanics, and such deviations are greatest, other factors being equal, for particles of small mass. This last point will be justified in more detail in the subsequent discussion.

Large hydrogen isotope effects were found experimentally very soon after the discovery of deuterium in 1932, and there is now an extensive literature on the subject, recently supplemented by work with tritium. Much of this relates to the kinetics of reactions involving proton transfer, and there is a smaller amount of information on acid-base equilibria. A large proportion of the kinetic work has had the semi-quantitative aim of discovering or confirming a reaction mechanism, usually by deciding whether or not the binding of particular hydrogen atoms has been modified in forming the transition state of the reaction. In this type of problem it is usually sufficient to know whether the isotope effect is large, small, or absent, and the experimental conditions are often not well adapted to quantitative interpretation. This application of isotope effects is now well known, and in this chapter we shall deal mainly with the problem of the quantitative interpretation of isotope effects in reactions of known mechanism.

The magnitude of the effects to be expected can be estimated by considering the dissociation energies of the bonds X—H and X—D. To a very good approximation the electron distributions in these two bonds are the same for a given internuclear distance, and the curves relating energy to internuclear distance are therefore identical. The dissociation energies, however, are not the same, since according to the quantum theory the lowest energy level is higher than the minimum point in the energy curve by the *vibrational zero-point energy*, which is different for the two isotopes. More specifically, the zero-point energy is given by $E_0 = \frac{1}{2}h\nu$, where ν is the vibration frequency, and the difference between the two dissociation energies is

$$\Delta E_0 = E_0 - E_0' = \tfrac{1}{2}h(\nu - \nu') \tag{83}$$

where ν and ν' refer respectively to the bonds X—H and X—D.[1] For a particular case the values of ν and ν' can be obtained from vibrational spectra; moreover, since the hydrogen or deuterium atom is always attached to a much heavier atom, it is a good approximation to write $\nu/\nu' = 2^{\frac{1}{2}}$, so that (83) becomes

$$\Delta E_0 = \tfrac{1}{2}h\nu(1 - 2^{-\frac{1}{2}}) = 0.146h\nu \tag{84}$$

where it is now only necessary to know the frequency in the hydrogen compound. For polyatomic molecules there will also be contributions to the zero-point energy from bending vibrations of the bond X—H, though these will be smaller because of the lower frequencies of bending vibrations.

Values of ν and ΔE_0 for typical C—H, N—H, and O—H bonds are given in Table 21. Apart from any other effects, a difference ΔE_0 in bond energy will contribute a factor $\exp(\Delta E_0/RT)$ to the isotope effect in equilibria or velocities, and values of this factor at 25°C are also given in the table. They all differ very considerably from unity.

We shall now consider in detail the isotope effect in equilibria of the type

$$AH + B \rightleftharpoons A + HB \tag{85}$$

TABLE 21.—ZERO-POINT ENERGIES FOR STRETCHING VIBRATIONS IN HYDROGEN AND DEUTERIUM COMPOUNDS

Bond	$\nu(\text{cm.}^{-1})$	$\Delta E_0(\text{cal/mole})$	$\exp(\Delta E_0/RT)$ at 25°C
C—H	2,800	1,150	6.9
N—H	3,100	1,270	8.5
O—H	3,300	1,400	10.6

[1] Throughout this chapter unprimed and primed quantities refer respectively to the light and heavy isotopes, usually H and D.

where A and B are either atoms or groups. If the process concerned is the transfer of a hydrogen atom, all the species will bear the same charge, while if a proton is being transferred there will be a unit difference of charge between the pairs AH—A and B—HB. The treatment which follows applies to either case. If the equilibrium constant for reaction (85) is K, and K' is the corresponding constant when H is replaced by one of the heavier isotopes D or T, then the ratio K/K' is the equilibrium constant for the isotopic exchange reaction

$$AH + H'B \rightleftharpoons AH' + HB. \tag{86}$$

At absolute zero the increase in internal energy $\Delta\epsilon_0$ in reaction (86) is given by the difference of zero-point energies, i.e.,

$$\Delta\epsilon_0 = E_0(AH) - E_0'(AH) - \left\{ E_0(HB) - E_0'(HB) \right\} \tag{87}$$

and the ratio K/K' is then given by standard statistical mechanics as

$$\frac{K}{K'} = \frac{Q_{HB}Q_{AH}'}{Q_{HB}'Q_{AH}} e^{\Delta\epsilon_0/kT} \tag{88}$$

where the Q's are internal partition functions for the species concerned.

Each Q is a product of translational, rotational, and vibrational parts, $Q = Q_t Q_r Q_v$, and it is of interest to see how each of these parts depends on the masses of the atoms concerned. Omitting constants which are independent of the mass, the usual expressions give

$$Q_t \propto M^{\frac{3}{2}}, \qquad Q_r \propto (XYZ)^{\frac{1}{2}}$$
$$Q_v = \prod_{3n-6} (1 - e^{-h\nu_i/kT})^{-1} = \prod_{3n-6} (1 - e^{-u_i})^{-1} \tag{89}$$

where M is the total mass of the species X, Y and Z are its moments of inertia, ν_i is a vibrational frequency, and n is the number of atoms which the species contains.[2] Since the quantities M, Z, Y, X, and u_i are all affected in different ways by isotopic substitution, it might appear that no simple general expression could be obtained for K/K'. However, the position is greatly simplified by introducing the *product rules*, which have general validity provided that the different degrees

[2] Equation (89) must be modified for linear molecules, which have only two rotational degrees of freedom, and hence an extra vibration. Similar modifications occur in the product rule (90), and the final expression for K/K' differs from (92) only in the number of vibrational terms. Analogous modifications for linear molecules (or transition states) must be made in the expressions given later for the kinetic isotope effect. These are not given separately, though the case in which A and B are atoms does of course involve linear molecules throughout.

of freedom are independent and the vibrations are harmonic.[3] The most convenient form of the rule for our present purpose states that if a single atom in any molecule is isotopically substituted, then the following relation holds between the properties of the substituted and the unsubstituted molecules,

$$\left(\frac{X'Y'Z'}{XYZ}\right)^{\frac{1}{2}}\left(\frac{M'}{M}\right)^{\frac{3}{2}}\left(\frac{m}{m'}\right)^{\frac{3}{2}}\prod_{3n-6}\frac{u_i}{u_i'} = 1, \tag{90}$$

where as before $u = h\nu/kT$. If this is combined with (89), we find for the ratio of the internal partition functions

$$\frac{Q}{Q'} = \left(\frac{m}{m'}\right)^{\frac{3}{2}}\prod_{3n-6}\frac{u_i(1 - e^{-u_i'})}{u_i'(1 - e^{-u_i})} \tag{91}$$

and hence for the ratio of equilibrium constants (88)

$$\frac{K}{K'} = \frac{f_{HB}}{f_{AH}} e^{\Delta\epsilon_0/kT} \tag{92}$$

where the function f is defined as

$$f = \prod_{3n-6}\frac{u_i(1 - e^{-u_i'})}{u_i'(1 - e^{-u_i})}. \tag{93}$$

Since

$$\Delta\epsilon_0 = \frac{1}{2}\sum_{AH}(u_i - u_i') - \frac{1}{2}\sum_{HB}(u_i - u_i'),$$

this simple expression involves only the vibrational frequencies of the molecules, the masses and moments of inertia having disappeared.[4] It can also be written in the alternative form.

$$\frac{K}{K'} = \prod_{HB}\frac{u_i \sinh \frac{1}{2}u_i'}{u_i' \sinh \frac{1}{2}u_i} \bigg/ \prod_{AH}\frac{u_i \sinh \frac{1}{2}u_i'}{u_i' \sinh \frac{1}{2}u_i}. \tag{92a}$$

It may be noted that, if we let $h \rightarrow 0$, then $\Delta\epsilon_0 \rightarrow 0$ and $f \rightarrow 1$, so that $K/K' \rightarrow 1$; i.e., in the classical limit there is no discrimination between isotopes, and the discrimination which actually occurs is a purely quantal effect.[5]

---

[3] O. Redlich, *Z. physikal. Chem.* **28B**, 371 (1935).

[4] This simplification was first introduced by H. C. Urey, *J. Chem. Soc.*, 569 (1947), and by J. Bigeleisen and M. G. Mayer, *J. Chem. Phys.*, **15**, 261 (1947).

[5] Even in the classical case K/K' is not necessarily unity if the molecules have certain symmetry properties; for example, the reaction $H_2 + D_2 \rightleftharpoons 2HD$ has a

Although the values of $\exp(\Delta E_0/RT)$ in Table 21 differ greatly from unity, Equation (87) shows that $\exp(\Delta \epsilon_0/\mathbf{k}T)$ involves a good deal of canceling out and may be quite close to unity unless A and B differ greatly from one another. Similarly, inspection shows that the term f_{HB}/f_{AH} will not be very different from unity. A single term in the product (93) tends to unity for high frequencies or low temperatures (large u_i) and to u_i/u_i' for low frequencies or high temperatures (small u_i). In comparing hydrogen and deuterium we have approximately $u_i/u_i' = 2^{\frac{1}{2}}$ for any vibration directly involving the isotope in question. In practice the isotopic substitution of a single hydrogen will affect only a small number of frequencies, so that f_{HB}/f_{AH} is probably closer to unity than is $\exp(\Delta \epsilon_0/\mathbf{k}T)$; i.e., the difference of zero-point energy will be the main factor causing isotopic discrimination.

Equations such as (92) contain only vibrational frequencies, which can be derived from spectroscopic observations for species of not too great complexity. It should thus be possible to predict the isotope effect on simple equilibria, and this has been done successfully for a number of reactions in the gas phase. The problem is more difficult for reactions in solution, and no such quantitative predictions have been made for acid-base equilibria, though existing experimental data can be rationalized to some extent.

The available experimental material consists of a few measurements of the dissociation constants of deutero-acids in D_2O, which may be compared with the dissociation constants of the undeuterated acids in H_2O. The relevant equilibria are thus

$$XH + H_2O \rightleftharpoons X^- + H_3O^+ \quad (K_H)$$
$$XH + D_2O \rightleftharpoons X^- + D_3O^+ \quad (K_D). \tag{94}$$

For all measurable dissociation constants XH will be a much weaker acid than H_3O^+ and will have the proton bound more tightly; hence the process of dissociation will involve a decrease in zero-point energy. This decrease will be smaller for the deuterated system, and deuteration should thus lower the tendency to dissociate, i.e., we should have $K_H > K_D$. Moreover, the O—H stretching force constant would be expected to decrease in going from H_2O to H_3O^+, and there is experimental evidence that this is so;[6] this also tends to decrease the zero-point energy and to make $K_H > K_D$. By the same arguments, in a

---

classical equilibrium constant of 4 because HD has a lower symmetry than either H_2 or D_2. For the sake of simplicity we have omitted these symmetry numbers, which are equivalent to the statistical corrections previously discussed in connection with dissociation constants (p. 98) and rates (p. 158).

[6] M. Falk and P. A. Giguère, *Canad. J. Chem.*, **35**, 1195 (1957).

TABLE 22.—DISSOCIATION CONSTANTS OF DEUTEROACIDS
IN DEUTERIUM OXIDE

Acid	pK_H	K_H/K_D	Reference
[Oxonium ion	−1.74	1.00]	—
Chloroacetic	2.76	2.74	(1)
2,6-Dinitrophenol	3.58	2.84	(2)
2,4-Dinitrophenol	4.02	3.28	(2)
Benzoic	4.21	3.13	(3)
Acetic	4.74	3.33	(4, 5)
2,5-Dinitrophenol	5.17	3.32	(2)
Bromothymol blue	6.15	3.40	(2)
3,5-Dinitrophenol	6.70	4.11	(2)
Dihydrogen phosphate ion	7.19	3.62	(3)
p-Nitrophenol	7.24	3.61	(2)
o-Nitrophenol	7.25	3.71	(2)
Bicarbonate ion	10.25	3.95	(6)
Hydroquinone	10.58	4.16	(3)
2,2′,2″-Trifluoroethanol	12.37	4.5	(7)
2-Chloroethanol	14.31	5.0	(7)
Water	15.74	6.5	(8)

1. G. N. Lewis and P. W. Schutz, *J. Am. Chem. Soc.*, **56**, 1913 (1934).
2. D. C. Martin and J. A. V. Butler, *J. Chem. Soc.*, 1366 (1939).
3. C. K. Rule and V. K. LaMer, *J. Am. Chem. Soc.*, **60**, 1974 (1938).
4. S. Korman and V. K. LaMer, *ibid.*, **58**, 1396 (1936).
5. V. K. LaMer and J. P. Chittum, *ibid.*, **58**, 1642 (1936).
6. J. Curry and Z. Z. Hugus, *ibid.*, **66**, 653 (1944).
7. P. Ballinger and F. A. Long, *ibid.*, **81**, 2347 (1959).
8. R. W. Kingerly and V. K. LaMer, *ibid.*, **63**, 3256 (1941).

series of similar acids the ratio K_H/K_D should increase with decreasing acid strength.

These predictions are borne out by the rather scanty experimental data. There is general agreement that $K_H > K_D$, as was shown at an early date by Rule and LaMer[7] and by Martin and Butler.[8] The available data (omitting some early measurements of doubtful accuracy) are given in Table 22 and plotted in Figure 18.

Table 22 shows clearly the trend to be expected, and it is seen from Figure 18 that log K_H/K_D is roughly a linear function of log K_H (omitting the values for H_3O^+ and H_2O, since the pK values for these species involve the doubtful figure 55.5 as the concentration of water molecules in pure water). The slope of the line drawn is 0.020, so that we have

[7] C. K. Rule and V. K. LaMer, *J. Am. Chem. Soc.*, **60**, 1974 (1938).
[8] D. C. Martin and J. A. V. Butler. *J. Chem. Soc.*, 1366 (1939).

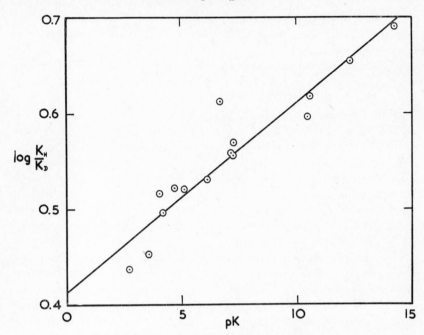

F$_{\text{IG}}$. 18—Hydrogen isotope effect for acid dissociation constants.

$$d \log (K_{\mathrm{H}}/K_{\mathrm{D}}) = - 0.020 \, d \log K_{\mathrm{H}}. \tag{95}$$

It is easy to show that the numerical coefficient in (95) is of the order of magnitude to be expected in terms of zero-point energies. For a small change in the frequency of the proton we have from (84)

$$\mathbf{k}T d \ln (K_{\mathrm{H}}/K_{\mathrm{D}}) = d\Delta E_0 = \tfrac{1}{2}\mathbf{h}(1 - 2^{-\frac{1}{2}})d\nu. \tag{96}$$

In the same way, in a series of similar acids the dissociation constant should vary with the dissociation energy of the proton, D, according to the relation

$$\mathbf{k}T d \ln K_{\mathrm{H}} = - dD. \tag{97}$$

The observed relation (95) follows from (96) and (97) provided that there is a linear relation between the vibrational quantum $\mathbf{h}\nu$ and the dissociation energy D. There are two ways in which such a relation can be derived from spectroscopic data, as follows:

(a) If $\mathbf{h}\nu$ is plotted against D for the 18 diatomic hydrides listed by Herzberg,[9] the points lie roughly about a straight line of slope 0.10.

[9] G. Herzberg, *Spectra of Diatomic Molecules*, 2nd ed. (New York, 1950), table 39.

(b) If it is assumed that the binding of the proton in the acids considered can be represented by a series of Morse curves having the same anharmonicity constant x, then the standard treatment[10] gives $D = h\nu/4x$. The 26 diatomic hydrides listed by Herzberg have an average value of $x = 0.02$ (extreme values 0.014 and 0.032), giving $h(d\nu/dD) = 0.08$.

With the mean value $h(d\nu/dD) = 0.09$, (96) and (97) give $d \log (K_H/K_D) = -0.013 \, d \log K_H$. The agreement with (95) is as good as could be expected in view of the crude picture employed.

Although the variation of K_H/K_D with acid strength can thus be interpreted semiquantitatively, it is certainly not possible to estimate the actual magnitude of the isotope effect, and it is even doubtful how much reliance can be placed on the qualitative explanation advanced for $K_H/K_D > 1$. This depends on estimates of the zero-point energies of the species H_2O and H_3O^+, both of which certainly exist in solution in close association with other solvent molecules. The true zero-point energies thus present a very complicated problem,[11] and it is likely that the change from H_2O to D_2O also affects the entropies of dissociation. The measurements of Rule and LaMer (*loc. cit.* [7]) for benzoic acid at three temperatures do in fact suggest that a large proportion of the isotope effect is due to an entropy difference, but this result is sensitive to experimental errors and should be confirmed. In general further experimental work on isotope effects in acid-base equilibria would be highly desirable, since little has been done during the last twenty years. It would be of particular interest to investigate solvents not containing exchangeable hydrogen atoms, since the H—D comparison could then be made without a simultaneous change of solvent.

We shall now turn to *kinetic isotope effects* in acid-base reactions. It is convenient to begin by considering what predictions can be made theoretically, first in the simplest possible terms and then using a more sophisticated model.

The energy curve for a proton-transfer reaction has already been discussed, and the full curve in Figure 19 has the same significance as those in Figures 12–15 of Chapter X. Since intermolecular and interatomic forces are almost unaffected by a change in nuclear mass, it is a very good approximation to use the same curve for any of the hydrogen isotopes. On the other hand, the lowest energy levels of the initial and final states will depend on the isotopic mass, as illustrated

[10] See, for example, Herzberg, *op. cit.*, (9), p. 100.

[11] Estimates for solid H_2O and D_2O have been made by E. Whalley, *Trans. Faraday Soc.*, **53**, 1578 (1957).

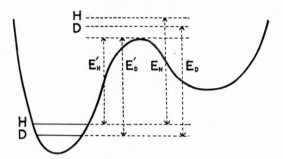

Fig. 19.—Zero-point energies and hydrogen isotope effect for a proton-transfer reaction.

by the zero-point energies for H and D indicated in the figure. The natural assumption is that the corresponding activation energies will differ by the same amount; i.e., for the reaction from left to right they will be E'_H and E'_D in the figure. The corresponding ratio of velocity constants would then be $k_H/k_D = \exp(\Delta E_0/RT)$, typical values of which have been given in Table 21, and for any particular reaction k_H/k_D would be predictable in principle from spectroscopic data for the reacting species. Since the reaction velocity in one direction is unaffected by the properties of the products, there is no partial cancellation of zero-point energy differences of the kind met with in equilibria (cf. Equation 87). and the isotope effect on reaction velocities should be much greater than on equilibrium constants, as is indeed found to be the case.

There are, however, two reasons why this simple view of the situation is inadequate. The first of these is the neglect of *zero-point energy in the transition state*. There are of course many vibrations both in the initial and in the transition state which are not shown in Figure 19, but many of these are not affected by a change in the mass of the atom being transferred. However, in a reaction of the type $AH + B \rightarrow A + HB$ the transition state contains a bending vibration whose frequency is sensitive to the mass of the hydrogen atom. This can be represented as

$$A \cdots \overset{\uparrow}{\underset{\downarrow}{H}} \cdots \underset{\downarrow}{B}.$$

and is doubly degenerate, since a vibration of identical frequency could take place in a plane at right angles to the paper. If A and B are atoms, it is easy to count the degrees of freedom involved. The molecule AH has 3 translational, 2 rotational, and 1 vibrational degree of freedom $(3T + 2R + V)$, so that the system $AH + B$ can be represented by $6T + 2R + V$. The transition state (assumed linear) has $3T$ and $2R$, leaving four degrees of freedom to be accounted for. One of these is the "internal translation" of zero frequency corresponding to motion along the reaction co-ordinate and represented by

$$\overset{\leftarrow}{A}\text{------}\vec{H}\text{------}\overset{\leftarrow}{B}.$$

Since A and B are much heavier than H, they will be almost stationary in this vibration. A second vibration has the form

$$\overset{\leftarrow}{A}\text{------}\overset{(?)}{H}\text{------}\vec{B},$$

where the hydrogen will not be stationary except in the symmetrical case. This vibration will be somewhat affected by the isotopic mass of the hydrogen, but since its frequency will be low the contribution to the observed isotope effect will be small. The remaining two degrees of freedom are represented by the degenerate bending vibration already mentioned, so that the total degrees of freedom of the transition state are $3T + T^* + 2R + 3V$, where T^* represents the internal translation. The formation of the transition state from $AH + B$ thus involves an increase of two in the vibrational degrees of freedom and an increase of one in vibrations which are sensitive to isotopic replacement. The position is somewhat different when A and B are not atoms, as is usually the case. If they contain respectively m and n atoms and are not linear, then for the change $AH + B \rightarrow A\text{----}H\text{----}B$ the change in degrees of freedom is $6T + 6R + (3m + 3n - 9)V \rightarrow 3T + T^* + 3R + (3m + 3n - 4)V$. The formation of the transition state is thus attended by an increase of five in the number of vibrations (or four if the transition state contains an internal rotation not present initially), but not all of these will be sensitive to isotopic changes in the hydrogen atom. We may in fact regard the bending vibrations in the transition state as being derived from two bending modes in the initial species AH (which of course do not exist if A is an atom), so that there is now a decrease of one in the isotopically sensitive vibrations, corresponding to the disappearance of the stretching vibration of AH.

The idea of bending vibrations in the transition state may seem an unfamiliar one, but it has a close parallel in the description of the reaction process given by the collision theory. This supposes that in the reaction between AH and B a particular direction of approach (usually collinear) gives a lower activation energy than any other direction. This means that the energy of a bent configuration is higher than that of the straight configuration, which is equivalent to saying that the vibration

$$\text{A} \cdots\cdots \overset{\uparrow}{\underset{\downarrow}{\text{H}}} \cdots\cdots \underset{\downarrow}{\text{B}}$$

has a finite frequency, as assumed above.

Returning to Figure 19, we see that the energy of the transition state is not given correctly by the maximum of the full curve but will be higher by an amount corresponding to the zero-point energy, and hence different for the two isotopes. The zero-point energy will of course change continuously as AH approaches B. If the course of the reaction is represented in the usual way by the motion of a point on a surface in three dimensions, then this effect corresponds to a change in the steepness of the sides of the valley up which the point moves on its way to the col. The full line in the figure represents a section along the path of the particle but gives no information about the energy contours at right angles to this. The true energy paths therefore lie somewhat above the full line and will differ slightly for the two isotopes, the activation energies being now E_H and E_D. The difference in activation energies is now $E_\text{D} - E_\text{H} = \Delta E_0 - \Delta E_0^{\ddagger}$, where $\ddagger$ refers as usual to the transition state. Unlike ΔE_0, $\Delta E_0^{\ddagger}$ is not calculable from spectroscopic data, and its evaluation depends on a detailed knowledge of the frequencies of the transition state, which are not accessible experimentally and which cannot be calculated theoretically by present methods.

We have seen that the main contribution to $E_0^{\ddagger}$ comes from two bending modes which replace two bending modes in the initial state. A possible analogue is the bending vibration of the symmetrical ion HF_2^-, which has $\nu = 1225$ cm.$^{-1}$ [12] For a transition state in which the proton is still close to two centers it seems likely that the bending frequency will be greater than that in a normal molecule, in which case $E_\text{D} - E_\text{H}$ is likely to be somewhat less than ΔE_0 for the stretching vibration alone, so that the figures in the last column of Table 21 would represent the *maximum* H − D isotope effects which could be expected for these bonds.

The second modification to the simple expression

[12] G. L. Coté and H. W. Thompson, *Proc. Roy. Soc.*, A, **210**, 206 (1951).

$$k_{\mathrm{H}}/k_{\mathrm{D}} = \exp\,(\Delta E_0/RT)$$

depends upon the effect of isotopic substitution on the pre-exponential factor of the Arrhenius equation (or, in the language of the transition-state treatment, on the entropy of activation). This is best seen by applying the transition-state method to the isotope effect on the velocity of the reaction $\mathrm{AH} + \mathrm{B} \rightarrow \mathrm{A} + \mathrm{HB}$, just as in equations 87 to 93 we have considered the equilibrium isotope effect. In this case the reaction co-ordinate x can be closely represented by the position of the proton between the two centers A and B, and if we define the transition state as including all systems in which x lies in a small arbitrary range δ in the neighborhood of the energy maximum, then the velocity constant is given by

$$k = \kappa(K/\delta)(\mathbf{k}T/2\pi m_{\ddagger})^{\frac{1}{2}}. \tag{98}$$

In this equation $m_{\ddagger}$ is the reduced mass for motion along the reaction co-ordinate (in this case close to the mass of the hydrogen isotope in question), κ is a transmission coefficient which will be referred to later, and K is the complete equilibrium constant for the formation of the transition state from $\mathrm{AH} + \mathrm{B}$.[13] As before, the equilibrium constant is expressed in terms of partition functions and the expression for the effect of isotopic substitution simplified by using a product rule, but the special nature of the transition state introduces some modifications. In place of

$$Q_v^{\ddagger} = \prod_{3n-6} (1 - e^{-u_i})^{-1}$$

(Equation 89) we must write

$$Q_v^{\ddagger} = (2\pi m_{\ddagger}\mathbf{k}T)^{\frac{1}{2}}(\delta/\mathbf{h}) \prod_{3n-7} (1 - e^{-u_i})^{-1} \tag{99}$$

since one vibration is replaced by an internal translation along the reaction co-ordinate. Similarly, in the product rule (90)

$$\prod_{3n-6} (u_i/u_i')$$

is replaced by

$$(m_{\ddagger}/m_{\ddagger}')^{\frac{1}{2}} \prod_{3n-7} (u_i/u_i').$$

[13] An alternative form of (98) uses an incomplete expression for the equilibrium constant, omitting the degree of freedom corresponding to the reaction co-ordinate; the velocity constant is then obtained by multiplying this equilibrium constant by $\mathbf{k}T/\mathbf{h}$. The same result is obtained finally, but the form given in (98) shows a closer analogy to the statistical treatment of equilibria.

This gives finally for the ratio of the velocity constants,

$$\frac{k}{k'} = \left(\frac{m_{\ddagger}'}{m_{\ddagger}}\right)^{\frac{1}{2}} \frac{f_{\ddagger}}{f_{\mathrm{AH}}} e^{\Delta\epsilon_0/kT} \tag{100}$$

in which

$$f_{\ddagger} = \prod_{3n-7} \frac{u_i(1 - e^{-u_i'})}{u_i'(1 - e^{-u_i})}, \qquad f_{\mathrm{AH}} = \prod_{3n-6} \frac{u_i(1 - e^{-u_i'})}{u_i'(1 - e^{-u_i})} \tag{101}$$

$$\Delta\epsilon_0 = \Delta E_0 - \Delta E_0^{\ddagger} \tag{102}$$

and the transmission coefficient κ is assumed to be the same for the two isotopes. In Equation (101) the values of n for $f_{\ddagger}$ and f_{AH} are of course different, being equal to the numbers of atoms in the transition state and AH respectively. Similarly, the values of u_i in each expression refer to the appropriate species. Since

$$\Delta\epsilon_0/\mathbf{k}T = \tfrac{1}{2} \sum_{\mathrm{AH}} (u_i - u_i') - \tfrac{1}{2} \sum_{\ddagger} (u_i - u_i'),$$

(100) can also be written as

$$\frac{k}{k'} = \left(\frac{m_{\ddagger}'}{m_{\ddagger}}\right)^{\frac{1}{2}} \prod_{\ddagger} \frac{u_i \sinh \tfrac{1}{2}u_i'}{u_i' \sinh \tfrac{1}{2}u_i} \Big/ \prod_{\mathrm{AH}} \frac{u_i \sinh \tfrac{1}{2}u_i'}{u_i' \sinh \tfrac{1}{2}u_i}. \tag{100a}$$

It is of interest to see what happens to (100) in the classical limit, i.e., when $\mathbf{h} \to 0$. $\Delta\epsilon_0$ then tends to zero and each factor $u/(1 - e^{-u})$ to unity, so that $k/k' \to (m_{\ddagger}'/m_{\ddagger})^{\frac{1}{2}}$. In contrast to the equilibrium expression (92) there is still an isotope effect under these conditions, and the factor $(m_{\ddagger}'/m_{\ddagger})^{\frac{1}{2}}$ represents the ratio of the vibration frequencies. For hydrogen and deuterium this factor has a maximum value of $2^{\frac{1}{2}}$, and since $k_{\mathrm{H}}/k_{\mathrm{D}}$ often exceeds this value in practice it is clear that quantal effects are also operating.

Equation (100) is of very general validity, being dependent only on the following assumptions, of which the first two are also implicit in equation (92) for equilibria:

(a) The vibrations have been assumed simple harmonic. This will not cause any serious error unless the temperature is high, and such errors will partially cancel when comparing the two isotopes.

(b) The limiting value has been taken for the rotational partition functions (cf. Equation 89). This assumption will fail only at temperatures far below room temperature, and then only for molecules with low moments of inertia, i.e., simple hydrides.

(c) The transmission coefficient κ has been assumed to be the same for the two isotopes.   This is a classical effect depending on the shape of the energy surface and is not to be confused with the "tunnel effect" treated later in this chapter.   It cannot be calculated without a knowledge of the energy surface but will not be much less than unity for simple reactions.   Although no calculations have been made, it seems intuitively probable that it will have closely the same value for the hydrogen isotopes, since these are considerably lighter than the atoms to which they are attached.

(d) The passage of the proton through the transition state has been treated by classical mechanics.   This is much more doubtful than the three preceding assumptions, and we shall return to it in connection with the tunnel effect.   However, we shall follow common practice in retaining this assumption for the present.

The above treatment was first given by Bigeleisen.[14]   For heavier isotopes, such as those of carbon, it is convenient to write $m' = m + \Delta m$ and to expand the expressions in powers of $\Delta m/m$, but this is rarely advantageous for the isotopes of hydrogen.

In the problem considered here many of the vibrations of AH or the transition state will be little affected by the mass of the atom transferred, and the corresponding terms in (100a) or (101) will be equal to unity.   A realistic assumption is that the only changes involved in the isotope effect are the disappearance of the A—H stretching frequency and a change in the frequencies of two bending vibrations.[15]   Equation (100) then becomes

$$\frac{k}{k'} = \left(\frac{m'_{\ddagger}}{m_{\ddagger}}\right)^{\frac{1}{2}} \prod_{3} \frac{u'(1 - e^{-u})}{u(1 - e^{-u'})} \prod_{2} \frac{u_{\ddagger}(1 - e^{-u'_{\ddagger}})}{u'_{\ddagger}(1 - e^{-u_{\ddagger}})} e^{\Delta \epsilon_0/kT} \qquad (103)$$

where u and $u_{\ddagger}$ refer to the initial state and the transition state respectively.   In comparing hydrogen and deuterium we have very nearly $(m'_{\ddagger}/m_{\ddagger})^{\frac{1}{2}} = u/u' = u_{\ddagger}/u'_{\ddagger}$.   If it can be assumed that $e^{-u} \ll 1$ throughout, then (103) assumes the simple form

$$k/k' = e^{\Delta \epsilon_0/kT}. \qquad (104)$$

This assumption is certainly justified for the initial state near room temperature and probably also applies to the transition state.   However, since we have no real knowledge of the latter, it should be noted that the extreme assumption $u_{\ddagger} \ll 1$ leads to $k/k' = \frac{1}{2}e^{\Delta \epsilon_0/kT}$.   Intermediate values are obviously also possible.   At sufficiently high tem-

[14] J. Bigeleisen, *J. Chem. Phys.*, **17**, 675 (1949).

[15] This is the model employed recently by C. G. Swain and his collaborators (*J. Am. Chem. Soc.*, **80**, 5885 [1958]) in calculating the relation between the isotope effects for deuterium and tritium.

peratures we should have $u \ll 1$, $u_{\ddagger} \ll 1$, and hence $k/k' = 2^{\frac{1}{2}}e^{\Delta \epsilon_0/kT}$, but this will certainly not apply to proton-transfer reactions in solution, though it may be relevant for gas reactions involving the transfer of hydrogen atoms at high temperatures.

It is convenient to summarize the rather meager results of the above theoretical treatment of the reaction $AH + B \rightarrow A + HB$, as follows:

(1) The major contribution to the kinetic isotope effect lies in the loss of the A—H stretching frequency in the transition state, since the contributions of bending frequencies tend to cancel out.

(2) Most of the isotope effect should reside in a difference in activation energies rather than in the pre-exponential factor A. Extreme possible values for A_H/A_D are $2^{\frac{1}{2}}$ and $\frac{1}{2}$, and values much closer to unity are to be expected.

(3) In consequence k_H/k_D should be close to the values of $\exp(\Delta E_0/RT)$ in Table 21, though lower values may be expected in some reactions.

We shall now consider how far these predictions are borne out by experiment. Previous chapters have given many examples of the measurement of rates of proton transfer, whether by the direct observation of acid-base reactions or indirectly in processes such as racemization or acid-base catalysis. A considerable amount of work has been done on the effect of deuterium substitution on these reactions; this has recently been reviewed by Wiberg.[16] However, caution is necessary in the quantitative interpretation of these results, for a number of reasons. It is obviously desirable that the reaction studied should consist of a single rate-determining step, and it has been shown in Chapter IX that in many reactions (especially those catalyzed by acids) an equilibrium precedes the rate-determining proton transfer. Further, it is necessary to avoid isotopic substitution of atoms other than the one being transferred, since these will affect the reaction velocity if their binding is affected in the transition state.[17] These *secondary isotope effects* have been studied in a number of cases and are far from negligible. They are also operative in equilibria; for example, the dissociation constant of $C_6H_5CD_2CO_2H$ in H_2O is 12 percent lower than that of $C_6H_5CH_2CO_2H$ in the same solvent.[18] Some of the clearest

[16] K. B. Wiberg, *Chem. Rev.*, **55**, 713 (1955).

[17] Isotopic substitution of nonreacting atoms can in principle affect the reaction velocity even if their binding remains unchanged in the transition state, since the change of mass will affect the vibrational frequencies of both the initial and the transition states, and hence the zero-point energies. However, calculation on the basis of simple models shows that this effect cannot contribute more than a few per cent to the isotope effect (personal communication from Dr. M. Wolfsberg).

[18] A. E. Halevi, *Tetrahedron*, **1**, 174 (1957); A. E. Halevi and M. Nussim, *Bull. Res. Council Israel*, **5A**, 263 (1956).

examples of secondary kinetic hydrogen isotope effects occur in reactions where hydrogen is not primarily concerned, for example, those which involve the formation of a carbonium ion by splitting off a halide or sulfonate anion.   Some examples are given in Table 23, which is taken from the review of Wiberg.

Many of these effects are large, and they suggest that the β-carbon-hydrogen bond is weakened in the transition state, either by hyperconjugation or by an inductive effect.   Similar behavior is found in

TABLE 23.—SECONDARY DEUTERIUM ISOTOPE EFFECTS IN
CARBONIUM ION REACTIONS

Compound	Solvent	Temperature	k_H/k_D	Reference
$CH_3CD_2CCl(CH_3)_2$	H_2O—EtOH	25°	1.40	(1)
$CH_3CH_2CCl(CD_3)_2$	H_2O—EtOH	25°	1.78	(1)
$CH_3CD_2CCl(CD_3)_2$	H_2O—EtOH	25°	2.35	(1)
$(CH_3)_2CDCCl(CH_3)_2$	H_2O—EtOH	25°	1.28	(2)
$CH_3CH_2CD_2CH(CD_3)OSOCl$	Dioxan	77.5°	1.41	(3–5)
$CH_3CH_2CD_2CH(CD_3)OSOCl$	Iso-octane	95.5°	3.34	(3, 5)
$CH_3CH_2CD_2CH(CD_3)Br$	HCO_2H	98°	1.39	(5)
$CH_3CH_2CD_2CH(CD_3)OSO_2C_7H_7$	$MeCO_2H$	78.4°	1.57	(5)
$CH_3CH_2CD_2CH(CD_3)OSO_2C_7H_7$	HCO_2H	39.9°	1.69	(5)
$CH_3CH_2CD_2CH(CD_3)OSO_2C_7H_7$	H_2O—EtOH	58.2°	1.40	(5)
p—CD_3—$C_6H_4CH(CH_3)Cl$	$MeCO_2H$	50°	1.10	(6)
p—CH_3—$C_6H_4CH(CD_3)Cl$	$MeCO_2H$	50°	1.28	(6)

1. V. J. Shiner, *J. Am. Chem. Soc.*, **75**, 2925 (1953).
2. V. J. Shiner, *ibid.*, **76**, 1603 (1954).
3. C. E. Boozer and E. S. Lewis, *ibid.*, **76**, 794 (1954).
4. E. S. Lewis and C. E. Boozer, *ibid.*, **74**, 6306 (1952).
5. E. S. Lewis and C. E. Boozer, *ibid.*, **76**, 791 (1954).
6. E. S. Lewis and G. M. Coppinger, *ibid.*, **76**, 4495 (1954).

proton-transfer reactions when deuterium is substituted on a neighboring atom; for example, in the bromination of the ketones

$$C_6H_5COC\underset{|}{\overset{CH_2 \cdot CH_2}{H}}\underset{CH_2 \cdot CH_2}{} \quad \text{and} \quad C_6H_5COC\underset{|}{\overset{CD_2 \cdot CH_2}{H}}\underset{CD_2 \cdot CH_2}{}$$

catalyzed by acetate ions in 90 percent acetic acid, $k_H/k_D = 1.24$, although the same proton (underlined above) is being removed in each case.[19]

[19] W. D. Emmons and M. F. Hawthorne, *J. Am. Chem. Soc.*, **78**, 5593 (1956).

We may also expect a secondary isotope effect if deuterium is sub-stituted in the base which is receiving the proton, and this is most easily seen by comparing the effectiveness as basic catalysts of the pairs OH^-—OD^- or H_2O—D_2O. If we confine ourselves to well-established cases of general base catalysis, in which the proton transfer is the rate-determining process, it is found that OD^- is more effective than OH^- by about 40 percent in the neutralization of nitroethane and 2-nitropropane,[20] and by about 20 percent in the bromination of ace-tone.[21] Conversely, H_2O is a more effective basic catalyst than D_2O by 30–40 percent in the bromination of nitromethane[22] and of methyl-acetylacetone.[23]

It is doubtful, however, whether these figures represent secondary isotope effects in the ordinary sense, since changes of a similar magni-tude are often produced on changing the solvent from H_2O to D_2O even in reactions where the solvent (or species derived from it) take no formal part in the reaction. This appears most clearly from the accurate measurements of Robertson and Laughton on the rate of hydrolysis of organic chlorides, bromides, and benzenesulfonates in H_2O and D_2O,[24] which show that hydrolysis is faster in H_2O than in D_2O by amounts varying from 6 percent to 30 percent. Similar effects are found in the bromination of acetone catalyzed by acetate ions,[25] the bromination of nitromethane catalyzed by acetate ions and by mono-chloroacetate ions,[26] the bromination of methylacetylacetone catalyzed by acetate ions,[27] and the bromination of 2-carbethoxycyclopentanone catalyzed by monochloroacetate ions.[28] In all of these cases the reac-tion is 20 to 40 percent faster in H_2O than in D_2O. The comparison is always made with the same substrate in each solvent, and the ratio of rates is nearly the same for deuterated and undeuterated substrates. Although the solvent does not enter explicitly into the reaction equa-tion as usually written, it is of course involved in the solvation of any ionic species, and the effects observed must be due to the difference of the solvating powers of H_2O and D_2O for the reactants or the transition

[20] S. H. Maron and V. K. LaMer, *J. Am. Chem. Soc.*, **60**, 2588 (1938).

[21] Unpublished measurements by Dr. M. H. Ford-Smith.

[22] O. Reitz, *Z. physikal. Chem.*, **176A**, 363 (1936).

[23] F. A. Long and D. Watson, *J. Chem. Soc.*, 2019 (1958).

[24] R. E. Robertson and P. M. Laughton, *Canad. J. Chem.*, **35**, 1319 (1957).

[25] O. Reitz and J. Kopp, *Z. physikal. Chem.*, **184A**, 429 (1939).

[26] Reitz, *loc. cit.* (22).

[27] Long and Watson, *loc. cit.* (23).

[28] R. P. Bell, J. A. Fendley, and J. R. Hulett, *Proc. Roy. Soc.*, A, **235**, 453 (1956).

state. The same difference is presumably responsible for the differences observed in the solubilities of salts in H_2O and D_2O.[29]

There are thus several conditions which must be fulfilled before an
observed kinetic hydrogen isotope effect can be interpreted quantitatively in terms of a simple molecular model, as follows:

(a) The reaction must involve a single rate-determining step, without a pre-equilibrium.

(b) The values of k_H and k_D must be compared in the same solvent.

(c) Isotopic substitution in either reaction partner must be confined
to the proton which is transferred during the reaction.

Not many investigations satisfy all these conditions, and almost all
of them refer to the zero-order bromination of ketones and similar substances, so that in presence of basic catalysts the rates measured refer
to the transfer of a proton or deuteron between the substrate and the
catalyst. The results are collected in Table 24. In each case the
deuterated compound is specified, and the comparison is made with
the undeuterated compound with the same catalyst and solvent. In
the acid-catalyzed reactions there is believed to be a pre-equilibrium of
the type $HS + H^+ \rightleftharpoons HSH^+$ followed by a rate-determining proton
transfer $HSH^+ + B \rightarrow SH + A$, where SH is the enol form and A is
the acid species whose catalytic effect is being measured (cf. Chapter
IX). If we can neglect the secondary isotope effect on the pre-
equilibrium, then the observed values of k_H/k_D represent primary isotope effects for the removal of a proton or deuteron from the cation
of the substrate. In most of the examples in Table 24 catalysis by
H_3O^+ or D_3O^+ is being studied, so that the base involved in the proton
transfer is H_2O or D_2O, but the second result for acetone refers to
catalysis by acetic acid, and the base concerned is therefore the acetate
ion.

Even the base-catalyzed reactions in Table 24 are not all strictly in
accordance with the model which we have considered. In the compounds acetone-d_6 and nitromethane-d_3 all the deuterium atoms are
equivalent to the one which is being removed, but nevertheless the
removal of any one of them is likely to be affected by the mass of the
others attached to the same carbon atom. There is therefore a kind
of secondary isotope effect present, though this could only be dis-
entangled from the primary effect by working with compounds such
as CH_2DNO_2 and making isotopic analyses of the reactant or product.

The values of k_H/k_D in Table 24 are all within the limits predicted
by theoretical considerations, being sometimes above and sometimes

[29] R. D. Eddy and A. W. C. Menzies, *J. Phys. Chem.*, **44**, 207 (1940); E.
Lange and W. Martin, *Z. physikal. Chem.* **180A**, 233 (1937).

TABLE 24.—PRIMARY DEUTERIUM ISOTOPE EFFECTS IN
BROMINATION REACTIONS AT 25°C

Substrate	Solvent	Catalyst	k_H/k_D	Reference
Basic catalysis				
Acetone-d_6	H_2O	$CH_3CO_2^-$	7	(1)
	H_2O	OH^-	10.2	(2)
	D_2O	OD^-	11.7	(2)
Methylacetylacetone-d_3	H_2O	H_2O	3.5	(3)
	H_2O	$CH_3CO_2^-$	5.8	(3)
	D_2O	D_2O	3.3	(3)
	D_2O	$CH_3CO_2^-$	5.6	(3)
2-Carbethoxycyclo-pentanone-d_1	D_2O	D_2O	3.4	(4)
	D_2O	F^-	2.7	(4)
	D_2O	$CH_2ClCO_2^-$	3.7	(4)
Nitromethane-d_3	H_2O	H_2O	3.8	(5)
	H_2O	$CH_2ClCO_2^-$	4.3	(5)
	H_2O	$CH_3CO_2^-$	6.5	(5)
	D_2O	$CH_2ClCO_2^-$	5.2	(5)
	D_2O	$CH_3CO_2^-$	6.9	(5)
Phenyl cyclopentyl ketone-d_1	CH_3CO_2H—H_2O	$CH_3CO_2^-$	6.2	(6)
2-*o*-Carboxybenzylin-dan-1-one-d_1	CH_3CO_2H	$CH_3CO_2^-$	4.4	(7)
Acid catalysis				
Acetone-d_6	H_2O	(H_3O^+)—H_2O	7.7	(1, 8)
	H_2O	(H_3O^+)—CH_3COO^-	7.7	(1)
	D_2O	(D_3O^+)—D_2O	7.7	(1)
Phenyl cyclopentyl ketone-d_1	CH_3CO_2H—H_2O	(H_3O^+)—H_2O	4.0	(6)
Phenyl cyclohexyl ketone-d_1	CH_3CO_2H—H_2O	(H_3O^+)—H_2O	6.7	(6)

1. O. Reitz and J. Kopp, *Z. physikal. Chem.*, **184A**, 429 (1939).
2. R. P. Bell and M. H. Ford-Smith, to be published.
3. F. A. Long and D. Watson, *J. Chem. Soc.*, 2019 (1958).
4. R. P. Bell, J. A. Fendley, and J. R. Hulett, *Proc. Roy. Soc.*, A, **235**, 453 (1956).
5. O. Reitz, *Z. physikal. Chem.*, **176A**, 363 (1936).
6. W. D. Emmons and M. F. Hawthorne, *J. Am. Chem. Soc.*, **78**, 5593 (1956).
7. C. L. Wilson, *J. Chem. Soc.*, 1550 (1936).
8. O. Reitz, *Z. physikal. Chem.*, **179A**, 119 (1937).

below the value of 6.9 deduced by considering only the vibrational zero-point energy of the initial state (cf. Table 21). Other values in the same range could be quoted, for example, $k_H/k_D = 6.6$ in an azo-coupling reaction,[30] 6.7 in the oxidation of isopropyl alcohol by chromic acid,[31] and 4.0 in the iodination of phenol,[32] though all these reactions involve a change which is more complicated than a simple proton transfer.

It does not seem possible at present to give any detailed analysis of the figures in Table 24, but it may be noted that in basic catalysis there is a tendency for the isotope effect to increase with increase in the basic strength of the catalyst; for example, in the bromination of nitromethane-d_3 the values are 3.8, 4.3, and 6.5 for catalysis by H_2O, $CH_2ClCO_2^-$, and $CH_3CO_2^-$ respectively.[33] This trend is in the opposite direction to what might be expected, since with a stronger base the C—H bond should be less extended in the transition state, and the higher bending frequency in this state should serve to reduce the isotope effect. A trend in this direction is in fact found for the isotope effect in the abstraction of H (or D) from toluene by radicals of varying reactivity,[34] so that other factors must operate in the base-catalyzed ionization of C—H bonds. It has been suggested by Swain[35] that with the stronger anion bases the bonding in the transition state is more ionic than covalent, thus losing its directional character. This is a plausible explanation, and a further study of the magnitude of the isotope effect with different reagents should give useful information about the nature of the transition states involved.

The other prediction of our molecular picture was that the isotope effect should appear mainly in the activation energy and should have only a minor effect upon the pre-exponential factor of the Arrhenius equation. Since for reactions which go at a convenient speed the expected difference in activation energies is only a small fraction of the total activation energy, a test of this prediction demands accurate measurements over a large temperature range. It is also particularly important to avoid the solvent effect produced by a change from

[30] H. Zollinger, *Helv. Chim. Acta*, **38**, 1597, 1617, 1623 (1955).

[31] F. H. Westheimer, *Chem. Rev.*, **45**, 419 (1949). This review refers to isotope effects of similar magnitude in a number of oxidation reactions.

[32] E. Grovenstein and D. C. Kilby, *J. Am. Chem. Soc.*, **79**, 2972 (1957).

[33] A figure of $k_H/k_D = 10$ has been quoted for the analogous neutralization of nitroethane-d_2 by hydroxide ions (W. F. K. Wynne-Jones, *J. Chem. Phys.*, **2**, 381 [1934]) but is subject to considerable uncertainty.

[34] For a summary see Wiberg, *loc. cit.* (16).

[35] C. G. Swain, E. C. Stivers, J. F. Reuwer, and L. J. Schaad, *J. Am. Chem. Soc.*, **80**, 5885 (1958).

H₂O to D₂O, since the careful work of Robertson and Laughton (*loc. cit.* [24]) shows that in the solvolysis of organic halides and benzene-sulfonates the solvent effect appears mainly as entropy rather than as energy of activation, presumably because of the orientation involved in solvation. There is in fact only one investigation which provides reliable values for the isotope effect on activation energies in a proton-transfer reaction, and this refers to the base-catalyzed bromination of 2-carbethoxycyclopentanone and its singly deuterated analogue.[36] Measurements were carried out at 5° intervals from 10° to 70°C, and the solvent was throughout D₂O. The results obtained are given in Table 25. These results are unexpected, in that the values of A_H^*/A_D^* fall outside the limits 0.5 to 1 suggested by the theoretical treatment,

TABLE 25.—OBSERVED ARRHENIUS PARAMETERS IN THE BROMINATION OF 2-CARBETHOXY-CYCLOPENTANONE IN DEUTERIUM OXIDE

Catalyst	D₂O	$CH_2ClCO_2^-$	F⁻
$k_H/k_D(25°)$	3.42	3.91	2.66
$E_D^* - E_H^*$ (kcal/mole)	1.21 ± 0.08	1.45 ± 0.08	2.44 ± 0.10
A_H^*/A_D^*	0.44 ± 0.05	0.35 ± 0.05	0.042 ± 0.008

the discrepancy being especially marked for catalysis by fluoride ion. A related discrepancy is apparent in the value of $E_D^* - E_H^*$ found for fluoride catalysis. This could only be accounted for by bringing in the full zero-point energies of stretching and bending in the initial state, though the rather low value of k_H/k_D demands that there should be considerable compensation from the zero-point energy of the transition state.

Before considering the reason for these discrepancies we must examine carefully the way in which the observed Arrhenius parameters (denoted by an asterisk in this section) are derived from the observed reaction velocities. The usual procedure, which was used to obtain the values in Table 25, is expressed by the equations

$$E^* = RT^2 d \ln k/dT,$$
$$\ln A^* = \ln k + E^*/RT. \tag{105}$$

If the reaction velocity can be represented exactly by an expression of the form $k = A \exp(-E/RT)$, where A and E are strictly independent of temperature, then E^* and A^* can be identified with E and A respectively, but if either A or E is temperature-dependent this identi-

---

[36] Bell, Fendley, and Hulett, *loc. cit.* (28).

fication is no longer possible and considerable errors may arise even when the deviations from the simple Arrhenius expression are not directly detectable over the experimental temperature range. In our theoretical expressions for the isotope effect (Equations 100 and 103) the energy in the exponential term is temperature-independent, since it involves differences of zero-point energy. On the other hand, the pre-exponential term will vary slowly with the temperature since it involves $u = \mathbf{h}\nu/\mathbf{k}T$. To investigate the effect of this it is sufficient to consider the effect of a single term $(1 - e^{-u})^{-1}$ in A, since the ratio u/u' is independent of temperature; i.e., we write

$$k = A(1 - e^{-u})^{-1} \exp(-E/RT) \tag{106}$$

where A and E are temperature-independent. Combining (105) and (106) we find

$$-\ln A^*/A = \ln(1 - e^{-u}) + ue^{-u}/(1 - e^{-u}). \tag{107}$$

This expression has a maximum near $u = 1.7$ (corresponding to $\nu = 350$ cm.$^{-1}$ at 300°K) where A^* is about 20 percent less than A. However, the discrepancy in the isotope effect is smaller, and for hydrogen and deuterium we find a maximum discrepancy of $A_H^*/A_D^* \simeq 1.07 \, A_H/A_D$ in the range $u = 2.5$ to $u = 4$ and a smaller discrepancy in the opposite direction for $u < 1.7$. It is clear, therefore, that the large discrepancy in Table 25 cannot be explained in this way, though this kind of treatment is necessary in any exact comparison of theory and experiment.

Another possible source of error lies in the presence of a small quantity of hydrogen in the deuterium compound being used. If a fraction α is present, the observed initial reaction velocity is given by

$$k_D^* = A\{\alpha \exp(-E_H/RT) + (1 - \alpha) \exp(-E_D/RT)\} \tag{108}$$

taking A to have the same value for the two isotopes. Applying (105) we find

$$\ln \frac{A_D^*}{A} = \ln\{(1 - \alpha) + \alpha e^{\Delta E/RT}\} - \frac{\alpha \Delta E}{RT} \cdot \frac{e^{\Delta E/RT}}{(1 - \alpha) + \alpha e^{\Delta E/RT}} \tag{109}$$

where $\Delta E = E_D - E_H$ and A is supposed temperature-independent. The error in A_D^* is of the same order of magnitude as that in k_D^* but opposite in sign; for example, if $\Delta E/RT = 2$, $\alpha = 0.02$, then k_D^* will be 15 percent higher than k_D, but A_D^* 16 percent less than A_D. However, this error will be much diminished if the reaction is studied over a considerable proportion of its course, and in any case it produces discrepancies in the opposite sense to those in Table 25.

It seems probable that the explanation of the observed discrepancies is to be found in the so-called *tunnel effect* for the motion of the proton and (to a lesser extent) of the deuteron, and the remainder of the chapter will deal with this topic. The essence of the tunnel effect can be illustrated by considering the behavior of a particle of mass m and

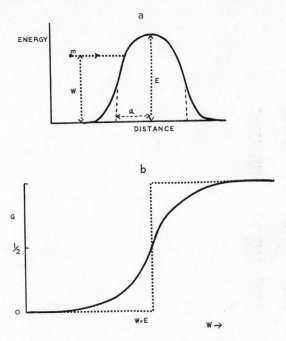

Fig. 20.—Barrier permeabilities in classical and in quantum theory.

energy W moving toward an energy barrier of height E as in Figure 20(a). If G is the probability that the particle shall cross the barrier (often described as the *permeability* of the barrier), then classical mechanics predicts $G = 0$ for $W < E$ and $G = 1$ for $W > E$, corresponding to the broken line in Figure 20(b). According to quantum theory, on the other hand, the permeability is a continuous function of W, $G(W)$, as shown by the full line in Figure 20(b). The most striking contrast with classical behavior lies in the finite probability predicted for $W < E$, which in classical mechanics would correspond to negative kinetic energies (or imaginary velocities) near the center of the barrier, and it is this feature which has led to the name "tunnel effect." It is, however, equally inconsistent with the classical picture that $G < 1$ for values of W a little greater than E, i.e., that some of the particles in this energy range should be reflected back.

The quantal result depends upon the wave-particle duality of matter, and there is a close optical analogue. If a ray of light inside a piece of glass strikes the surface at an angle greater than the critical angle, there will be total internal reflection. However, the position is altered if a second piece of glass is brought close to the first so that the width of the air gap between them is not very great compared with the wavelength of the light being used. As illustrated in Figure 21, there will then be a transmitted ray as well as a reflected one, and the intensity

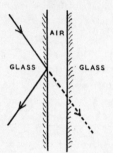

GLASS   AIR   GLASS

Fig. 21.—Optical analogue of the tunnel effect.

of the transmitted ray increases exponentially as the width of the gap decreases. This phenomenon is incomprehensible in terms of ray optics, or a corpuscular theory of light, but is predicted quantitatively by the wave theory.

The De Broglie relation assigns a wavelength $\lambda = \mathbf{h}/mv$ to a particle of mass m and velocity v, and we shall therefore expect the largest deviations from classical behavior for particles of low mass. It is generally accepted that the motion of electrons on a molecular scale cannot be treated even approximately by classical mechanics, and one of the earliest applications of the tunnel effect was to the emission of electrons from metals in strong electric fields. It is found that the energies of the electrons emitted are much lower than the maximum potential energy in the region through which they have passed, and a quantitative theoretical treatment[37] predicts correctly the dependence of emission upon field strength. A similar treatment can be applied to the emission of α-particles from radioactive nuclei. Although the mass of the α-particle is much greater than that of the electron, corresponding to a shorter wavelength, the energy barrier surrounding the nucleus is a very narrow one (about 10^{-12} cm.) so that the permeabil-

[37] R. H. Fowler and L. Nordheim, *Proc. Roy. Soc.*, A, **119**, 173 (1928); L. Nordheim, *ibid.*, **121**, 626 (1928).

ities are appreciable. A quantitative treatment leads to a relation between the half-life of the nucleus and the energy of the α-particle emitted, which was originally established empirically under the name of the Geiger-Nuttall relation.[38]

In chemical reactions the passage of an electron through an energy barrier may sometimes be important in oxidation-reduction processes which can be formulated as electron transfers,[39] but in most types of reaction the motion of nuclei is also involved. It is clear that appreciable deviations from classical behavior can only be expected for light nuclei, notably protons, and calculation shows that for protons moving with thermal velocities at ordinary temperatures the wavelength $\lambda = \mathbf{h}/mv$ has values in the range 10^{-8} to 10^{-9} cm. Since the barriers appropriate to chemical reactions have a total width of a few Ångström units, we may expect the tunnel effect to be of some importance in at least some proton-transfer reactions, especially at low temperatures. This was suggested at an early date by a number of authors,[40] though without any experimental evidence.

It is, however, misleading to regard the tunnel effect as an optional or additional effect outside the framework of the usual treatment of reaction kinetics, since it has in fact just the same logical status as zero-point energy. Both of these phenomena depend on the quantum theory and can be related to the operation of the uncertainty principle for motion along one co-ordinate, the difference being that for the tunnel effect the co-ordinate is one in which the potential energy passes through a maximum, whereas for zero-point energy it passes through a minimum. It might even be anticipated that the two effects would be of the same order of magnitude in the transition state, and we shall see later that this is in fact the case. These considerations do not of course apply to the initial or final states of the system, in which the energy is at a minimum for any type of displacement, and in general the tunnel effect has no relevance for any equilibrium problem. However, in any kinetic treatment which is sufficiently refined to take into account the zero-point energy of the transition state it is not justifiable to neglect the tunnel effect.

In carrying out a quantitative treatment of the tunnel effect it is usual to regard it as a one-dimensional problem, as illustrated by

[38] See, e.g., G. Gamow, *Structure of Atomic Nuclei and Nuclear Transformations* (Oxford, 1937), ch. v.

[39] J. Weiss, *Proc. Roy. Soc.*, A, **222**, 128 (1954); R. J. Marcus, B. J. Zwolinski, and H. Eyring, *J. Phys. Chem.*, **58**, 432 (1954).

[40] D. G. Bourgin, *Proc. Nat. Acad. Sci.*, **15**, 357 (1929); R. M. Langer, *Phys. Rev.*, **34**, 92 (1929); S. Roginsky and L. Rosenkewitsch, *Z. physikal Chem.*, **10B**, 47 (1930); E. Wigner, *ibid.*, **19B**, 203 (1932); R. P. Bell, *Proc. Roy. Soc.*, A, **139**, 466 (1933).

Figure 20(a).   There is no strict justification for thus separating out the reaction co-ordinate from other types of motion, but the error is probably similar to that involved in ignoring the interaction between different vibrational modes.   For a particle of given mass and energy the value of the permeability depends not only on the height of the barrier, but also on its shape, and in particular on its curvature at the top.   Since we have no detailed knowledge of the shape of the energy surface in the neighborhood of the transition state, it is natural to approximate the true barrier by means of a parabola, as shown by the broken curve in Figure 20(a).   The discrepancy at the base of the curve will not be important unless the main contribution to the reaction velocity is made by particles of low energy, and we shall see that this is not likely to be the case in chemical problems, except perhaps at very low temperatures.   The assumption of a parabolic barrier is analogous to the harmonic oscillator approximation for vibrations and gives correspondingly simple results.

The evaluation of the permeability is simple in principle, depending upon the conditions of continuity for the wave function in passing from one part of the energy diagram to another, and it is frequently unnecessary to obtain an explicit expression for the wave function.   It is convenient to define the curvature of the barrier at the top by a frequency ν_t given by

$$\nu_t = E^{\frac{1}{2}}/\pi a(2m)^{\frac{1}{2}} \tag{110}$$

where E and a are the height and half-width of the parabola as shown in Figure 20(a).   (ν_t is actually the frequency with which a particle of mass m would vibrate in a parabolic potential well having the same curvature as the barrier, and this is often expressed symbolically by saying that motion in the reaction co-ordinate corresponds to an imaginary frequency $i\nu_t$.)   The permeability of the barrier for a particle of energy W is then given by the expression[41]

$$G(W) = \left\{1 + \exp\left[2\pi(E - W)/\mathbf{h}\nu_t\right]\right\}^{-1}. \tag{111}$$

Equation (111) for $G(W)$ represents a curve like that in Figure 20(b), which is symmetrical about the point $W = E$, $G(W) = \frac{1}{2}$.

Equation (111) expresses the reaction probability for particles of a given energy.   In a chemical reaction we are dealing with systems having a thermal distribution of energies, and in order to obtain an

[41] R. P. Bell, *Trans. Faraday Soc.*, **55**, 1 (1959).   In this paper expression (111) was regarded as an approximate one, since it was based on the Brillouin-Wentzel-Kramers (B.W.K.) approximate solution of the wave equation.   However, in this particular case the result is exact (E. C. Kemble, *Fundamental Principles of Quantum Mechanics* [New York, 1937], ch. iii; D. L. Hill and J. A. Wheeler, *Phys. Rev.*, **89**, 1140 [1953]).

expression for the reaction velocity it is necessary to average $G(W)$ appropriately over all possible energies. The most convenient assumption (strictly true when the energy can be expressed as two classical square terms) gives a simple Boltzmann distribution for the energy. If the motion of the proton is treated classically, this leads to the expression $\exp(-E/kT)$ for the integrated reaction probability, and we can thus formulate Q_t, the tunnel-effect correction to the reaction velocity, as

$$Q_t = \exp(E/kT) \int_0^\infty \frac{1}{kT} \exp(-W/kT) G(W) dW \qquad (112)$$

with $G(W)$ given by (111). The evaluation of (112) depends upon the numerical magnitude of the quantities involved, but provided that

$$\exp\left(\frac{E}{kT} - \frac{2\pi E}{h\nu_t}\right) \ll 1,$$

which will usually be the case for chemical reactions at ordinary temperatures, it becomes[42]

$$Q_t = \tfrac{1}{2}u_t / \sin \tfrac{1}{2}u_t \qquad (u_t = h\nu_t / kT). \qquad (113)$$

Equation (113) has several points of interest. It bears a remarkable formal resemblance to the quantum correction for a real harmonic frequency in the transition state, which is $Q = \tfrac{1}{2}u/\sinh \tfrac{1}{2}u$ (cf. Equation 100a), and can in fact be derived from it by replacing the real frequency ν by the imaginary one $i\nu_t$. If (113) is expanded in powers of u_t we obtain

$$Q_t = 1 + \frac{u_t^2}{24} + \frac{7u_t^4}{5760} + \cdots \qquad (u_t < 2\pi) \qquad (114)$$

$$\ln Q_t = \frac{u_t^2}{24} + \frac{u_t^4}{2880} + \cdots \qquad (u_t < 2\pi) \qquad (115)$$

which are identical with the corresponding expansions for a harmonic oscillator[43] except that all the terms are positive instead of being alternatively positive and negative. The term $u_t^2/24$ in (114) was de-

---

[42] A more accurate expression is

$$Q_t = \frac{\tfrac{1}{2}u_t}{\sin \tfrac{1}{2}u_t} - \frac{u_t}{2\pi - u_t} \exp\left\{\frac{E}{kT}\left(\frac{u_t}{u_t - 2\pi}\right)\right\} \qquad (u < 2\pi).$$

and expressions for $u \geq 2\pi$ are given by Bell (*loc. cit.* [41]).

[43] J. Bigeleisen, *Proceedings of International Symposium on Isotope Separation*, (Amsterdam, 1958), p. 148.

rived by Wigner (*loc. cit.* [40]) on very general grounds as the first correction, assumed small, for the tunnel effect. It differs only in sign from the corresponding correction for zero-point energy in the transition state, and to this approximation the two corrections are of the same order of magnitude provided that the curvature of the energy surface in the direction of the reaction co-ordinate does not differ greatly from the curvatures in other directions. However, this is no longer true when the corrections are not small. The expression

$$1 + \frac{1}{24} u_t^2$$

has sometimes been used as a tunneling correction even when this amounts to 40 to 50 percent, for example in the gas reactions $H + HCl$ and $H_2 + CH_3$,[44] and this is hardly justifiable.

We shall now consider the experimental consequences of the tunnel effect, first with reference to the kinetics of proton transfers in general and then for hydrogen isotope effects. If the tunnel effect is the only cause for deviations between the observed quantities A^* and E^* and the corresponding classical quantities A and E, then we can combine (105) with (113), giving

$$E^* - E = \mathbf{k}T(\tfrac{1}{2}u_t \cot \tfrac{1}{2}u_t - 1) \tag{116}$$

$$\frac{A^*}{A} = \frac{\tfrac{1}{2}u_t}{\sin \tfrac{1}{2}u_t} \exp \left(\tfrac{1}{2}u_t \cot \tfrac{1}{2}u_t - 1\right). \tag{117}$$

Equations (113), (116), and (117) (or the corresponding expressions valid for larger values of u_t) lead to the following predictions:

(1) E^* should decrease with decreasing temperature, eventually becoming almost zero. This may be a useful test at very low temperatures, but small variations of E^* in the readily accessible temperature range may be due to other causes.

(2) $E^* < E$. Since an accurate theoretical calculation of the barrier height is not yet possible even for the simplest reactions, this prediction cannot be tested in practice.

(3) A^* should be temperature-dependent and less than A. Any exact theory for A demands a detailed knowledge of the properties of the transition state, and a test is again impracticable, except perhaps at very low temperatures, where abnormally low values of A^* are to be expected. It seems at first sight unreasonable that the tunnel effect should lead to low rather than high values of A^*. The reason for this

[44] J. Bigeleisen and M. Wolfsberg, *J. Chem. Phys.*, **23**, 1535 (1955); J. C. Polanyi, *ibid.*, **23**, 1505 (1955).

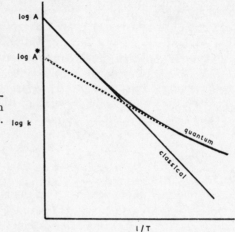

Fig. 22.—Temperature variation of reaction velocity with and without the tunnel correction.

is illustrated in Figure 22, which shows the usual plot of log k against $1/T$ with and without the tunnel correction. The value of log A is equal to the extrapolated intercept at $1/T = 0$, and it will be seen that when this extrapolation is made from measurements over a finite temperature range it will lead to $A^* < A$ because of the curvature of the plot.

Since the mass of the particle enters into the expressions for ν_t (Equation 110) and hence also for u_t, the use of the isotopes of hydrogen offers a much better chance of detecting the tunnel effect. For the isotopes H and D the following theoretical predictions can be made:

(i) k_H/k_D should be greater than the value calculated without taking into account the tunnel effect. This is not a sensitive test, since the calculated value demands a knowledge of the frequencies of the transition state; however, very large values of k_H/k_D might be observed at low temperatures.

(ii) $E_D^* - E_H^*$ should be larger than the appropriate difference of zero-point energies. This again demands a knowledge of the properties of the transition state but may be useful if the effect of tunneling is considerable.

(iii) $A_H^* < A_D^*$. This appears to be the most likely method of detecting the tunnel effect, since we have seen that in its absence the transition-state theory predicts limits of 0.5 to 1 for the ratio A_H^*/A_D^*, with values close to unity most probable. Certainly, experimental values of $A_H^*/A_D^* < 0.5$ would provide strong evidence of an appreciable degree of tunneling.

These predictions are borne out by the experimental results given in Table 25 for $E_D^* - E_H^*$ and A_H^*/A_D^* in the catalyzed bromination of

2-carbethoxycyclopentanone, and it seems likely that the apparent anomalies can in fact be explained by means of the tunnel effect. This is confirmed by a quantitative calculation. If it is assumed that A_H^*/A_D^* would be equal to unity in the absence of tunneling, then Equations (116) and (117) can be used to derive the values of E_H, E_D, and a from the experimental values of E_H^*, E_D^*, and A_H^*/A_D^*. In this calculation it is assumed that the width of the barrier $2a$ is the same for hydrogen and deuterium, though the barrier heights E_H and E_D will differ because of the zero-point energy differences. Table 26 shows the values obtained; these differ slightly from those given in the original paper, in which a less accurate expression for the tunnel correction was used. The values of $2a$, the width of the parabola at its base (cf.

TABLE 26.—BARRIER DIMENSIONS IN THE BROMINATION OF
2-CARBETHOXYCYCLOPENTANONE

E in kcal/mole^{-1}, a in Å

Catalyst	E_H	E_H	$2a$	E_H^*/E_H	E_D^*/E_H
D_2O	13.17	13.55	1.26	0.90	0.96
$CH_2ClCO_2^-$	12.53	12.95	1.17	0.88	0.95
F^-	18.01	18.07	1.17	0.81	0.94

Fig. 20a) are very reasonable, since the actual distance between the two equilibrium positions of the proton will be something like twice this. E_D is in each case somewhat greater than E_H, but the differences are considerably smaller than the differences of zero-point energy in the initial state, indicating an appreciable compensation from the transverse vibrations of the transition state. For catalysis by fluoride ion $E_D - E_H$ is almost zero, suggesting a particularly stiff transverse vibration in the transition state; this may be related to the strong hydrogen bonds formed by fluorine, and the rather high frequency of 1225 cm.$^{-1}$ found for the bending vibration of the ion HF_2^-.[45]

If we accept the barrier dimensions in Table 26, the theoretical equations can be used to predict the temperature at which the temperature dependence of reaction velocity should deviate largely from the simple Arrhenius relation. The limiting value at high temperatures is E_H (or E_D), and although the observed values of E_H^* are appreciably lower than this they would vary only by a few percent in the temperature range 10 to 70°C on which Table 25 is based. If we calculate the temperature at which $E_H^* = \frac{1}{2}E_H$, we find -60°C for ca-

[45] Coté and Thompson, *loc. cit.* (12).

talysis by deuterium oxide or monochloracetate ion and − 20°C for catalysis by fluoride ion.   Deviations should be readily detectable at these temperatures, and this has been recently confirmed experimentally.[46]   The kinetics of bromination were studied down to − 20°C, using 5-molar sodium bromide as solvent in order to prevent freezing. The rate of the fluoride-catalyzed reaction at − 20°C is about twice as great as would be predicted by the Arrhenius equation applying above 0°C, while this behavior is not shown in catalysis by water or by the acetate ion.   This correspondence between the isotope effect and the deviations from the Arrhenius equation constitutes strong evidence that the interpretation in terms of the tunnel effect is the correct one.

The above evidence rests on the study of single reaction, there being no other proton-transfer reaction for which the temperature coefficient of the isotope effect has been studied with sufficient accuracy to yield a reliable value of A_H^*/A_D^*.   Values of A_H^*/A_D^* or A_H^*/A_T^* considerably less than unity have been reported recently for a number of reactions of different types.[47]   None of these are as striking as the example quoted above, but it is possible that they can be explained in the same way.   Since the magnitude of the tunnel effect is sensitive to the exact shape and dimensions of the energy barrier, its importance may well vary considerably as between reactions which are formally very similar, for example the three catalysts in Tables 25 and 26.

It should be emphasized that the molecular picture of proton-transfer reactions at ordinary temperatures is not modified in any major way by the inclusion of tunnel effects of the order of magnitude discussed above.   The quantity E^* is a measure of the average excess energy of the reacting systems, and Table 26 shows that this amounts to 80 to 90 percent of the height of the barrier for hydrogen and 94 to 96 percent for deuterium.   In particular, the semiquantitative use of hydrogen isotope effects for drawing conclusions about reaction mechanisms remains valid, since it is still true to say that a large isotope effect implies a considerable loosening of hydrogen in the transition state.   The tunnel effect does, however, become important in any quantitative treatment, especially of the separate factors A^* and E^*.   If the treatment given above is accepted, the values of k_H/k_D observed in the bromination of 2-carbethoxycyclopentanone depend as much upon the

[46] J. R. Hulett, *Proc. Roy. Soc.*, A, **251**, 274 (1959).

[47] V. J. Shiner, *J. Am. Chem. Soc.*, **76**, 1603 (1954); J. R. McNesby and A. S. Gordon, *ibid.*, **76**, 1416 (1954); **77**, 4719 (1955); **78**, 3570 (1956); R. H. Lindquist and G. Rollefson, *J. Chem. Phys.*, **24**, 725 (1956); R. E. Weston, *ibid.*, **26**, 975 (1957).   Dr. G. A. Ropp (personal communication) has recently found A_H^*/A_D^* = 0.3 in the dehydration of formic acid by sulfuric acid.

different tunneling propensities of H and D as upon their different zero-point energies.   Even for heavier isotopes such as those of carbon, it is not justifiable to neglect the tunnel effect in any treatment which is sufficiently refined to take into account the zero-point energy of the transition state, though in these cases a correction of the form $1 + u_t^2/24$ (cf. Equation 114) is sufficiently accurate.

The rather detailed account which has been given of the tunnel effect makes it necessary to omit two aspects of hydrogen isotope effects to which a good deal of attention has been given.   The first of these deals with catalyzed reactions in which there is a pre-equilibrium between substrate and catalyst, as is commonly the case in acid catalysis.   This may often lead to an inverse isotope effect $(k_H/k_D < 1)$. The second is concerned with the way in which the reaction velocity varies when the composition of the solvent is changed continuously from 100 percent H_2O to 100 percent D_2O.   References to early work on these topics is given in reviews of the subject,[48] and both of them have been recently studied by Long and his co-workers.[49]

    [48] R. P. Bell, *Acid-Base Catalysis* (Oxford, 1941), p. 143; Wiberg, *loc. cit.* (16).
    [49] F. A. Long and J. G. Pritchard, *J. Am. Chem. Soc.*, **78**, 6008 (1956); B. C. Challis, F. A. Long, and Y. Pocker, *J. Chem. Soc.*, 4679 (1957); Long and Watson, *loc. cit.* (23).   See also E. L. Purlee, *J. Am. Chem. Soc.*, **81**, 263 (1959).

Author Index

215

Subject Index

Acetaldehyde, 136
Acetaldehyde hydrate, 151, 158, 164, 178
Acetic acid:
  as solvent, 37, 54, 55
  rate of dissociation, 112
Acetone:
  acidity of, 105
  aldol condensation of, 138
  halogenation of, 144, 148, 153, 199
Acetonedicarboxylic acid, 128
Acetophenone, 105, 144
Acetylacetone, 105
Acetylene, 104, 121
Acidic solvents, 37
Acidity function, 75 ff.
Acids:
  carbon, 103
  Lewis, 12, 13
  primary, 12
  pseudo, 12, 13, 164, 173
  secondary, 11
Acridines, 17
Alcohols:
  acid-base properties of, 43–45
  as solvents, 36, 49
Aldol condensation, 136
Amides, 140
Amines:
  acid-base properties of, 27, 53, 58, 66, 67, 175
  rate of protolysis, 111, 118, 122
  reaction with nitroparaffins, 109
Ammonia:
  acid-base properties of, 27, 88
  as solvent, 40
  proton affinity of, 21
  rate of protolysis of, 112, 117, 122
  reaction of, with nitroparaffins, 109
Ammonium hydroxide, 27
Anhydro-bases, 10

Anisole, as solvent, 56
Anthocyanines, 16
Aprotic solvents, 41, 145
Aquo-bases, 10
Azo-coupling reaction, 138, 202

Barium hydroxide, 126
Bases:
  anhydro, 17
  aquo, 17
  carbinol, 16
  pseudo, 13
Benzene, as solvent, 56
Bicarbonate ion, 178
Bifluoride ion, 179
Boric acid, 13, 34, 92, 114, 179
Brönsted relation, 155 ff.

Calcium hydroxide, 126
2-Carbethoxycyclopentanone, *see* 2-Ethoxycarbonylcyclopentanone
Carbon acids, 103
Carbon dioxide, 29
Carbonic acid, 29, 93, 178
Carboxylic acids, 56, 96
Chlorobenzene, as solvent, 56, 58
4-Chlorodiazobenzene, 139
Chloroform, as solvent, 56
Concerted mechanisms, 147
Conductivity:
  at high field strengths, 31, 112
  at high frequencies, 113
  of strong acids, 75
Conjugate acids and bases, 7
Consecutive mechanisms, 147
m-Cresol, as solvent, 56
Crystal violet, 16

Decarboxylation reactions, 128
Degenerate activity coefficients, 59
Deutero-acids, 187